The Open University

TOPIC 5
Climate change

Prepared for the Course Team by Kiki Warr

This publication forms part of the Open University course S250 *Science in Context*. Details of this and other Open University courses can be obtained from the Student Registration and Enquiry Service, The Open University, PO Box 197, Milton Keynes, MK7 6BJ, United Kingdom: tel. +44 (0)870 333 4340, email general-enquiries@open.ac.uk

Alternatively, you may visit the Open University website at http://www.open.ac.uk where you can learn more about the wide range of courses and packs offered at all levels by The Open University.

To purchase a selection of Open University course materials visit http://www.ouw.co.uk, or contact Open University Worldwide, Michael Young Building, Walton Hall, Milton Keynes MK7 6AA, United Kingdom for a brochure. tel. +44 (0)1908 858785; fax +44 (0)1908 858787; email ouwenq@open.ac.uk

The Open University
Walton Hall, Milton Keynes
MK7 6AA

First published 2006. Second edition 2007.

Edited and designed by The Open University.

Typeset by The Open University.

Printed and bound in the United Kingdom by Halstan Printing Group, Amersham.

ISBN 978 0 7492 1890 4

2.1

The S250 Course Team

Andrew J. Ball (*Author, Topic 2*)

John Baxter (*Author, Topic 6*)

Steve Best (*Media Developer*)

Kate Bradshaw (*Multimedia Producer*)

Audrey Brown (*Associate Lecturer and Critical Reader*)

Mike Bullivant (*Course Manager*)

James Davies (*Media Project Manager*)

Steve Drury (*Author, Topic 3*)

Lydia Eaton (*Media Assistant*)

Chris Edwards (*Course Manager*)

Mike Gillman (*Author, Topic 4*)

Debbie Gingell (*Course Assistant*)

Sara Hack (*Media Developer*)

Sarah Hofton (*Media Developer*)

Martin Keeling (*Media Assistant*)

Richard Holliman (*Course Themes and Author, Topic 1*)

Jason Jarratt (*Media Developer*)

Simon P. Kelley (*Author, Topic 2*)

Nigel Mason (*Topic 7*)

Margaret McManus (*Media Assistant*)

Elaine McPherson (*Course Manager*)

Pat Murphy (*Course Team Chair and Author, Topic 1*)

Judith Pickering (*Media Project Manager*)

William Rawes (*Media Developer*)

Shelagh Ross (*Author, Topic 7*)

Sam Smidt (*Author, Topic 7*)

Valda Stevens (*Learning Outcomes and Assessment*)

Margaret Swithenby (*Media Developer*)

Jeff Thomas (*Author, Topics 6 and 7*)

Pamela Wardell (*Media Developer*)

Kiki Warr (*Author, Topic 5*)

The Course Team would like to thank the following for their particular contributions: Benny Peiser (*Liverpool John Moores University; Author, Topic 2*), David Bard (*Associate Lecturer; Author, Topic 6*) and Barbara Brockbank (*Associate Lecturer; Author, Topic 6 and Critical Reader*).

Dr Jon Turney (*University College London and Imperial College London*) was External Assessor for the course. The External Assessors for individual topics were: Professor John Mann (*Queen's University, Belfast*); Professor John McArthur (*University College London*); Dr Richard Reece (*University of Manchester*); Dr Rosalind M. Ridley (*University of Cambridge*); Dr Duncan Steel (*Macquarie University, Australia*); Dr David Viner (*University of East Anglia*) and Professor Mark Welland FRS (*University of Cambridge*).

Frontispiece

Contents

Chapter 1

Climate change in context

1.1 Introduction

The Earth's climate changes. On a geological time-scale, the steamy swamplands of the dinosaur age have come and gone. Vast ice sheets have spread down from the poles and retreated again. In the more recent past, historical and other records paint an increasingly rich and detailed picture of the vagaries of climate and their impact on the environment and on human affairs.

Natural variations in climate form an important backdrop to the material in this book. However, its central concern is an issue now being billed as a major threat to humanity, and to the plants, animals and other organisms with which we share this planet: global climate change due to human interference with the composition of the atmosphere. For now, it is enough to outline the main elements of the argument. In a nutshell:

> Carbon dioxide (CO_2) and other so-called 'greenhouse gases' are accumulating in the atmosphere due to the prodigious amounts emitted by burning fossil fuels (mainly coal, oil and natural gas) and other human activities. By amplifying the Earth's natural greenhouse effect, this has contributed to an overall warming of the planet.

Almost daily it seems, we read or hear about the effects of this 'global warming', and the potential consequences of allowing it to continue unchecked. The headlines (Figure 1.1, overleaf) often conjure up images of an unfolding crisis, with the world headed towards climatic mayhem, rising sea levels and large-scale environmental change and damage. References to climate change turn up in the news, during weather forecasts, in magazines or TV/radio programmes on anything from current affairs to gardening and natural history. Countless popular scientific articles (e.g. in publications like *New Scientist* or *Scientific American*) and many books have been written about climate change. It has been the subject of major TV programmes, and has inspired science-fiction novels and films (e.g. *The Day After Tomorrow*, 2004). Never before has there been such widespread public awareness of the climate change issue.

Human-induced, or **anthropogenic**, climate change is now widely seen as a pressing environmental issue that demands clear and effective action. Since the early 1990s, many world leaders have spoken publicly about their concerns. Environmental organisations, prominent scientists, religious leaders and other public figures have added their voices to the chorus of appeals for urgent action to address climate change, before it is too late and things get out of control. For example, in an article in the prestigious scientific journal *Science* in January 2004, Sir David King characterised climate change as 'the most severe problem that we are facing today – more serious even than the threat of terrorism'. Strong words from the chief scientific adviser to the UK government, and widely reported by the media.

Much of this topic is taken up with the science that lies behind this rising tide of concern. How do we know that the Earth really is warming up? And if it is, are

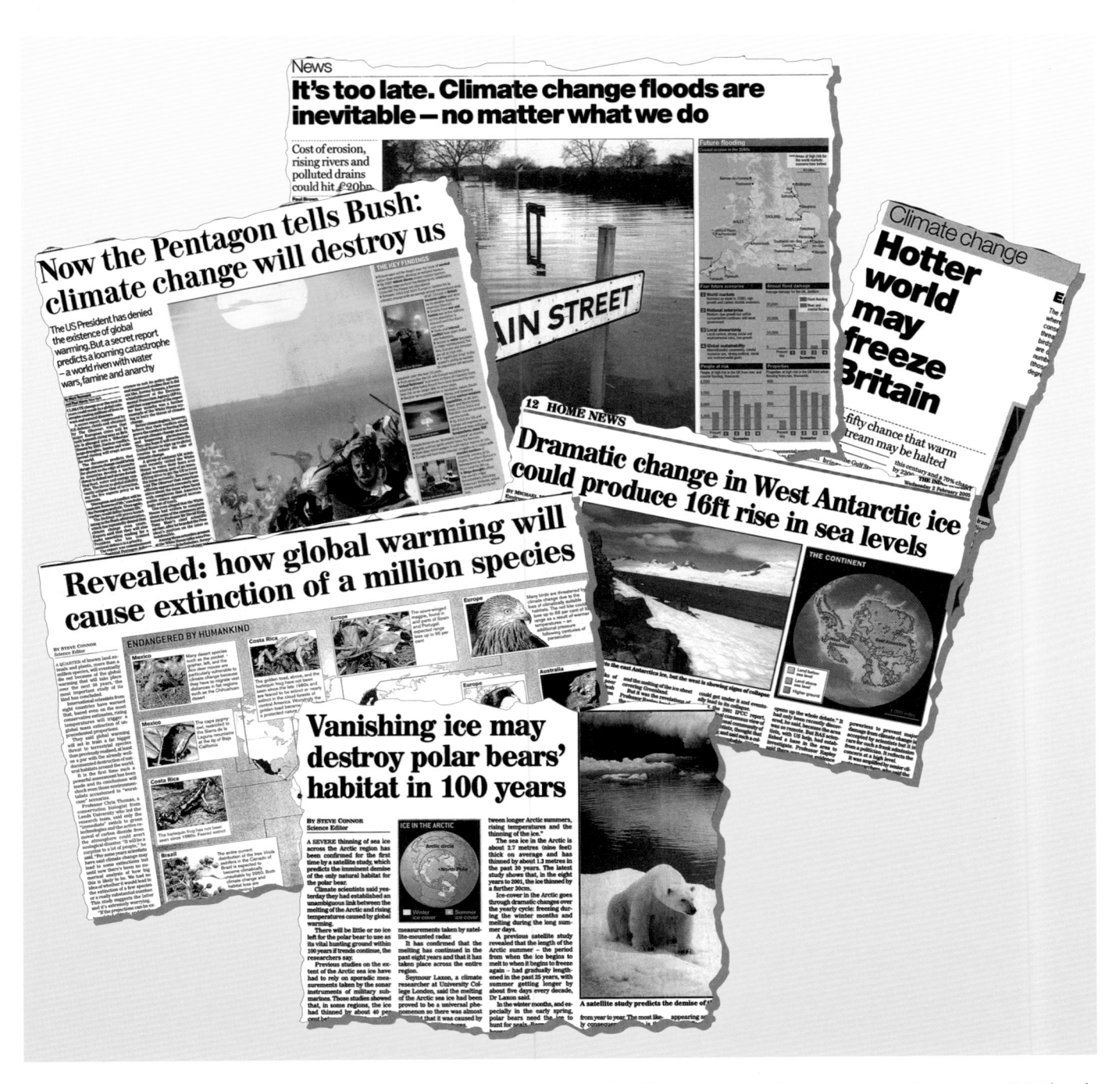

Figure 1.1   The view from the media. Cuttings from newspaper stories on climate change published in the early 21st century (October 2003 to February 2005). Sources: *The Independent*, *The Guardian* and *The Observer*.

the observed changes a result of human activities or due to other causes? What is the basis for claims that dramatic changes could lie ahead – of the kind referred to in Figure 1.1, for example? And what are the implications for different human societies and natural environments around the world? There are a host of such questions.

As you will see, the Earth's 'climate system' effectively takes in the entirety of the living and non-living systems on the planet, and is bound together by the complex interplay of many dynamic processes. Unravelling the workings of this extraordinary 'interconnected' system is one of the most challenging and truly interdisciplinary intellectual puzzles facing researchers. It requires the knowledge and expertise of scientists from a wide range of different disciplines: among others, these include meteorology, atmospheric chemistry and physics, oceanography, glaciology, geochemistry, ecology, marine biology, and so on. Many scientists around the world are spending a large part of their working lives refining knowledge of what amounts to one small element in a much bigger picture. Much progress has been made, but there are still many unknowns.

The uncertainties that haunt the science of climate change will be a recurrent theme throughout this topic. What's more, climate scientists are keenly aware of an uncomfortable truth. The Earth's climate system is so complex – there are so many factors involved, each influencing the others – that some measure of uncertainty is unavoidable. In particular, even with massive investments in research, there will always be uncertainty over how the effects of global warming will unfold in the years, decades and even centuries to come. As one commentator on environmental issues has put it (Clark, 2003):

> It is one thing to acknowledge uncertainty, however, and quite another to actually live in the light of this knowledge. Taking uncertainty into account – working with it, through it and around it – is a central part of the environmental challenge.

It is here that we can begin to make connections with three of our course themes. Uncertainty has implications for assessments of the *risks* associated with allowing greenhouse gases to go on accumulating in the atmosphere, and for the *communication* of those risks to *decision makers*, journalists and the wider public. It lies at the heart of debates about the scientific case for action on climate change.

In the rest of this opening chapter, we put detailed study of the underlying science 'on hold', and focus on setting the climate change issue in a broader historical, social, economic and political context. The overall aim is to sketch out the dimensions of the 'problem' as we conceive it today, and to highlight aspects that will allow further development of the course themes, and the way they are interwoven with one another and with the science. As implied above, the main emphasis throughout is on risk, communication and decision making, and the uncertainty that lurks behind all three. But we shall also touch on the *ethical* aspects of climate change.

Before embarking on that wider discussion though, it is important to be clear about some basic terminology. In the context of this topic, the terms 'global warming' and 'global climate change', or just 'climate change', are often used interchangeably. So do they mean the same thing?

1.2 What do we mean by 'climate change'?

Let's start with the notion of '**climate**'. Crudely, you can think of this as the *average* weather conditions in a given place. Weather is pretty easy to understand; if you go outside right now, you can probably give a fairly good description in terms of temperature, rain, wind-strength, sunshine, cloud cover

Figure 1.2   Tropical cyclones (also known as hurricanes or typhoons in different parts of the world) are particularly destructive, due in part to the combination of very high winds and intense rain. The photograph shows the aftermath of Hurricane Mitch which wreaked havoc across the Central American countries of Honduras, Guatemala and Nicaragua in October 1998. At its peak, winds near the storm's centre averaged over 290 km per hour; torrential rain (more than 1.5 m in less than a week in some areas) resulted in floods and mudslides. This single event caused an estimated 11 000 deaths, destroyed homes, swept away roads and bridges and ravaged agricultural production; it had a devastating effect on the economies of the affected countries.

and so on. Unlike weather, however, it is not possible to observe your local *climate* directly. A description of climate always refers to **climatological averages** – values of important parameters (such as the mean surface temperature or mean precipitation for each month of the year), averaged over a period of years. The statistics also incorporate some measure of year-to-year variability, including the frequency of the 'extreme weather events' that any given region may experience from time to time. The hazards to human societies from such events include the damage, hardship and death caused by droughts, floods (e.g. due to torrential rainfall), windstorms (especially tropical cyclones or hurricanes; Figure 1.2) and heat waves or extreme cold.

In short, 'climate is what you can expect; weather is what you get' (Peake, 2003). With this notion of climate in mind, we all know that climatic conditions vary widely around the world – from the heat and rain that prevails in tropical regions near the Equator, to the cold, ice-bound wastes at the highest latitudes (Figure 1.3). In between, there are hot, dry deserts; regions with a 'Mediterranean' type of climate; mild 'temperate' regimes like that in Britain; and so on. Some regions (e.g. the tropics; Figure 1.3a) experience much the same temperature all year round. Elsewhere, in the continental interiors of the Northern Hemisphere for instance, temperature varies markedly with the seasons. Equally, some regions can have rain in any month (Figure 1.3a); others have a well-defined wet or dry season, or receive little precipitation (as rain or snow) throughout the year (Figure 1.3b).

Given this rich variety of climatic regimes (more on which in Chapter 4), what do we actually mean by *global* climate? As implied earlier, the key indicator of human impact on climate is global warming – the Earth is warming up. But do we mean all of it, or just some of it? The difficulty is that temperatures around the world vary dramatically in both space and time. In any one place,

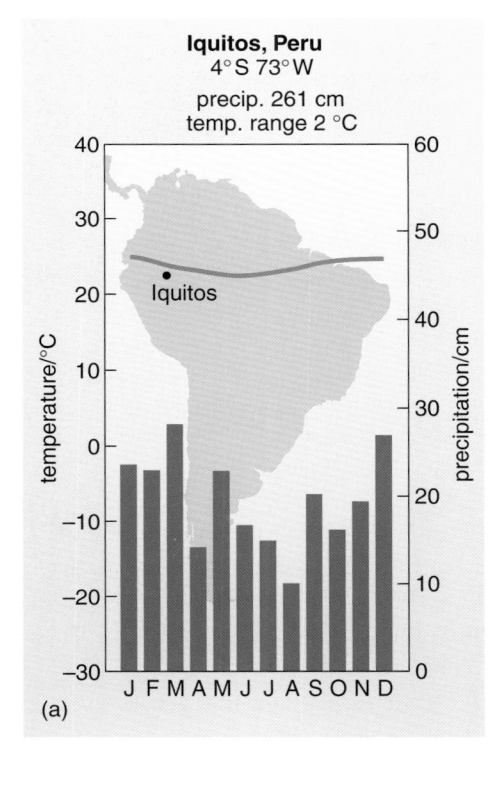

Iquitos, Peru
4° S 73° W
precip. 261 cm
temp. range 2 °C

(a)

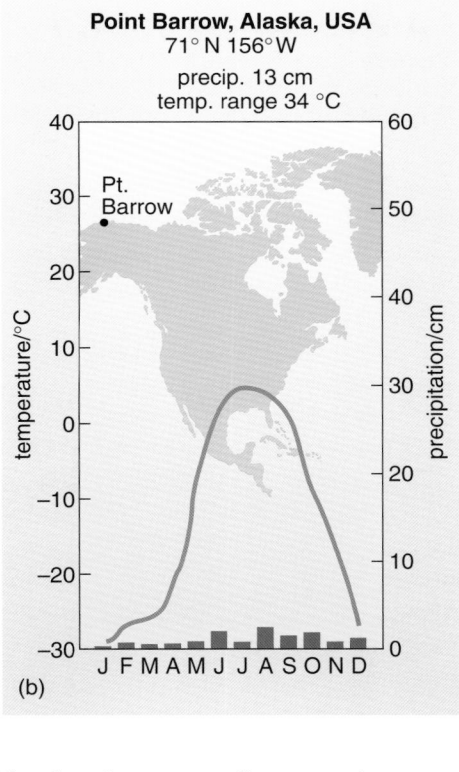

Point Barrow, Alaska, USA
71° N 156° W
precip. 13 cm
temp. range 34 °C

(b)

Figure 1.3   Climate diagrams like these are a useful way of summarising average weather conditions. In both cases, there is a temperature scale (in °C) on the left and a red line connects mean monthly temperatures. A precipitation scale (measured as depth in cm) is on the right, and blue bars show average monthly precipitation totals. Clearly, the average climatic conditions in Iquitos, Peru (a), are very different from those in Point Barrow, Alaska (b). Note that the location of each site is given in terms of its latitude (in degrees north (N) or south (S) of the Equator) and longitude (in degrees east (E) or west (W) of the Greenwich Meridian).

temperature changes during the course of the day; it can vary from one day to the next, over the month, and by season. The temperature regime varies from one place to another depending on latitude (Figure 1.3) and other local factors; it also varies from land to sea. So how do we measure the Earth's temperature? In practice, this is a far from straightforward task (see Chapter 3). But in brief, it involves combining thousands of measurements made over time and in different places around the world into a single, somewhat artificial, globally averaged temperature. This is called the Earth's **global mean surface temperature**, or **GMST**, the figure commonly quoted for the contemporary world being 15 °C. An upward trend in GMST is referred to as **global warming**.

There is now widespread agreement that a rise in GMST will have various (albeit still uncertain) effects on *regional* climates – not just an expected increase in average temperatures in particular areas, but also shifts in precipitation patterns and other weather elements, including possible changes in variability and extremes. It is also expected to have other effects, such as a global rise in sea level and the 'disappearance' (i.e. melting) of ice cover in various parts of the world (both referred to in Figure 1.1). The term '**climate change**' embraces all these indirect effects of a rise in the Earth's GMST. The potential impacts of climate change are likely to be strongly dependent on the interplay of these kinds of changes at the regional level – an issue we return to in Section 1.5.

First, we take a brief look at the developments that saw climate change emerge as a major environmental issue and move into the mainstream of international politics in the early 1990s.

1.3 Greenhouse warming: from scientific curiosity to global politics

Who made the 'discovery' of **greenhouse warming**? If we take this to mean the realisation that the CO_2 released by burning fossil fuels could build up in the atmosphere and bring on global warming, then the early pioneers were Svante Arrhenius (back in 1896) and a later advocate of his curious proposition, G. S. Callendar (around 1938). Based as it was on sparse and uncertain measurements and hand-waving arguments, Callendar's claim that greenhouse warming was underway was given scant credence at the time.

By the late 1950s however, new research findings had begun to cast doubt on the 'traditional' view that CO_2 from human activity could never become a problem. A few scientists began to speak out, notably the highly respected oceanographer Roger Revelle. In voicing his concerns to journalists and government officials, he used a potent metaphor: by consuming fossil fuels at an ever-increasing rate, he warned, people were conducting 'a large-scale geophysical experiment' on the planet.

Revelle's high public profile was deliberate – his part in a worldwide campaign for research funds that culminated in the International Geophysical Year (IGY) in 1957/58 (Figure 1.4). And that allowed a seminal development. The first continuous monitoring of the level of CO_2 in the atmosphere was set up – in the pristine air high atop the Mauna Loa volcano in Hawaii (Figure 1.5). Almost immediately, a year-on-year rise was apparent. Today, the record reveals a jagged but inexorably upward trend, tangible evidence that we really are changing the composition of the atmosphere on a global scale.

That much has been clear since the early 1960s, yet global warming only began to make headline news around the world in the late 1980s. Why did it take so long? In some ways, this deceptively simple question provides the *leitmotif* that runs through this topic, but part of the answer is simple enough. In the 1950s and 1960s, there was no climate science 'community' as such. The expertise that would be needed to unravel the implications of the warning signal from Mauna Loa was scattered among researchers working in diverse and almost entirely separate fields. Only gradually would the barriers to communication across discipline boundaries begin to break down as scientific interest took off in the 1970s. Until then, many of the findings that would prove crucial to the

Figure 1.4 The logo of the IGY. Among other things, this international effort saw a major expansion of the permanent scientific presence in Antarctica (reflected in the tilt of the globe, with the South Pole towards us). In the years ahead, this would prove crucial to the discovery of the 'ozone hole' (Figure 1.6d) and to several studies that underpin current concerns about climate change.

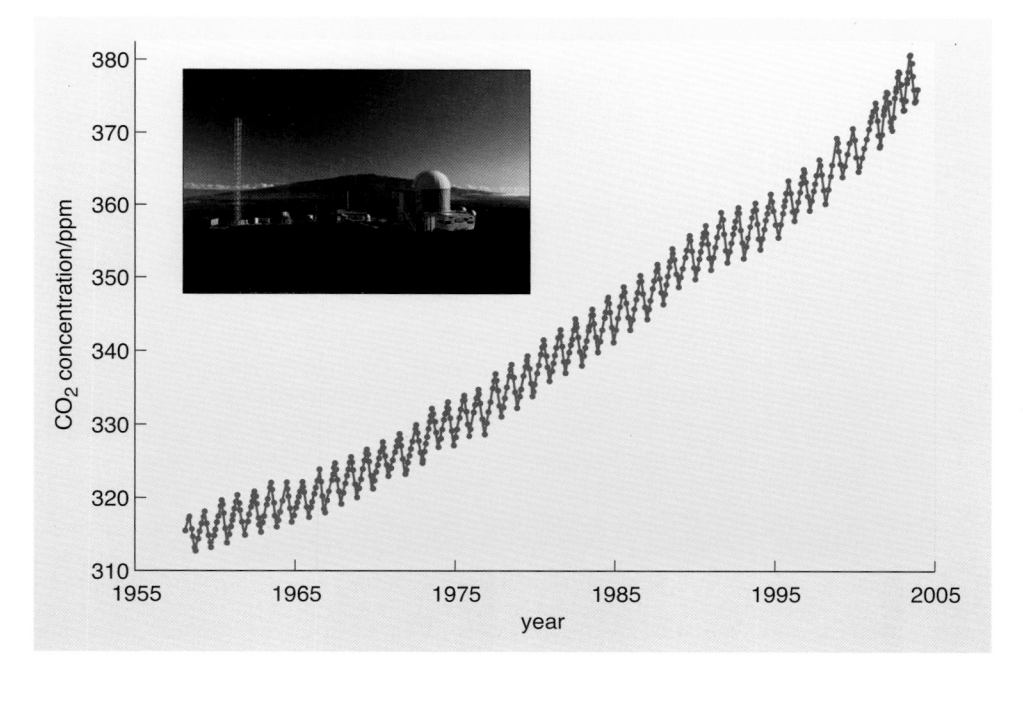

Figure 1.5   Data for the CO_2 concentration (in parts per million, ppm; see Box 2.3 in Chapter 2) from the Mauna Loa record, up to 2004. Annual oscillations arise from seasonal variations in photosynthesis and other biological processes (discussed in Chapter 5). The instrumentation needed to measure the CO_2 level in the atmosphere was developed by Charles Keeling and installed in the Mauna Loa climate observatory (inset) in 1958.

development of climate science emerged from research programmes that did not have the study of climate – much less CO_2 as an agent of climate change – as a primary goal. As Spencer Weart points out in *The Discovery of Global Warming* (Weart, 2004):

> Following the Second World War, the United States Federal government funded many kinds of basic research, much of it connected to Cold War concerns, and some of this happened to relate to climate change. During the 1960s, the government created major agencies for space, atmospheric and ocean science, and in the 1970s, as public concern for the environment mounted, the agencies increasingly supported research targeted directly at climate change.

Here, we can make connections with the central message of this course – science *in context*. Put baldly, all research has to be funded. The political, social, cultural – and one might even say 'psychological' – environment in which scientists operate exerts a major influence over which lines of research flourish, or are neglected, in particular places and times.

Note in particular that the quote above makes reference to what has been dubbed the 'first wave' of modern environmentalism, which burst onto the scene in the early 1970s. This is not the place to attempt an analysis of the many factors behind this movement – nor of the reasons why it later waned, only to re-emerge as a more enduring force in the mid- to late 1980s. However, we can point to some of the factors that have fed general concerns about the effects of using the atmosphere as a free 'dumping ground' for our waste products:

- *Local air pollution*   This has been a problem for centuries. But people in the affluent West have become increasingly aware of the health

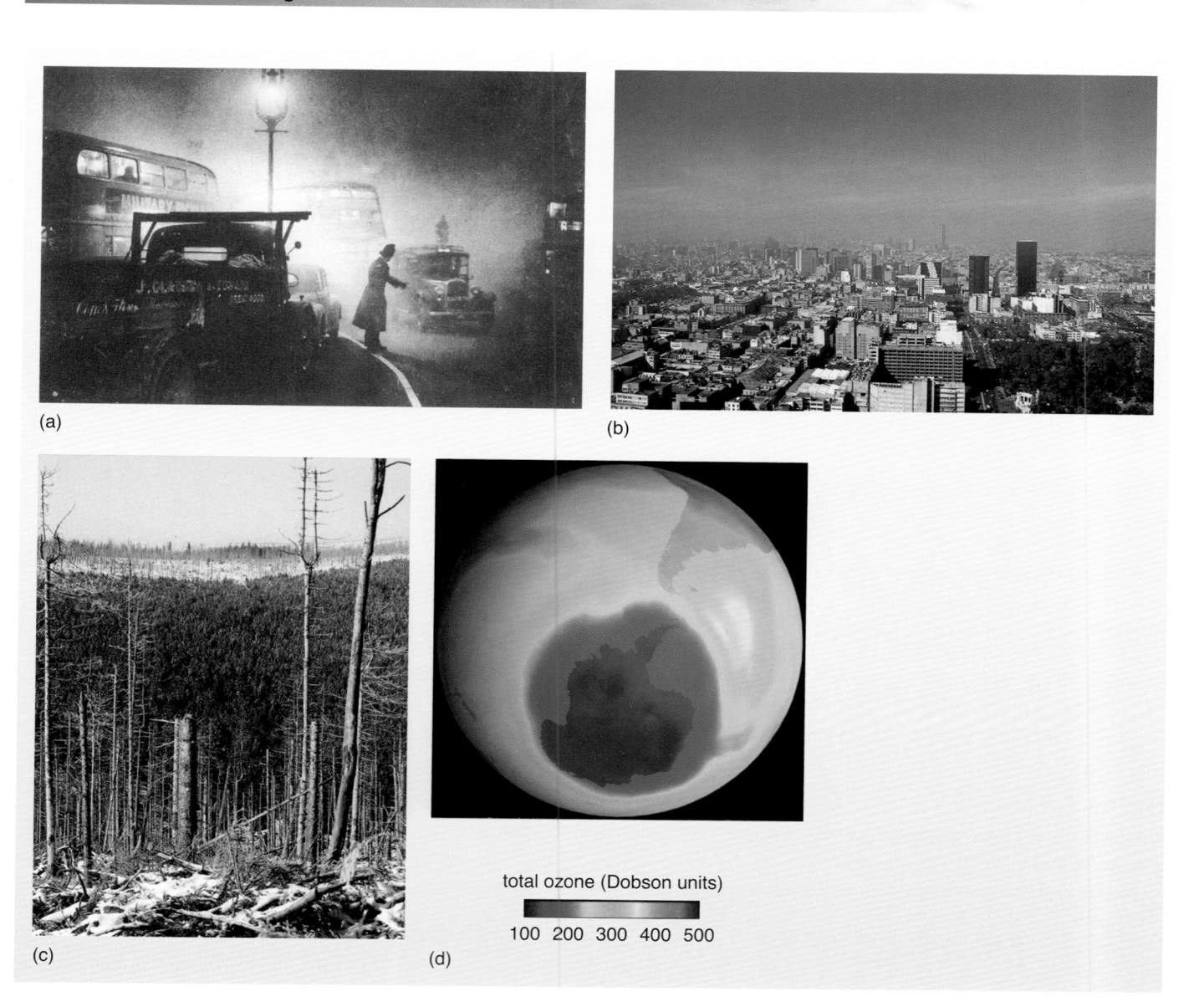

Figure 1.6 (a) The 'killer' smog that gripped London for a week in December 1952 left 4000 people dead. (b) View over Mexico City showing the murky haze of 'photochemical' smog, a noxious brew of chemicals and particles generated by the action of sunlight on vehicle exhaust fumes. (c) Tree death caused by acid rain. (d) The Antarctic ozone hole, made 'visible' by computer-processing the ozone data collected by satellite-borne instruments.

hazards associated with the more visible manifestations of air pollution – such as the smokes and fogs of industrial cities (Figure 1.6a), or the summer smogs that began to afflict Los Angeles during the 1940s and are now commonplace in major cities across the world (Figure 1.6b).

- *Transboundary pollution*   During the early 1980s, debates about acid rain demonstrated that power plants in one region could result in environmental degradation in another. Dramatic images of lakes devoid of life and dying forests (Figure 1.6c) captured the public imagination in Europe and North America.

- *Local acts – global effects*   In the mid-1970s, scientists in the US began to warn that continued release of chlorofluorocarbons (CFCs, then widely used as propellants in spray cans, refrigerants and solvents) posed a threat to the ozone layer. Located several miles above our heads, the ozone layer acts as a filter, protecting life on Earth from the full intensity of the Sun's damaging ultraviolet radiation. There was widespread publicity about the dangers of ozone loss, the link with an increased risk of skin cancer being a particularly emotive issue. The first tangible sign of actual damage came with the discovery of the 'ozone hole' over Antarctica in 1985; the ozone loss was far more severe than scientists had predicted, and there were graphic images to hammer the message home (Figure 1.6d).

On the public side, a decade or so of agitation on these and other environmental issues did much to drive home how severely human technologies and development patterns could affect the natural world, even the air itself. Certainly, it was shocking for people to realise that such everyday activities as using a hairspray or deodorant (with a CFC-based propellant) could have such a drastic impact on the Earth's ozone shield, and half a world away. Here was disturbing evidence that tampering with the atmosphere could have serious consequences – not just on a local or regional scale, but on a truly global one. The message was not lost on the scientific community.

Meanwhile, knowledge of how climate could change had pushed on in a direction informed by studies of the Earth's past climate history, and by field observations, laboratory measurements and theoretical considerations. Global surveillance from space by satellite-borne instruments was playing an increasing role as well. No less important, several large multinational and interdisciplinary research programmes helped to foster cooperation and communication among experts in different fields and from many countries – a vital factor in building a worldwide network of climate scientists. Over the years, their achievement was not just to gather and analyse great heaps of data, but also to fit it all together into an emerging (if still murky) picture of how the climate system functions (reviewed in Chapters 4 and 5).

Here another key development can again be traced back to the late 1950s – the first attempts to represent atmospheric behaviour by using computers, the beginnings of numerical weather forecasting. With more information to chew on, modellers embarked on an ambitious project that continues to this day: the elaboration of their weather-forecasting models into the tools needed for a serious assessment of the climate's response to an atmosphere enriched in CO_2. From the mid-1970s on, the visions of the future generated by these 'climate models' (explored in Chapter 6) did much to fuel growing scientific concerns about how the 'experiment' going on in the real world might turn out.

The period through to the mid-1980s was marked by many controversies and twists and turns in experts' views about what might happen to the climate (a point we revisit later on). But it also saw the majority scientific opinion gradually harden behind the view that allowing CO_2 to go on accumulating in the atmosphere was a 'legitimate cause for concern', with the potential to bring about significant climate change in future. And then, in 1986, there was another important development – publication of the first reliable record of variations in GMST back to the mid-19th century. It provided hard evidence for the reality of global warming (a main focus of Chapter 3).

By that time, scientific efforts to get a hearing for their concerns had already registered with government officials and decision makers in many parts of the world. In the US, for example, a series of 'expert panel' reviews of the climate change issue by the National Academy of Sciences was especially influential in legitimising scientific concerns, and in raising public and political awareness. A report by such a prestigious scientific body (the UK equivalent is the Royal Society) is relatively hard to dismiss. Moreover, the production of such reports itself acted to crystallise a set of beliefs and attitudes among climate scientists, and did much to foster the majority view noted above.

As expert-panel studies, government committee hearings and international conferences proliferated through the 1980s, there was a gathering momentum behind the insistent warnings by leading climate scientists – a pressure for action that would eventually sweep climate change onto the world's agendas in the early 1990s. Some of the major milestones during this period are collected in Box 1.1. Two UN agencies – the *World Meteorological Organisation* (WMO) and the *United Nations Environment Programme* (UNEP) – played a central role in facilitating these developments. However, in the wake of the Toronto Conference (Box 1.1), their involvement went beyond sponsoring conferences, coordinating international research programmes, etc. With mounting scientific, public and

---

Box 1.1 Breaking into global politics

1979 First World Climate Conference (Geneva) called on governments to 'foresee and prevent man-made changes in climate'. World Climate Research Programme launched to coordinate international research.

1985 First major international conference of climate experts (held in Villach, Austria) concluded that 'in the first half of the next century a rise of global mean temperature could occur which is greater than any in man's history', and called on governments to consider international agreements to restrict emissions.

1988 World Conference on the Changing Atmosphere, nicknamed the Toronto Conference. For the first time, a group of leading scientists called on the world's governments to set strict, specific targets for reducing greenhouse gas emissions: a cut of 20% below 1988 levels by 2005.

1990 Second World Climate Conference (Geneva). Government representatives from 137 countries formally agreed that the risk of climate change was sufficiently well established scientifically to warrant a concerted international response. Shortly after, the UN General Assembly established a negotiating committee charged with drafting an international 'climate convention'.

1992 The **UN Framework Convention on Climate Change (UNFCCC)** was opened for signature at the UN Conference on Environment and Development (dubbed the first Earth Summit) held in Rio de Janeiro, Brazil, in June 1992.

1994 The UNFCCC came into force on 21 March 1994. Today, it has near-universal membership and has become the centrepiece of the international response to climate change. The declared objective of the convention is 'to achieve [...] stabilization of greenhouse gas concentrations in the atmosphere at a level that would prevent dangerous anthropogenic interference with the climate system.'

official concern in many countries, there was pressure for the creation of a new type of international body – one with the official status and connections (the 'clout', in other words) to give force to its recommendations. The result was the **Intergovernmental Panel on Climate Change (IPCC)**, established under joint WMO/UNEP auspices in 1988.

One last point before we take a closer look at how the IPCC functions. As you may have noticed already, the topic of climate change is littered with abbreviations! For reference, these are collected in the Appendix to this topic.

1.4 Climate science and climate policy: the central role of the IPCC

As you will see in later chapters, there are many strands to the story of the human impact on the Earth's climate. For example, the other manifestations of atmospheric pollution mentioned in Section 1.3 are all woven in, in one way or another. But there is one factor that, above all others, makes human-induced climate change a deeply *political* issue: the link between CO_2 emissions and energy production – a major driving force behind economic growth since the dawn of the industrial age.

Any proposal to limit climate change by curbing global CO_2 emissions connects with powerful economic, social and political forces. It comes up against the vested interests of the fossil fuel industries and oil-exporting countries for example, and may challenge strongly held views about what is and is not technologically, economically or politically feasible. Moreover, it gets tangled up with complex issues involving fairness and the balance of power between industrialised and developing countries. To quote George Carey, the former Archbishop of Canterbury:

> A child born in a wealthy country is likely to consume, waste, and pollute more in his lifetime than 50 children born in developing nations. Our energy-burning lifestyles are pushing our planet to the point of no return. It is dawning on us at last that the life of our world is as vulnerable as the children we raise.

■ Which of our course themes is implicit in this remark?

▨ There is a 'moral' or ethical dimension to climate change. Carey invokes the argument that the 'problem' is largely the responsibility of the rich countries of the world – historically (and still today) the main source of CO_2 emissions as they have, in effect, 'combusted their way' to their current living standards. Yet people everywhere will be affected by the impacts of climate change – as will future generations, and indeed, life in general.

Can people in affluent countries like the UK be persuaded to cut back on their energy-intensive lifestyles (Figure 1.7)? And what about the legitimate aspirations of people in the world's poorer countries? Will they insist on their rights to power the process of economic development on cheap fossil fuels, as we have done in the past? The argument that less-developed nations have a right to benefit from

Figure 1.7 The 'Save It' campaign was a prominent part of the UK government's response to the 'oil crisis' that unfolded in the wake of the Yom Kippur War (between Egypt and Israel) in 1973. We can make connections between early public awareness campaigns to save energy in the home, and the implications of policies to combat climate change.

economic growth in the same way that developed nations have in the past adds a further ethical dimension to debates about climate change.

From the outset, the IPCC has operated within the context of these wider issues. It was an explicitly *intergovernmental* undertaking, set up to provide a mechanism whereby the scientific community could make a more effective contribution to decision making on climate change by the world's governments. In this sense, the IPCC is neither a strictly scientific body nor a strictly political one; it is a hybrid. In its own words (IPCC, 2004):

> The role of the IPCC is to assess […] the scientific, technical and socio-economic information relevant for the understanding of the risk of human-induced climate change […] The IPCC does not carry out research nor does it monitor climate-related data or other relevant parameters. It bases its assessment mainly on peer reviewed and published scientific/technical literature.

To date (2006), the IPCC has produced three major assessments of the 'current state of knowledge' on climate change: the first in 1990; the second in 1996; and most recently the **Third Assessment Report (TAR)**, published in 2001. The fourth report is due in 2007, and will provide food for thought in the years that follow. Here, we shall make frequent reference to the findings in the **IPCC TAR**, though we shall also draw on results that have emerged from research since then. Like its predecessors, the TAR comes in several weighty tomes (Figure 1.8); three working groups (referred to as Working Groups I, II and III, often abbreviated as WGI, etc.; see Box 1.2) each produced a report on a different aspect of climate change, and there is also a synthesis report (IPCC, 2001d).

Figure 1.8   Taken together, the four volumes of the IPCC TAR are 3062 pages long, 14 cm thick and weigh 8.6 kg!

Box 1.2 Managing the complex, interdisciplinary climate change puzzle

The IPCC's remit is not only to draw together the best available scientific knowledge on climate change from around the world, but also to assess the implications of this information for policy purposes. In one way or another, this huge task involves a significant proportion of the global community of natural scientists, economists, social scientists and technical experts engaged in climate change-related research. As in earlier reports, the IPCC divided up the work for the TAR among three working groups:

Working Group I: the scientific aspects of the climate system and climate change (IPCC, 2001a).

Working Group II: the vulnerability of socioeconomic and natural systems to climate change, the negative and positive consequences of climate change, and options for adapting to it (IPCC, 2001b).

Working Group III: options for limiting greenhouse gas emissions and otherwise mitigating climate change (IPCC, 2001c).

The report from each working group (Figure 1.8) contains a short **'Summary for Policymakers' (SPM)**, a longer 'Technical Summary', and the main body of the text. Few non-specialists attempt to grapple with the highly technical detail in the main report. When the IPCC's conclusions are reported in the media, the most frequently quoted source is the SPM. These summaries are also freely available through the IPCC's website.

Over the years, the IPCC has established itself as the most authoritative and comprehensive source of information on the science of climate change. Its political influence rests on the way the Panel functions. IPCC reports are the result of a painstaking effort to draw nearly all the world's climate experts into the process of assessing the latest scientific findings, coupled with a determination to hammer out a consensus view through an exhaustive (and exhausting!) cycle of review, discussion and revision. We shall have more to say about this process later on (Chapter 3). Here, we want to underline the emphasis on *consensus*.

In practice, this means that any final conclusions about the evidence for human-induced climate change, and its implications for the future, are phrased in terms that no knowledgeable scientist could fault on scientific grounds. These carefully crafted consensus statements are collected in a 'Summary for Policymakers' (SPM; Box 1.2), which is an important part of each report. So much so, that the wording of the SPM must be agreed unanimously at an IPCC 'plenary' meeting. According to one commentator (Peake, 2003): 'This involves high-level government officials sitting behind national flags in UN fashion going through the summaries, line by line, word by word, and, frequently, comma by comma'.

This aspect of the IPCC process is highly political. Conflicts among many kinds of nations tend to surface at this point. For example, representatives of countries most at risk from the impacts of climate change (such as small island nations; see Section 1.5) can be expected to argue for strong statements. Equally, large fossil-fuel-consuming and oil-producing nations do not hesitate to press their interests, and may attempt to 'water down' the consensus statements endorsed by the climate science community. In short, the conclusions that emerge from this final round of negotiations – and hence the final wording of the 'Summary for Policymakers' – often reflect the strains of political compromises. They represent what some have termed the 'lowest common denominator' of scientific opinion. But therein lies their strength; the IPCC's conclusions have solid credibility, and cannot be readily brushed aside by the policy-making community.

■   How do the summaries to IPCC reports act as an important vehicle for communicating climate science to the wider public as well?

▨   Through the media reports based on them, or via the IPCC's website (Box 1.2).

Within two years of its establishment, the IPCC was already playing a pivotal role in the world's response to the threat of climate change. Its first report (in 1990) provided the scientific input to the Second World Climate Conference (Box 1.1), and effectively triggered the events that led to the adoption of an international 'climate convention' (officially, The United Nations Framework Convention on Climate Change, UNFCCC; Box 1.1), which included targets for reducing greenhouse gas emissions. On the face of it, this is science and decision making writ large! In reality, as Weart points out (Weart, 2004):

> The agreement's evasions and ambiguities left governments enough loopholes so they could avoid, if they chose, serious action to reduce [emissions] […] But the agreement did establish some basic principles, and it pointed out a path for further negotiation.

For our purposes, the key point is that the adoption of the climate convention effectively institutionalised the IPCC as an important driving force behind international climate policy. Roughly twice a decade, the Panel would issue an up-to-date assessment of the 'current state of knowledge'; and that would, in turn, provide the scientific basis to inform further action on climate change. For example, there is little doubt that the IPCC's second report (published in 1996) turned up the political heat as a new round of negotiations began on a tougher target for emissions reductions than that in the original text of the UNFCCC. While acknowledging many uncertainties, the report concluded not only that the world was getting warmer, but also that this was 'unlikely to be entirely natural in origin'. In the words of the report's most widely quoted sentence, 'The balance of evidence suggests that there is a discernible human influence on the global climate'. Careful wording perhaps, but the message was clear, and was seized upon with relish by the media. As the journal *Science* put it: 'It's official […] the first glimmer of greenhouse warming' had been seen.

Following tough and protracted negotiations, nations eventually agreed to what is undoubtedly the best-known face of the global climate policy regime to date – the **Kyoto Protocol**, signed in December 1997. There are some brief notes on this agreement in Box 1.3.

Box 1.3 The international climate policy regime: the UNFCCC and the Kyoto Protocol

The global politics of climate change are inextricably bound up with complex environment and development issues that are often portrayed in terms of the 'North–South divide'. Here, the 'North' is another term for the developed countries (referred to as **Annex I** in the UNFCCC) and takes in two broad groups:

- Countries with highly developed market economies (e.g. western Europe, the US, Japan, Australia, etc.).

- Countries with 'economies in transition' (EITs) – countries of the former Soviet Union and other eastern European states.

The 'South' is a crude umbrella term for developing countries (**Non-Annex I**, in the convention's jargon). It takes in everyone else, including very poor countries like Bangladesh and many African nations, oil-rich states in the Middle East, and rapidly industrialising countries such as China and India.

The UNFCCC makes it clear that the developed countries (historically, the largest contributors to greenhouse warming) should take the lead in reducing CO_2 emissions. For them, the Kyoto Protocol significantly strengthened the commitments in the original text: the new (and legally binding) target is an average cut of 5% below 1990 emission levels by 2012. Until then, developing countries are exempted from explicit regulations.

The Protocol also set the scene for a global market in 'carbon credits'. Put simply, developed countries are allowed to exceed their CO_2 emissions quotas at home in two main ways:

- Through 'emissions trading' – by buying the right to emit a given amount of CO_2 from another Annex I country with 'spare' emission rights (e.g. Russia, where the economic collapse in the early 1990s led to a dramatic fall in emissions).

- Through the 'clean development mechanism' – by investing in projects designed to reduce emissions in a developing country partner (e.g. paying to upgrade old and inefficient coal-fired power stations in China).

The finer details on how these mechanisms will actually work only began to emerge in 2001.

■ There is little, if any, disagreement among nations that the top priority for developing countries is the alleviation of poverty, and the pursuit of economic development. How does the global climate policy regime reflect this imperative?

■ In many ways, this ethical aspect of our response to climate change lies at the heart of the regime. For now, developing countries are not required to limit their CO_2 emissions. The burden rests with the developed world.

To enter into force as international law, the Protocol had to be ratified (agreed by the national legislature, i.e. Parliament in the UK) by enough developed countries to account for 55% of that group's CO_2 emissions in 1990. That did not happen until early 2005, and even then, *without* the involvement of the United States – the world's leading economic and political power, and largest single emitter of CO_2 (currently accounting for some 24% of global emissions). To many environmental activists (Figure 1.9), that means that progress on *effective* action to tackle climate change has been glacially slow.

Figure 1.9   Environmental campaigners demonstrate outside the climate negotiations in Bonn, Germany, in July 2001. Climate change connects with many general concerns about the damage being inflicted on the planet's living systems by human population growth and development patterns. It has a prominent place on the agenda of environmental NGOs (non-governmental organisations) such as *Greenpeace* and *Friends of the Earth*.

You will be in a better position to judge the merits of such claims, *from a scientific perspective*, when you have completed this topic. But we hope that one thing is already becoming apparent. The science of climate change feeds into debates about some of the most challenging environment and development issues that the international community has ever attempted to grapple with – debates that tend to revolve around issues of equity and the notion of 'sustainable' economic development. We shall not attempt to explore this notion in any detail, but simply note that, for all the rhetoric, there is little common vision about what it actually means. Different nations bring very different interests and values to the negotiating table; and there are many other non-governmental voices (ranging from environmental NGOs to large multinational corporations) contributing to these debates as well. From this wider perspective, it's fair to say that climate negotiations have come a long way in a relatively short time.

In short, 15 years on from the first IPCC report, the world had embarked on what Klaus Töpfer (the director of UNEP) has called 'only the first step on a long journey'. In the words of the climate convention, the ultimate goal of that journey is to 'prevent dangerous [human] interference with the climate system' (Box 1.1). But what exactly do we mean by 'dangerous'?

Activity 1.2

Allow 15–20 minutes

Before we move on, let's just pause to draw together your thoughts on the themes of communication and decision making. Hopefully, you have been tracking these through earlier sections, so have your notes on Activity 1.1 to hand.

(a) So far, we have identified several means by which the climate science community has communicated its findings on the 'greenhouse warming problem' to (i) government officials and policy makers, and (ii) the wider public. Note these down.

(b) How have governments, in turn, influenced the development of the science of climate change?

(c) What other (non-governmental) interest groups, organisations or public figures also have a stake in influencing the wider debate on the climate change issue?

(d) Now think about your own attitude to the climate change issue. Are you concerned about climate change, or pretty sceptical that there is anything to worry about? Whatever your views, try to identify what lies behind them. Do you feel that you have a reasonable grasp of the underlying science, for example? And if so, what is your main source of information: previous studies, popular scientific articles or books, the media? What other preconceptions, values and feelings have influenced your views?

1.5 Why is climate change a problem?

As implied at the outset, extraordinary statements are being made about the *risks* of human-induced climate change. For example, in early 2004, the Pentagon in the US (hardly a hotbed of environmental activists) waded in with its own highly charged perspective on a global-warming future: 'a world riven with water wars, famine and anarchy', according to one of the articles in Figure 1.1.

What are we to make of such doom-laden claims? Are they an accurate portrayal of the potential consequences of climate change, as conceived by current scientific understanding? In this context, it is not much help to learn that, in the more measured tones of the IPCC TAR (IPCC, 2001a): 'The globally averaged surface temperature [i.e. GMST] is projected to increase by 1.4 to 5.8 °C over the period 1990 to 2100'.

■ This statement is based on the climate modelling studies reviewed by the IPCC. How does it provide striking evidence of the uncertainties we referred to earlier?

▨ The range of projected global warming (i.e. the rise in GMST) by the end of this century is very wide; there is a factor-of-four difference between the top and bottom of the range of temperature change.

We shall probe the many sources of uncertainty in these model-based projections in later chapters. For now, it is enough to note that the IPCC gives no guidance about the relative likelihoods of various outcomes within this range. So how are we to interpret the Panel's findings? On the face of it, global warming at the bottom end of the model-projected range – a rise in GMST of 1–2 °C, say, over the next 100 years – does not sound that alarming. Indeed, the prospect of a slightly warmer climate could seem positively attractive to many people in the colder parts of the planet, for instance in northern Europe or Siberia or northern North America. But what if the size, and by implication, the *rate* of warming this century were actually four times as great? Either way, we need to get a feel for what continued global warming could mean in more tangible terms. How might human societies and **ecosystems** (natural communities of plants and animals) in different parts of the world be affected? What might it actually mean for the lives and livelihoods of people in this and future generations?

In the IPCC TAR, questions like these are addressed in the report from Working Group II (Box 1.2). Before we jump ahead and take a look at its conclusions, let's just pause to consider the range of *potential* impacts that could affect human welfare. Broadly, these can be traced back to the combined influence of the factors we identified at the end of Section 1.2:

- *Regional climate change* Alongside a trend to higher average temperatures, this takes in possible changes in the total amount of precipitation in a given locality, and/or its distribution through the year.

- *Extreme events* Possible changes in the frequency and/or severity of such events (floods, droughts, storms, heat waves, etc.).

- *Global sea-level rise* According to the TAR (IPCC, 2001a): 'Global mean sea level is projected to rise by 0.09 to 0.88 metres between 1990 and 2100'.

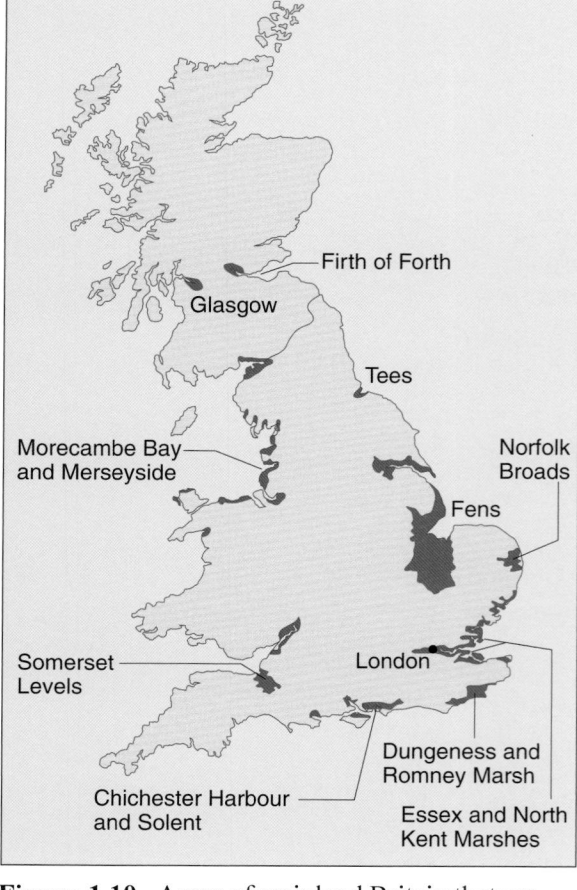

Figure 1.10   Areas of mainland Britain that are currently less than 5 m above sea level.

To focus the discussion, let's start with the final point: rising sea level is one of the most frequently cited reasons for concern about global warming. Again, current model-based projections (noted above) cover a wide range of possibilities. Suppose we take a sea-level rise of 50 cm by the end of the 21st century as a typical mid-range value. This might not sound much. But even in mainland Britain, it would threaten low-lying coastal areas (Figure 1.10), especially in southeast England, which has regional subsidence as well (see Chapter 3). For example, East Anglia (and the Fens, in particular) already relies on some major flood defences, as does London (the Thames Flood Barrier). In these and other vulnerable areas, extreme high water levels – due to a combination of high tides and 'storm surges' on top of a rise in average sea level – would become more frequent, with a higher risk of coastal flooding and erosion, or permanent inundation. What would this mean in social, economic and environmental terms?

■ Drawing on Figure 1.10 and your general knowledge of Britain (or another country you are more familiar with), try to come up with three or four examples of the potential consequences of sea-level rise that would affect the nature of the coastal zone, and the lives and livelihoods of people living there.

▪ The range of potential impacts is wide. Check your ideas with the points discussed below (some of which may well be unfamiliar).

For a start, there would be consequences for anything built on low-lying land near the coast. The list includes human settlements (from cities to isolated properties), industrial centres, power stations and other facilities (e.g. road and rail links) – with implications for the insurance industry as well. Moreover, productive farmland (e.g. in East Anglia) would be threatened with permanent inundation – or with 'salinisation' through periodic incursions of saltwater, which could also contaminate freshwater resources (e.g. groundwater). Land well above sea level could be lost as well. Cliffs along some stretches of Britain's coastline are crumbling away due to the erosion caused by wave action; rising seas would speed up this natural process.

Meanwhile, some beaches would disappear. Other coastal wildlife habitats, such as salt marshes and freshwater wetlands, would be flooded and could be lost if unable to re-establish further inland, due to urban growth or sea defences. On top of their ecological significance, coastal environments are some of the most biologically productive areas on Earth; worldwide, they provide habitat and breeding grounds for important fishery populations and seafood. Bear in mind too that they are areas of recreation and tourism.

Of course, it is possible to keep the sea at bay, but the cost is enormous. For example, without its system of dykes and sea walls, half the present area of The Netherlands would be under water; maintaining these sea defences takes roughly 6% of that country's gross domestic product (GDP). Even for wealthy countries like the UK or other western European nations, the costs of coping with, *and adapting to*, sea-level rise will be high. The issue will also raise difficult social and political questions. Should a country attempt to maintain its existing coastline, for instance? Or would it be more cost effective (in purely economic terms) to focus on protecting its more valuable 'assets' (cities, major towns, power stations, etc.), and plan for a 'managed' retreat elsewhere – by abandoning the farmland and smaller communities at greatest risk of flooding, say, and relocating people and facilities to higher ground? How would people faced with losing their homes, communities and livelihoods respond to that prospect?

The point we want to emphasise here is that the problems of coping with sea-level rise *alone* would be far sharper for many developing countries. In general, they have fewer financial and technical resources available for adaptive measures, and a weaker infrastructure for implementing them effectively. On top of that, some countries would face a problem on a staggering scale; that is, they are more *vulnerable* to the effects of sea-level rise.

■   Thinking back to earlier in the course, what country comes to mind in this context?

▨   As the world's major low-lying country, Bangladesh is especially vulnerable to sea-level rise. In the Ganges–Brahmaputra delta region, most of the land is less than 2 m above the sea, and already subsiding (due in part to the over-extraction of groundwater – the issue that was central to Topic 3, though in a different context).

According to the IPCC, a sea-level rise of 45 cm would (without adaptive measures) inundate about 11% of Bangladesh and displace around 5 million people; a 1 m rise (at the top end of current projections for the 21st century) would increase that figure to 15 million. Major low-lying coastal regions of other Asian countries,

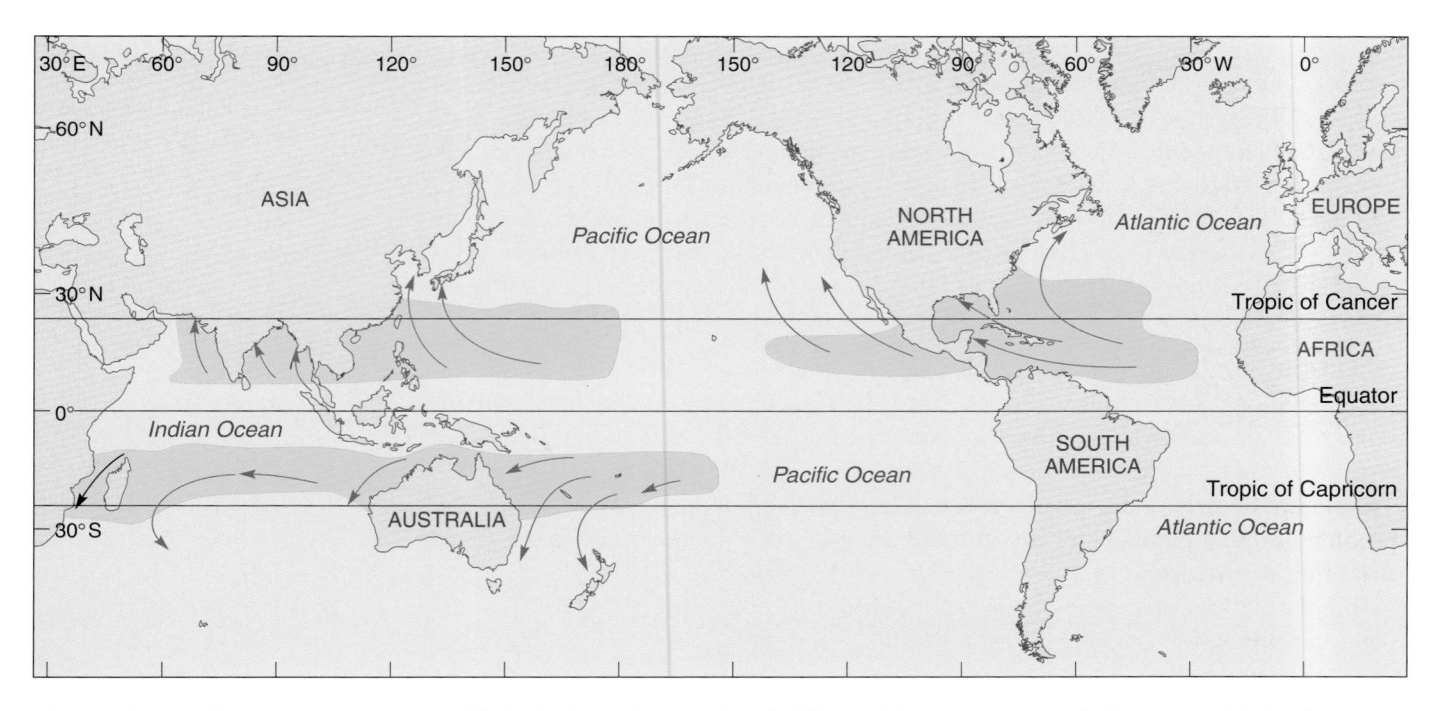

Figure 1.11 This world map shows the ocean areas where most tropical cyclones form, as well as the most common tracks they follow. Note that these storms seldom form over the South Atlantic or the eastern South Pacific (for reasons we revisit in Chapter 4).

with their densely populated cities and huge rural populations, would also be profoundly affected – southern China, India and Vietnam, in particular. Overall, many tens of millions of people in Asia may be displaced from what is, at present, productive farmland – raising the prospect of mass migrations of 'environmental refugees'. Sea-level rise would also cause extensive damage to the coastal fish and prawn industry, a major source of protein in local diets throughout southeast Asia and of revenue through exports.

For these and other nations in the tropics and subtropics (roughly 30° N to 30° S), there is another factor that would exacerbate the hazards of sea-level rise; their coastal zones are visited, periodically, by the destructive power of tropical cyclones (Figure 1.11). Along with the damage caused by high winds and rain (referred to in Figure 1.2), tropical cyclones can produce a massive surge in sea level (5 m or more, in extreme cases) as they move onshore, devastating coastal communities and leading to major loss of life. In 1991, for instance, a storm surge superimposed on normal high tide took the lives of at least 135 000 people in Bangladesh. Historically, some 76% of the total death toll from these storms has occurred here and in neighbouring India.

Other nations in regions prone to cyclonic activity may have even greater problems. They may be rendered uninhabitable, or be wiped from the map altogether. This stark perspective is evident in pleas from the leaders of a number of small island states (in the South Pacific and Indian Oceans, and in the Caribbean Sea) that are particularly low lying, several with maximum heights above sea level of just a few metres. In a statement to the UN General Assembly in September 2003, the Prime Minister of Tuvalu (Figure 1.12) put it like this:

> we live in constant fear of the adverse impacts of climate change. For a coral atoll nation, sea-level rise and more severe weather events loom as a growing threat to our entire population. The threat is real and serious, and is of no difference to a slow and insidious form of terrorism against us.

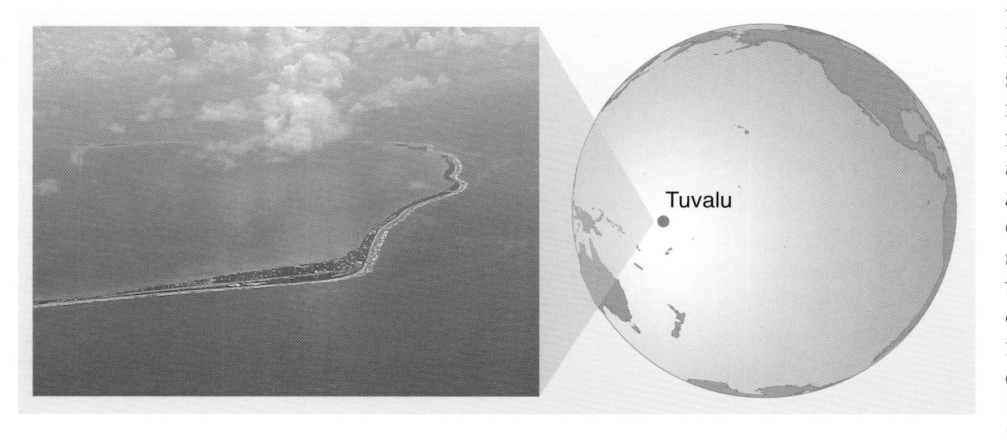

Figure 1.12 Funafuti is the main island in the collection of seamounts and coral atolls that make up Tuvalu (a dot on the map in the South Pacific). It has a coastline of about 24 km and a *maximum* height above sea level of just 5 m. A major tropical storm can devastate islands like this for decades. The government of Tuvalu has already begun to formulate evacuation plans, in case its population (around 11 000 in 2004) become the first 'refugees' of climate change.

To sum up: Clearly, there are no real 'winners' from sea-level rise, i.e. it is a problem for all nations with a coastline. But equally, the 'losers' (those most at risk of harm) are distributed very unevenly – both at the national level (e.g. within the UK) and, more importantly, across the globe. Some developing countries are both more vulnerable to sea-level rise and less able to bear the costs of coping with it. This picture of 'unevenness' in the distribution of impacts and vulnerabilities emerges with yet greater force once we begin to factor in the effects of regional climate change as well.

As you will see in Chapter 6, the details of how global warming will affect regional climates remain hazy. Nevertheless, there is widespread agreement that the range of potential impacts is broad. Some examples are given in Figure 1.13, collected under headings that represent 'sectors' likely to be particularly sensitive to changing climatic conditions.

Space does not allow us to attempt a comprehensive review of such possible impacts, though we shall come back to some of them in later chapters, once we have filled in the necessary scientific background. At this stage, our aim is to

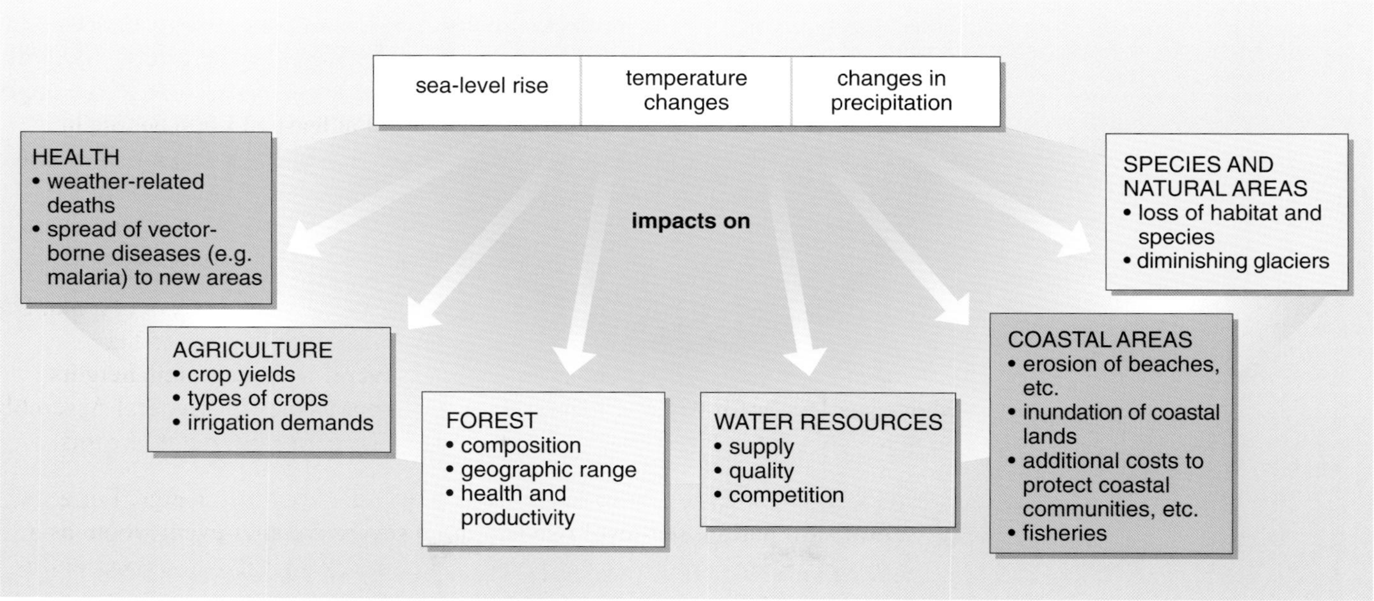

Figure 1.13 Examples of the potential impacts of climate change (including sea-level rise) in various sectors.

sea-level rise | temperature changes | changes in precipitation

impacts on

HEALTH
• weather-related deaths
• spread of vector-borne diseases (e.g. malaria) to new areas

AGRICULTURE
• crop yields
• types of crops
• irrigation demands

FOREST
• composition
• geographic range
• health and productivity

WATER RESOURCES
• supply
• quality
• competition

SPECIES AND NATURAL AREAS
• loss of habitat and species
• diminishing glaciers

COASTAL AREAS
• erosion of beaches, etc.
• inundation of coastal lands
• additional costs to protect coastal communities, etc.
• fisheries

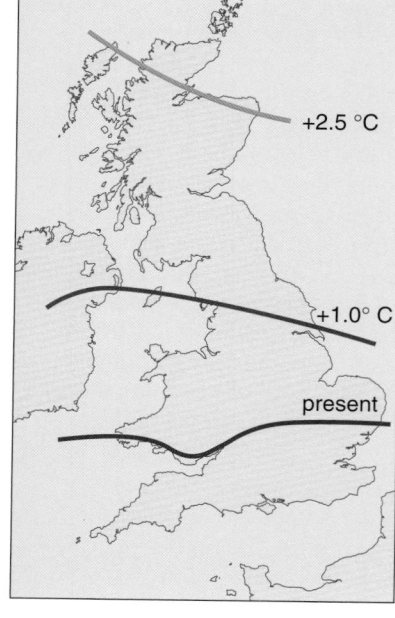

Figure 1.14 Possible shifts in the northern limit for the ripening of grain maize in the UK. The present limit in an average year is shown (lower plot), along with suggested future limits (maroon and orange plots) for a range of degrees of warming.

point out that the 'lottery' of climate change will bring benefits as well as costs. However, the 'balance sheet' of winners and losers will vary from region to region. Since food production is fundamental to human welfare, we take agriculture as our main example. Note that the relevant box in Figure 1.13 includes three points: crop yields; types of crops; and irrigation demands.

Underlying these points is the fact that the climatic conditions in a given region – mainly the temperature regime and availability of water – largely determine the types of plants (whether natural or cultivated) that will grow there. Different crops have their own particular temperature requirements, and this imposes constraints on the areas where they can be grown with a high chance of success (i.e. good yields). In Europe, for example, the present northern limit for growing grain maize is imposed by lack of warmth; in an average year, it takes in the parts of southern England shown in Figure 1.14. Elsewhere in the UK, the **growing season** (between the last frost of spring and first frost of autumn) is usually too short and summer temperatures are rarely high enough to ensure successful ripening of the grain. With a warmer UK climate, however, the growing limit would shift north, to an extent that would depend on the magnitude of the warming (i.e. the rise in average temperature).

This is just one example of the 'spatial shifts' in the potential for growing crops that are likely in a global-warming future. Such shifts in agricultural potential would have both beneficial and adverse effects. In northern Europe, Russia and North America, for example, a rise in average temperatures could open up new lands to cultivation – in areas at higher latitudes that are currently too cold to be very productive. Moreover, if warmer winters and a longer growing season become a reality in temperate regions at middle latitudes (roughly 40° to 55° N), yields of many existing crops might increase, and the changed conditions might suit many new ones as well. On the other hand, many staple crops (wheat, maize, rice, soya bean, etc.) are so 'fine tuned' to the prevailing temperature regime, in terms of their tolerance of *high* as well as low temperatures, that some existing growing areas would suffer a fall in productivity.

This is probably true of the 'corn belt' in the US, for instance, where a northward shift in agricultural potential is likely to be offset by losses further south. Towards the southern edge of the belt, summer temperatures are already close to the upper limit that wheat and maize can tolerate, especially at the time when the grain is maturing. If a warmer climate results in more very hot spells (as seems likely; see Chapter 3), crop yields could fall. Many regions already suffer large-scale agricultural losses during unusually hot summers (though this can be due, in part, to drier soil conditions rather than direct heat damage). One recent example was the prolonged and extreme heatwave that gripped Europe in 2003; across the EU, wheat production was reduced by about 10% on normal years, with much greater losses in the south than in the north.

- ■   With these fairly simple considerations in mind, what parts of the world are most likely to experience a decline in crop yields as average temperatures rise?

- ▨   Regions where important crops are already near to their maximum temperature tolerance. In general, this is likely to mean regions at low latitudes.

Bear in mind too that livestock (e.g. cattle, pigs and poultry) are all susceptible to heat stress – and so are people, of course.

■ What other aspect of regional climate change is likely to have a significant impact on agricultural output in a warmer world?

▨ Possible shifts in rainfall patterns, and hence in the water available to support plant growth in a given region. Some areas may receive less rainfall than they do today – potentially increasing requirements for irrigation and/or the risk of drought – while others get more, or the seasonal distribution could change. (Perhaps you also thought about the catastrophic effects of 'one-off' extreme weather events, an important issue we come back to in Chapter 7.)

Unfortunately, this is one area where model predictions of future climate change are generally acknowledged to be particularly unreliable (see Chapter 6), although there are some fairly robust features. Typically, estimated patterns of change include rainfall increases over northern mid- to high latitudes and some equatorial regions, and decreases in many sub-tropical and semi-arid regions (terms that are defined more precisely in Chapter 4). When these features are combined with projected changes in the temperature regime in different parts of the world, and fed into models of agricultural systems, most studies reach broadly similar conclusions. As reported in the TAR (IPCC, 2001b):

• Even nominal amounts of warming would reduce crop yields in the tropics and sub-tropics, a zone that takes in many developing countries; i.e. most of Africa, tropical Latin America, the Indian subcontinent and southeast Asia (Figure 1.11).

• Modest global warming (a rise in GMST of 1–2 °C) would improve productivity at mid- to high latitudes (provided adequate water is available).

• For average global warming greater than 2.5 °C, world food prices (taken to be a key indicator of world food production) would rise; productivity gains at mid- to high latitudes would diminish, and yield decreases in the tropics and sub-tropics are expected to be more severe.

These conclusions reinforce points we made in the context of sea-level rise. With shifts in optimal crop zones, changed yields and water availability, farmers across the globe would face new challenges in a warmer world. For more temperate, developed countries, adapting current agricultural practices to changed climatic conditions is probably both feasible and affordable, and food production as a whole is unlikely to be threatened by modest global warming; there may even be net gains in some regions. But once again, the negative impacts will fall disproportionately on vulnerable communities in the developing world – especially in those regions where a substantial proportion of the population is particularly poor, or lives in semi-arid (or indeed, coastal) areas, or depends on rain-fed (i.e. non-irrigated) agriculture. For example, climate change is expected to worsen food security in many parts of Africa – increasing the risk of hunger, or outright starvation, in areas where tens of millions of people already suffer from chronic undernourishment.

■ For the world as a whole, what other key point is implicit in the conclusions summarised above?

■ Put simply, the balance sheet of 'costs and benefits' depends not only on geographical location, but also on the *amount* of global warming. For a modest rise in GMST, there are positive effects in some regions (at mid- to high latitudes), and negative effects in others (in the tropics and sub-tropics) – potentially increasing the disparity in food production between developed and developing countries, in this case. But as global warming increases, the costs begin to outweigh the benefits, and the overall balance shifts towards a *net* negative outcome for human welfare (i.e. world food production is reduced).

Broadly similar conclusions emerge from studies of the potential impacts on the many other sectors that impinge on human welfare in different parts of the world (i.e. water resources; forests; coastal zones and fisheries; human health; human settlements; etc.; Figure 1.13). In general, the disparity in social, economic and environmental conditions between rich and poorer countries means that the latter are usually more vulnerable to the negative effects of sea-level rise and regional climate change. This is expected to exacerbate what are already enormous problems for many of the world's poorest people. But as the rise in GMST increases, so the adverse impacts on a wide range of sectors come to dominate the picture for all nations.

In the TAR, the IPCC elected to get this central message across via a striking (if somewhat impressionistic) diagram; it is reproduced here (in slightly modified form) as Figure 1.15. There are several points to note. First, the vertical scale represents the increase in GMST (above the 1990 value); it spans the range of current model-based projections for the 21st century (i.e. 1.4 to 5.8 °C). Secondly, each of the vertical bars represents one of the five categories of 'reasons for concern' about climate change identified by the IPCC; these are listed in Table 1.1, together with some brief explanatory notes.

Figure 1.15 Reasons for concern about projected climate change (I–V refer to categories given in Table 1.1).

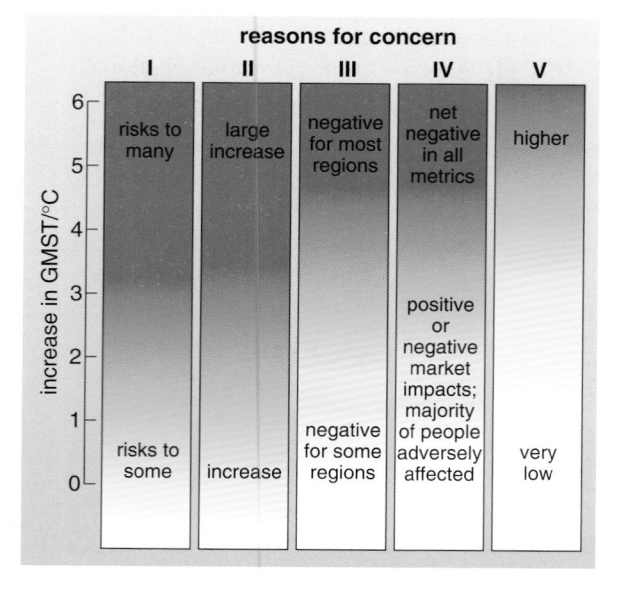

In this section, we have concentrated on examples that illustrate 'the unevenness and inequalities' of climate change impacts (category III in the table) – though we have also made reference to the damaging effects of extreme events (category II)

Table 1.1 The IPCC's five categories of 'reasons for concern' about climate change (IPCC, 2001b).

Risk category	Comments
I Risks to unique and threatened natural systems	Some species and ecosystems (e.g. coral reefs and coastal wetlands) are highly sensitive to environmental change, and could be irreversibly damaged or lost (see Chapter 3).
II Risks from extreme climate events (floods, droughts, storms, heat waves, etc.)	Some of the major impacts of climate change are expected to come from increases in the frequency and/or intensity of extreme events (see Chapter 7).
III Distribution of impacts	This relates to the issue of winners and losers; i.e. the inequalities and unevenness of the impacts that climate change will bring (as discussed in this section).
IV Global economic impacts	A measure of the total cost of climate change on the economy. The size of the human welfare loss is usually measured in terms of % of GDP, taking into account costs and benefits of climate change for a particular increase in GMST. Such assessments are still highly controversial (see text).
V Risks from future large-scale discontinuities	Global warming has the potential to trigger major changes in the climate system that would have widespread and sustained impacts. Two examples are referred to in Figure 1.1: a rapid disintegration of the West Antarctic Ice Sheet; and a cooling of the UK climate, due to a weakening or loss of the Gulf Stream (see Chapters 4 and 7).

in our current climate, and touched on the economic implications of climate change (category IV). There is a strand of economic modelling and research that seeks to quantify the costs and benefits of future climate change, and to put a price on the *net* impact on human welfare. We shall not attempt to explore the details of such assessments, but simply note that the answers they come up with are strongly dependent on the kinds of assumptions built into the models. In particular, there is a link here with difficult questions that also have an ethical dimension. For example, how do you place a monetary value on the impacts of climate change on the non-human world – the loss of species, habitats, or even entire ecosystems (category I in Table 1.1)? And what about the harm we might be doing to the prospects of *future* generations?

Economists have always brought 'thinking about the future' into their forecasts. But for the most part, this is done in a way (known as 'discounting') that emphasises human welfare in the present to the detriment of future generations and the environment. In effect, future gains or losses are seen as being less important than an equivalent gain or loss today. This is not too different from everyday human aspirations. As one commentator has put it (Smith, 2003): 'Most people with families want to maximise their economic security and share that security with their close relations in the present and near-future. Ties with distant future generations, whether kin or not, are altogether less compelling'.

Recognition of the long-term, intergenerational nature of the climate change problem has prompted some radical re-thinking on this front. In some assessments of the kind referred to above, efforts are being made to factor in the 'full' environmental costs of climate change impacts, and to represent the

Figure 1.16 In true disaster-movie fashion, *The Day After Tomorrow* depicts a terrifying global-warming-induced scenario – tidal waves sweeping through cities, snow piling halfway up New York's skyscrapers and hail the size of grapefruit devastating Tokyo. We can forgive Hollywood for artistic licence, but the credibility of climate change science is not well served by wild, implausible scenarios such as an imminent return of 'ice age' conditions to London or New York.

potential harm to future generations in a way that is less stacked in favour of the people alive today. We shall not pursue the matter further, but it's worth bearing in mind in your reading about the climate change issue. The more 'traditional' economists' mindset often underpins arguments that we should pursue economic development that rewards many in present generations, but only *may* be creating hazards and harm in the future.

To return to Table 1.1, the final category of 'reasons for concern' represents the more scary side of future climate change – the possibility that continued greenhouse warming could trigger sudden and dramatic changes, rather than a gradual shift in climatic conditions around the world. Stories of this kind often feature in the media (Figure 1.1), and have entered popular culture through films such as *The Day After Tomorrow* (Figure 1.16). We shall take a sober look at the science behind such concerns in later chapters.

The visual impact of Figure 1.15 comes from the colour code used in an attempt to communicate the varied 'calculus of risk' associated with projected global warming. The IPCC's official explanation of the colour key is:

- *white* indicates neutral or small negative or positive impacts or risks
- *yellow* indicates negative impacts for some systems or low risks
- *red* means negative impacts or risks that are more widespread and/or greater in magnitude.

The IPCC does not explain exactly what is meant by 'low' or 'high' risk in this context, so we are left to draw our own conclusions.

■   With reference to Figure 1.15, summarise in your own words the relationship between 'reasons for concern' and the projected increase in GMST.

▨   There is no one 'correct' answer here, but my own thoughts went as follows. In many cases, the chances of adverse effects appear to increase with the rise in GMST, but not always at an even pace and often distributed unevenly. However, for larger projected increases in GMST (above about 3 °C), there are significant risks of widespread damaging effects in all categories of reasons for concern, including an increased chance that major new hazards (of the kind represented by category V) may appear.

So we can interpret the colour code in clearer terms: red effectively means 'danger'. Although the details remain hazy, somewhere within the range of projected global warming for the end of the century (1.4 to 5.8 °C) the threshold introduced at the end of the previous section is crossed: dangerous interference with the climate system.

1.6 Taking stock and looking forward

The notion that human actions can modify climate on a global scale has travelled a long and rocky road on the way to being accepted by the majority of the climate science community. Though attitudes were already shifting in that direction by the late 1980s (Section 1.3), there is no doubt that critical appraisal of the 'current state of knowledge' in successive IPCC reports has consolidated a broad scientific consensus on the causes and implications of global warming. And that has, in turn, brought governments 'on board', through the UNFCCC and Kyoto Protocol. It was concerned scientists who played a pivotal role in bringing human-induced climate change to public attention, and scientific assessment now underpins the global political response.

As climate change has moved up the world's agendas, the policy debate – although ostensibly about the scientific case for action – has often taken on the characteristics of a propaganda war. Over the years, media coverage of this issue has been a fertile arena for polemic and highly polarised views, as various opposing advocate groups and other pundits have waded in with their own perspectives. This is not altogether surprising. Efforts to curb the growth in atmospheric CO_2 have far-reaching policy implications, involving socially and economically painful choices (Figure 1.17), technological challenges and an unprecedented level of international co-operation. On the other hand, climate

Figure 1.17 One of the great challenges of climate-change politics is that a global problem that is the result of millions of local activities requires that international agreements can result, through the actions of different governments, in changes in the behaviour of industry, business and commerce, and individual citizens at the local level. Politicians will always keep a weather eye on public opinion, keenly aware of the need to 'sell' whatever control measures they sign up to (e.g. the cutbacks in CO_2 emissions mandated by the Kyoto Protocol) to consumers and voters. Recent protests against fuel price increases in the UK perhaps provide a foretaste of the strong resentment and opposition that could be stirred up by any proposal to impose higher energy taxes.

change is a great attention grabber for environmental activists: the risks of large-scale environmental change and damage are real and significant. The issue also invites prescriptions about how people should live properly and equitably together on the same planet, and is a trump-card for those promoting sustainable development (Section 1.4). In short, the list of 'actors' with a stake in advancing their own interests or worldview is a particularly long one (recall your thoughts on Activity 1.2). Indeed, climate change, and what people decide to do about it, will affect all of us in one way or another.

To make matters more confusing for the concerned citizen, a vocal minority of scientists continues to question both the evidence for a link between global warming and human activity, and the credibility of the models used to project future climate change. In the highly charged context of the policy debate, media reports may seek to 'balance' the mainstream scientific consensus (embodied in IPCC reports) against the opposing views of a few high-profile sceptics; to the non-specialist, each position can seem equally credible. Even accurate reports of new findings by professional science journalists can be hard to take in, as the spotlight shifts with bewildering speed from one aspect of the climate change puzzle to another (a pattern evident in Figure 1.1).

Behind much of this confusion lies the 'uncomfortable truth' we flagged up at the outset (Section 1.1): the climate change issue is both extremely complex and so infused with uncertainties that it is still impossible to rule out either mild or catastrophic outcomes if the world simply carries on with 'business as usual'. Will the Earth's GMST be up by 1.4 °C by 2100, or by 5.8 °C? The difference (crystallised in Figure 1.15) is between relatively adaptable changes and very damaging ones. Or are these two polar opposites (i.e. either 'it will all be OK' or 'it will be catastrophic') actually the least likely possible outcomes?

As you will see, when scientists peer into the shadowy future for the Earth's climate using the best available knowledge, they are dealing with an outcome that will depend on a unique coming together of a range of factors and circumstances. The outcome will be something genuinely novel, one that cannot be predicted solely on the basis of what has happened in the past. Given the same body of information, different scientists can, and do, reach different subjective judgements about the odds on various climate futures. The challenge for climate scientists is how to communicate underlying levels of confidence in these 'expert judgements' without straying into one of the twin traps of ignoring the necessary caveats (due to uncertainties), or else producing statements so hedged in qualifications (because of the complexities) as to misrepresent what is really understood. Stephen Schneider (Figure 1.18) has referred to this as the 'ethical double bind'.

Figure 1.18 Stephen Schneider (right) is a leading climate researcher who has grappled with the problem of communicating the complexities of climate science to non-specialists for over 30 years. He has a high public profile in the US, as a witness before countless committees of the state and federal legislatures, in the media, through popular scientific articles and books, and via his website. Together with Richard Moss (left), he was influential in getting the IPCC to adopt in the TAR a more rigorous treatment of the uncertainties in the science (see Chapter 3). For this reason, the two have sometimes been dubbed the 'uncertainty cops'.

For the IPCC, the challenge of communicating the science of climate change comes down to the need to be clear and up-front about the degree of confidence it has in its conclusions, while at the same time explaining as far as possible the origins and nature of the uncertainties about our climate future. These themes run through the discussion of the detailed science in the rest of this topic. Our overall aim is to give you a firm basis from which to follow future developments in an informed and *critical* way – to judge for yourself the import of new findings as these are reported in the media and in popular scientific articles, and to weigh up the merits of various claims and counter-claims in the wider debate about climate policy. We have already touched on some of the major questions that will be addressed along the way. In brief:

- How do we know that the observed build up in atmospheric CO_2 and 'other' greenhouse gases is due to human activities, and why is this expected to lead to global warming?

- What is the evidence for global warming, and how confident can we be about the extent to which warming is attributable to human activity? What are the sceptics questioning, and what is the nature of the evidence they use?

- What do we mean by the Earth's 'climate system'?

- How confident can we be about the basic methods, assumptions and results of climate modelling studies? What are the main factors that feed into the uncertainties about our climate future? What happens if we don't do anything? What are the odds that the polar ice-caps will melt, for example? Or that the world will see more extreme weather conditions – more floods, droughts and storms?

- The UNFCCC calls for 'stabilization of greenhouse gas concentrations […] at a level that would prevent dangerous anthropogenic interference with the climate system'. What 'level' is this? And how are we going to get there? How deep, and how fast, do the cuts in global CO_2 emissions need to be?

Before you embark on this journey, take a few minutes to attempt Activity 1.3. It gives you a chance to check your existing understanding of some of the basic science of climate change.

Activity 1.3

Allow 10–15 minutes

Consider the following quote (in *The Guardian Weekly*, 10 February, 2000) from George Monbiot (writer and campaigner on environmental issues): 'Every time someone in the West switches on a kettle, he or she is helping to flood Bangladesh'.

(a) Can you readily describe the steps in the scientific argument that explains why burning fossil fuels (in a power station in this case) is expected to lead to sea-level rise? Try to jot down the various steps in the chain of cause and effects. Don't spend long on this, and don't worry if you cannot get very far, but do keep your notes. We shall come back to this exercise at the end of Chapter 3.

(b) What other aspect of the climate change issue is implicit in the statement above?

Summary of Chapter 1

1   The Earth's global climate is commonly characterised by a somewhat artificial globally averaged temperature, known as the global mean surface temperature (GMST). The focus of this topic is the 'global warming' (i.e. rise in GMST) caused by the build-up of greenhouse gases (especially CO_2) in the atmosphere due to human activities (notably burning fossil fuels), and the potential consequences of allowing this 'greenhouse warming' to continue unchecked. The term 'climate change' takes in the effects of a rise in GMST on regional climates (temperatures, precipitation patterns, extreme events, etc.) and global sea level.

2   Human-induced climate change is no longer the remote possibility first pointed out by Arrhenius over a century ago. It is now the subject of major international agreements (the United Nations Framework Convention on Climate Change, UNFCCC, and Kyoto Protocol; Boxes 1.1 and 1.3), and is widely seen as one of the most pressing, and challenging, environmental issues of our times. An evolving scientific understanding of climate change underpins this transformation from scientific curiosity to global political and cultural consciousness.

3   The study of climate change is an extreme example of an area that requires the integration of knowledge and expertise from dozens of different scientific communities. Barriers to communication, the inadequacies of available data and the sheer complexity of the climate system have long created difficulties for scientists seeking to assess the climatic effects of an atmosphere enriched in CO_2. A majority view that this is a 'legitimate cause for concern' only began to emerge amid the heightened environmental awareness of the mid- to late 1980s.

4   There are many means whereby 'expert knowledge' on climate change has informed and influenced individual governments, industries, interest groups and public opinion (see Activity 1.2). Since its establishment under UN auspices in 1988, the exhaustive reviews and negotiating sessions of the Intergovernmental Panel on Climate Change (IPCC) have effectively institutionalised this process at the international level. To date (2006), the IPCC has produced three major assessments of the 'current state of knowledge' on climate change. Carefully worded consensus statements are collected in a 'Summary for Policymakers' (SPM), which is an important (and politically sensitive) part of each report, and a major vehicle for communicating the Panel's findings to non-specialists.

5   The dynamics of the IPCC process has consolidated a broad scientific consensus on the causes and implications of climate change. At the same time, there are still many uncertainties about how human-induced climate change will evolve over the century ahead. This messy reality is a central part of the climate change challenge. It also provides opportunities for a minority of scientific sceptics to contest some of the IPCC's findings (see also Chapter 3).

6   Scientific assessment by the IPCC is now a major driving force behind international climate policy. The science and the politics of climate change are inextricably interlinked, and are also an integral part of wider debates about complex environment and development issues. Different nations and interest groups bring very different perspectives to these wider debates about equity and

'sustainable' development, and that can, in turn, colour attitudes to what can or should be done to combat climate change.

7   The range of potential impacts of climate change is very wide. Sea-level rise alone would have major socioeconomic and environmental consequences, especially for the inhabitants of island nations and other low-lying areas of developing countries (e.g. Bangladesh). In other sectors that impinge directly on human welfare (e.g. food production; Figure 1.13), modest global warming will bring both beneficial and adverse effects in different regions. Again, the negative impacts will fall disproportionately on vulnerable communities in the developing world. The inequalities and unevenness of climate change impacts raise difficult ethical and political issues about the responsibility of people elsewhere in the world for these threats.

8   The IPCC's Third Assessment Report (TAR) identified several categories of 'reasons for concern' about climate change (summarised in Table 1.1). The risks of widespread damaging effects in all categories increase significantly with the projected rise in GMST, including an increased chance that major new hazards (e.g. a weakening of the Gulf Stream) may appear. The details remain uncertain, but somewhere within the range of projected global warming for the end of the century (1.4 to 5.8 °C) an important threshold (identified in the UNFCCC) is crossed: dangerous interference with the Earth's climate system.

Chapter 2 Global climate and the greenhouse effect

At the beginning of the 21st century, terms such as the 'greenhouse effect', 'greenhouse gases' and 'greenhouse warming' are printed or spoken thousands of times a week in the context of climate change caused by human activities. This chapter is designed to consolidate your understanding of the basic science behind these terms, and then to review what is known about the human impact on the composition of the atmosphere since the dawn of the industrial age, commonly put (in this context) at around AD 1750.

We start with a couple of fundamental questions about global climate (as defined in Section 1.2). What determines the Earth's global mean surface temperature (GMST)? And how does the composition of the atmosphere come into that equation?

Box 2.1 Electromagnetic radiation

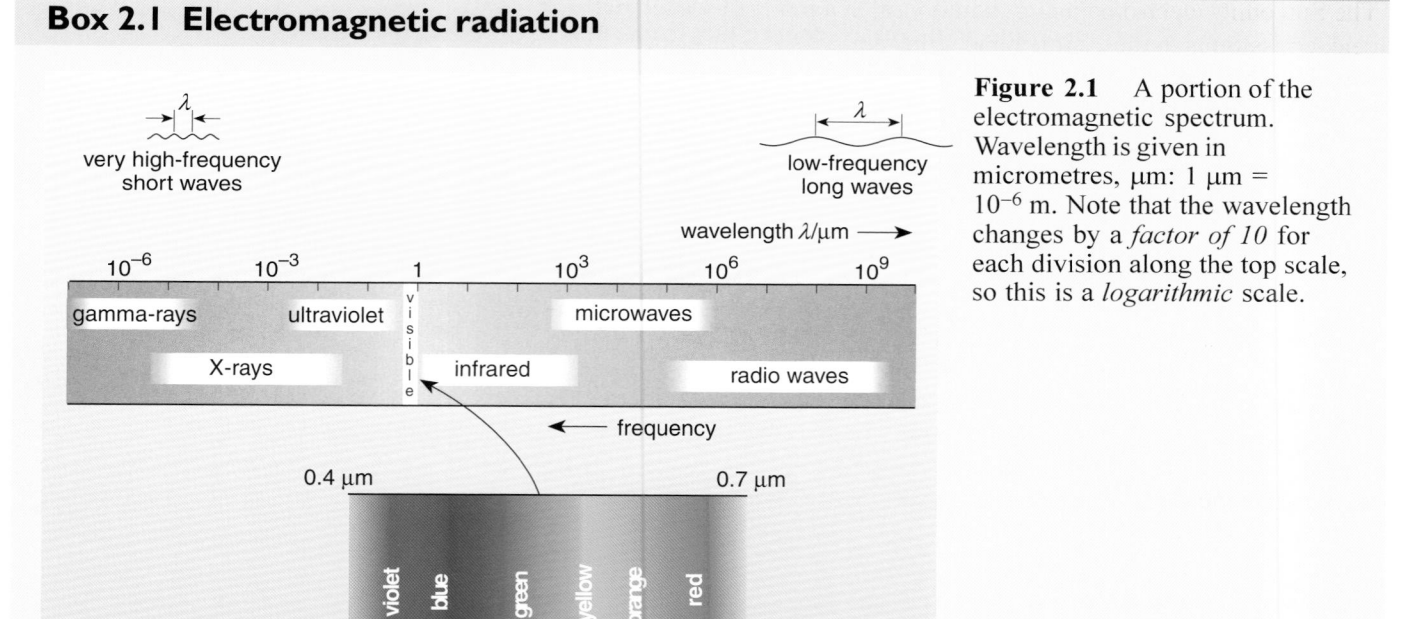

Figure 2.1 A portion of the electromagnetic spectrum. Wavelength is given in micrometres, μm: 1 μm = 10^{-6} m. Note that the wavelength changes by a *factor of 10* for each division along the top scale, so this is a *logarithmic* scale.

Electromagnetic radiation is the only form of energy transfer that travels through the vacuum of space, propagating as a wave. By convention, the full spectrum of electromagnetic radiation is carved up into regions, each characterised by a particular range of wavelengths (Figure 2.1). The **wavelength** (symbol λ) is just the distance between successive crests of a wave.

Our eyes are sensitive to **visible radiation**, which corresponds to the wavelength range from about 0.4 μm (violet light) to 0.7 μm (red light). When all wavelengths in this range are present, we perceive this as 'white light'. To either side of the visible band lie the ranges known as **ultraviolet (uv) radiation** (with wavelengths *below* that of violet light) and **infrared (ir) radiation** (with wavelengths *above* that of red light).

As with any propagating waves, the shorter the wavelength, the higher the frequency (f) (i.e. the higher the number of waves passing a point in a given time). For electromagnetic radiation, the two multiplied together give the speed of light (c): $c = f\lambda$.

2.1 What determines the Earth's GMST?

The Sun is the ultimate source of energy for the Earth's climate. A planet such as the Earth will have a stable temperature as long as there is a balance between the rate at which energy comes in from the Sun and the rate at which it is returned to space by the planet. If the two rates fail to match, the planet will either warm up or cool down until a balance is restored. Thus, it is appropriate to begin with a review of this global balancing act. The heart of the matter is that the energy flows to and from space are in the form of radiation – or to be more precise, **electromagnetic radiation**. You should consult Box 2.1 if you need to refresh your memory about this form of energy transfer.

2.1.1 Heating and cooling the Earth: the overall radiation balance

The Sun emits electromagnetic radiation with a range of wavelengths, but its peak emission is in the visible band – the sunlight that allows us to see. The wavelength of radiation has important climatic implications, as we shall see shortly. For now, we are mainly interested in the overall *rate* at which energy in the form of **solar radiation** reaches the Earth.

■ What is the SI unit for the rate of energy transfer, or 'power'?

▨ The watt (W), defined as $1\ \text{W} = 1\ \text{J s}^{-1}$ (joule per second).

Radiation streams out of the Sun at the prodigious rate of 3.85×10^{26} W. Located at an average distance from the Sun of some 150×10^{6} km, the Earth intercepts only a tiny fraction of this – an amount equivalent to the solar radiation falling on the flat, circular disc depicted to the left in Figure 2.2. Note that we imagine the disc to be just outside the Earth's atmosphere and aligned at right angles to the Sun's rays: the solar input *per unit area* (a square metre, say) of this disc is called the **solar constant**. Measurements from satellite-borne radiation sensors give the solar constant an average value over recent years of $1368\ \text{W m}^{-2}$. Of course, the Earth is a rotating sphere, not a flat disc. As explained in the caption to Figure 2.2, when averaged over the surface of the whole globe, the solar input per unit area at the top of the atmosphere comes down by a factor of four, to $342\ \text{W m}^{-2}$. For simplicity, we shall refer to this globally averaged value as '100 units', though you should remember that these are units of 'energy per unit time per unit area'.

Not all of the incoming solar radiation is available to heat the Earth: some of it is reflected directly back to space. The proportion of incident solar radiation that is reflected by a given surface is called the **albedo**. Now have a look at the Frontispiece. This is an image of the Earth from space formed from reflected sunlight (solar radiation at visible wavelengths). Clouds and the ice-covered mass of Antarctica (at the bottom of

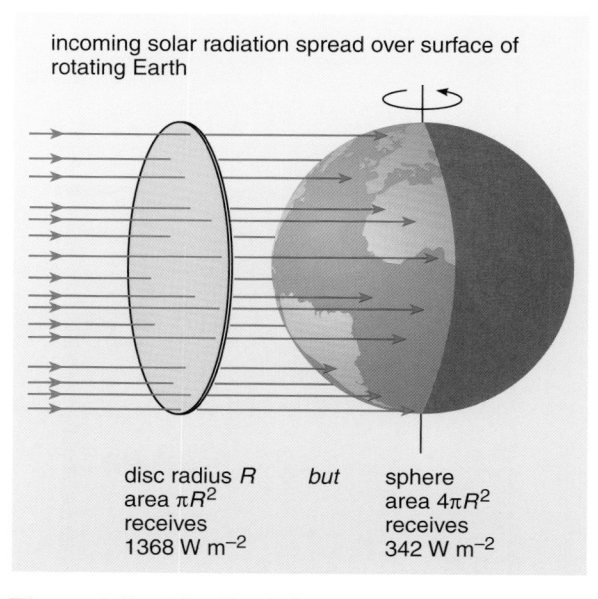

incoming solar radiation spread over surface of rotating Earth

disc radius *R*   but   sphere
area πR^2 area $4\pi R^2$
receives   receives
$1368\ \text{W m}^{-2}$ $342\ \text{W m}^{-2}$

Figure 2.2   The Earth intercepts an amount of solar radiation equivalent to that falling on a disc with the same radius (*R*) as the Earth, facing the Sun: this comes to $(1368 \times \pi R^2)$ W, where πR^2 is the area of the disc (in m²). However, the Earth is *spherical*, so the area presented to the incoming solar radiation by the rotating Earth (over a period of 24 hours or more) is $4\pi R^2$; i.e. four times as great. Thus, the solar input per unit area *averaged over the surface area of the whole Earth* is a quarter of the solar constant; i.e. $1368\ \text{W m}^{-2}/4 = 342\ \text{W m}^{-2}$.

the image) appear bright because they reflect strongly; i.e. they have a high albedo – up to 90% in the case of fresh snow and sea-ice. By contrast, the oceans have a low albedo (typically less than 5%) and appear dark in this image. In general, most land surfaces have moderate albedo, with values ranging from 10–20% for forests to around 35% for grasslands and deserts.

Evidently, the albedo can vary markedly around the world, depending on the cloud cover and surface characteristics. The **planetary albedo** is the combined figure for the Earth as a whole: on average, it has a measured value of 31% (31 units). The remainder (69 units) is absorbed by the atmosphere and materials at the Earth's surface (the oceans, soils, vegetation and so on).

■   What is the rate per unit area at which solar energy is absorbed by the Earth's atmosphere and surface?

▪   69 units is 69% of 342 W m^{-2} or (342 W m^{-2}) × (69/100) = 236 W m^{-2}.

Suppose now that the Earth's atmosphere is stripped away, but the planetary albedo is unchanged. (This may strike you as a curious proposition, but it will help to expose just how important the atmosphere really is.) The energy flows at the surface of this 'airless' world are shown in Figure 2.3. To the left of the figure, a nominal 100 units of solar radiation reach the planet; 31 units are reflected away and *all* of the remaining 69 units are absorbed by the surface.

■   By itself, what would be the effect of this continual input of solar energy?

▪   The surface would warm up; indeed, it would get progressively hotter and hotter.

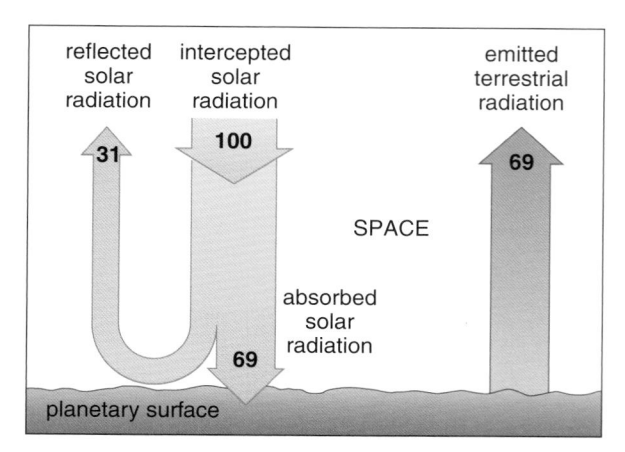

Figure 2.3   The steady-state balance between incoming and reflected solar radiation (orange arrows) and outgoing terrestrial radiation (reddish arrow) for an Earth-like planet without an atmosphere. 100 units represent the globally averaged rate per unit area at which solar radiation reaches the planet; i.e. 342 W m^{-2}.

Fortunately, there is a compensating cooling effect. Like the Sun, *all* objects (you and I included) emit electromagnetic radiation. Further, they do so at a rate that depends on the temperature of the object: the hotter an object becomes, the higher its radiative power – the rate at which it emits radiation. For our planet, a steady or *equilibrium* temperature is maintained by a dynamic balance: the rate at which solar energy is absorbed (the 69 units to the left in Figure 2.3) must be balanced by the rate at which the planet loses energy to space as emitted radiation (the 69 units to the right in Figure 2.3). Note that this *emitted* radiation originates with the 'jostling about' of atoms within the surface; it is *not* the same thing as the *reflected* solar radiation, which merely 'bounces off' the surface. To emphasise the distinction, we shall refer to the radiation emitted by the planet as **terrestrial radiation**.

Expressed in quantitative terms, the relationship between temperature and radiative power is the basis for a well-established law of physics. The appropriate calculations tell us that, for an Earth-like planet to emit radiation to space at a steady rate of 236 W m^{-2} (the 69 units depicted in Figure 2.3), it should have an equilibrium temperature of −19 °C.

This equilibrium temperature is known as the **effective radiating temperature** and, were it not for the atmosphere, this would also be the Earth's global mean *surface* temperature. Conditions would certainly be inimical to life as we know it. But how does the atmosphere perform the vital trick of keeping the GMST at a more temperate 15 °C (the value quoted in Section 1.2)? The answer is bound up with an important difference between 'solar' and 'terrestrial' radiation – one that again depends on the temperature of the source.

Question 2.1

Heated in an ordinary fire, a metal poker glows 'red-hot'; if heated to a higher temperature (in an oxy-acetylene flame, say), it would glow 'white-hot'. Generalising from this example, does the average wavelength of emitted radiation increase or decrease as the temperature of the emitting body rises? Include your reasoning.

The trend you identified in Question 2.1 is evident in Figure 2.4. Here, the curves record the distribution, or *spectrum*, of wavelengths emitted by the Sun (with an average surface temperature of some 5500 °C) and the Earth (with a GMST of 15 °C). The plots are schematic, in the sense that the vertical scale is not defined, but each shows how the radiative power is apportioned among the range of wavelengths emitted.

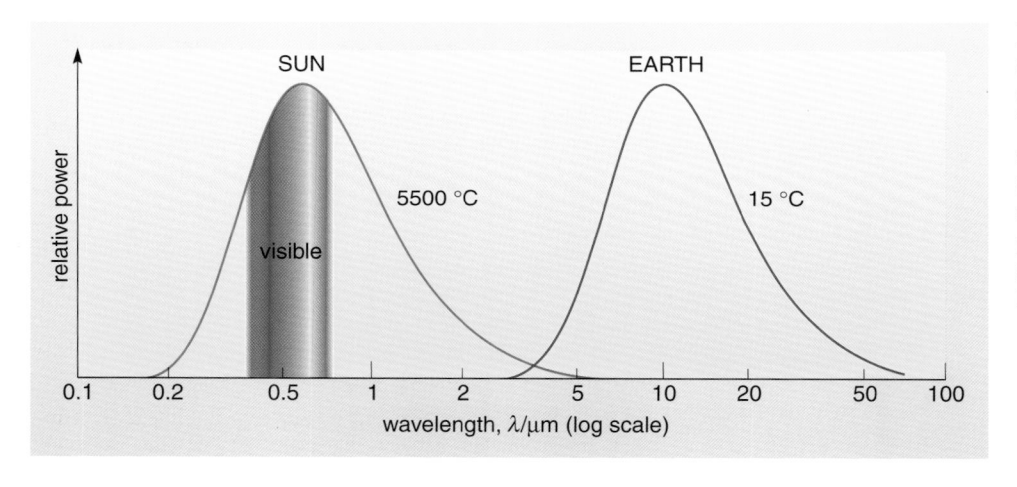

Figure 2.4   Wavelength spectrum of solar radiation (red) and terrestrial radiation (blue). The solar spectrum has been simplified and is for the solar radiation *intercepted* by the Earth (as in Figure 2.2), not the total power emitted by the Sun. Note again that the wavelength scale is logarithmic.

■   With reference to Figure 2.4, is it reasonable to use 'shortwave' and 'longwave' as a shorthand for incoming solar radiation and outgoing terrestrial radiation, respectively?

▓   Yes. The two curves in Figure 2.4 barely overlap: solar radiation peaks in the visible band, although there are contributions at both shorter wavelengths (in the ultraviolet, uv) and longer wavelengths (in a region often called the 'near' infrared). By contrast, radiation emitted at cooler terrestrial temperatures lies entirely at longer infrared (ir) wavelengths.

This pattern is important because the atmosphere is relatively transparent to incoming shortwave radiation, but *not* to outgoing longwave radiation. And that has a profound effect on the actual energy balance at the Earth's surface.

2.1.2 Bringing in the atmosphere: the natural greenhouse effect

> As a dam built across a river causes a local deepening of the stream, so our atmosphere, thrown as a barrier across the terrestrial rays, produces a local heightening of the temperature at the Earth's surface.

> (Tyndall, 1862, quoted in Weart, 2004)

Thus, writing in 1862, John Tyndall (Figure 2.5) described the key to our modern understanding of why the Earth's surface is so much warmer than the effective radiating temperature. Tyndall's careful experimental work had established what others only suspected: expressed in modern scientific terms, certain atmospheric gases absorb infrared radiation with wavelengths in the range spanned by outgoing terrestrial radiation (about 4 to 100 μm; Figure 2.4). These are the **greenhouse gases**. Tyndall identified water vapour and CO_2, but the list of *natural* greenhouse gases (naturally present in the atmosphere long before human activities began to make their mark) also includes methane (CH_4), nitrous oxide (N_2O) and ozone (O_3). The main mechanism by which these gases absorb infrared radiation is through the vibrations of their molecules. We shall not pursue the scientific principles that underlie this mechanism in any detail, but the key points we shall need are summarised in Box 2.2.

Figure 2.5   John Tyndall (1820–1893). Like many Victorian scientists, Tyndall was interested in a great many questions – contributing to such diverse areas as heat transfer, glacier motion and scattering of light in the atmosphere, where he is honoured for his explanation of why the sky is blue (the Tyndall effect). He was a keen alpinist, and attracted by one of the great riddles of his day: if vast sheets of ice had once covered all of northern Europe (hotly debated at the time), how could climate have changed so radically? One then-current hypothesis was a change in atmospheric composition, and it was this possibility that led to Tyndall's pioneering work on the physics of the greenhouse effect. He was also a committed communicator; during his time at the Royal Institution, he earned great renown for presenting science to the public. So it is fitting that one of the climate change research institutes in the UK, with a particular focus on an interdisciplinary approach and communication with the public, local authorities, business, etc., is named after him – the Tyndall Centre in Norwich.

Box 2.2 'Exciting' molecular vibrations

- The chemical bonds that hold a molecule together are like springs and, like them, they can stretch and flex, making the molecule vibrate. Molecular vibrations always have a characteristic frequency. If a molecule absorbs radiation of a matching frequency – *and hence with a characteristic wavelength* (see Box 2.1) – the energy it gains makes it vibrate more vigorously. The frequencies of molecular vibrations invariably correspond to wavelengths in the infrared part of the spectrum.

- To be 'infrared active' (i.e. to absorb infrared radiation through changes in the way it vibrates), a molecule must contain more than two atoms or, if there are just two atoms, these are of different elements. More complex molecules, such as the greenhouse gases, can vibrate in several ways, each with its own characteristic frequency. So they can absorb a range of wavelengths in the infrared.

- Once 'excited' by absorbing infrared radiation, a greenhouse gas molecule can lose energy again by *re-emitting* radiation of the *same* wavelength. Alternatively, it can pass energy on to other molecules in the air by bumping into them: the net effect is to increase the total 'energy content' of the air, warming it up.

Taken together, the natural greenhouse gases absorb infrared wavelengths throughout most of the terrestrial range; there is only one region, between 8 and 13 μm, where absorption is weak. Known as the 'atmospheric window', this allows some of the longwave radiation from the surface to escape *directly* to space, but most of it is intercepted by the atmosphere. That changes the simple picture in Figure 2.3 substantially. A better representation is shown in Figure 2.6. Now most of the longwave radiation from the surface is effectively 'trapped' and recycled by the atmosphere, being repeatedly absorbed and *re-emitted* in all directions by the greenhouse gases. This warms the atmosphere. Some of the re-emitted radiation ultimately goes out to space, maintaining an overall **radiation balance** *at the top of the atmosphere*, as shown in Figure 2.6. This prevents the whole Earth–atmosphere system from heating up without limit. The crucial difference is that much of the re-emitted radiation goes back down and is absorbed by the surface. It is this additional energy input – over and above the absorbed solar radiation – that keeps the Earth's GMST over 30 °C warmer than it otherwise would be.

> The surface warming attributed to the back radiation from the atmosphere is called the **greenhouse effect**.

The contribution each of the greenhouse gases makes to the total effect depends on two main factors: how efficient it is at absorbing outgoing longwave radiation, and its atmospheric concentration. The striking thing is that most of these gases are only minor atmospheric constituents, as shown by the information collected in Table 2.1 (p. 45). Here, concentrations are given as 'mixing ratios' – the

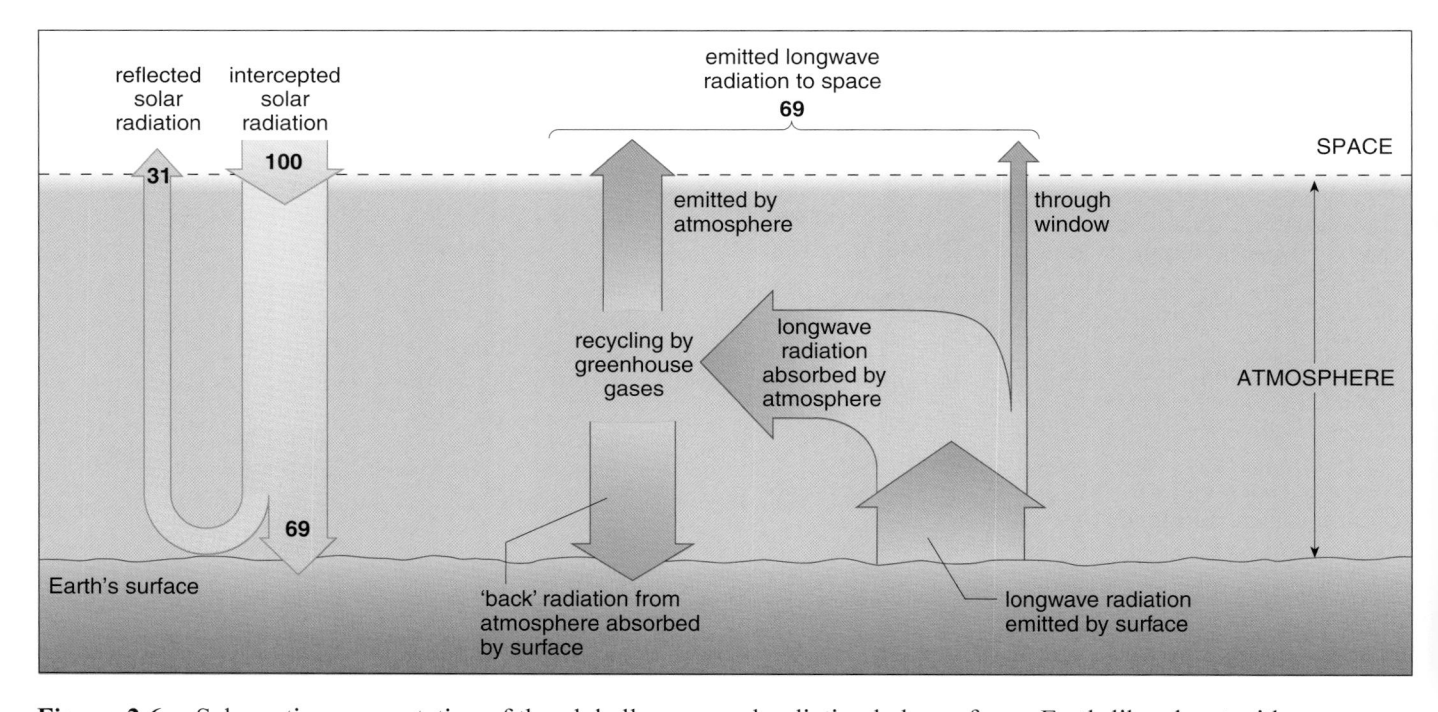

Figure 2.6   Schematic representation of the globally averaged radiation balance for an Earth-like planet with an atmosphere that absorbs and re-emits (both downward and upward) longwave radiation from the surface (reddish arrows). As in Figure 2.3, 69 units of solar radiation are absorbed by the planet and 69 units of longwave radiation go back out to space. However, this overall radiation balance is now at the top of the atmosphere, *not at the surface*, which receives an extra input of energy through the 'back radiation' from the atmosphere.

measure of atmospheric composition that has become familiar to policy makers and other stakeholders in the climate change debate (Figure 2.7). The term is explained in Box 2.3.

Figure 2.7   According to the 500 PPM company, 'Our name is our mission: 500 PPM means 500 parts per million – a critical value for climate protection, because it describes the point at which the concentrations of greenhouse gases in the atmosphere should be stabilized' (an issue we revisit in Chapter 7).

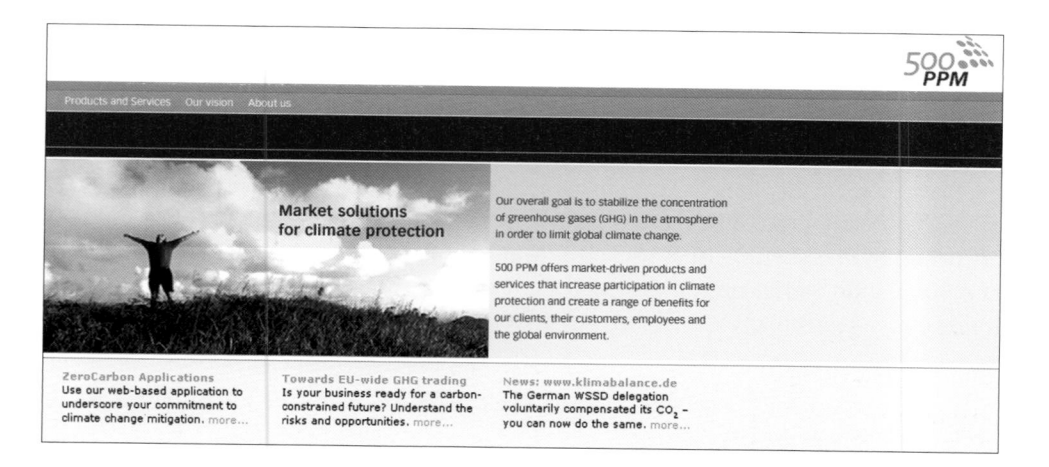

Box 2.3 Mixing ratios

Strictly, the mixing ratio (by volume) tells us about the 'fractional abundance' or proportion of a given atmospheric gas, although you will often find it referred to as the 'atmospheric concentration' (and we shall follow this practice). Taking oxygen (O_2) as an example, the formal definition is as follows:

$$\textbf{mixing ratio} = \frac{N(O_2)}{N_{total}} \tag{2.1}$$

where N_{total} is the total number of molecules in a given volume of air (a cubic metre, say) and $N(O_2)$ is the number of molecules of oxygen in the *same* volume of air. Expressing the fraction in decimal form or as a percentage (by multiplying by 100) is fine for the major atmospheric constituents (see the entries in Table 2.1), but it becomes unwieldy for minor constituents like the greenhouse gases. In this case, values are usually recorded as **ppm (parts per million, 10^6)** or as **ppb (parts per billion, 10^9)** – or even as **ppt (parts per trillion, 10^{12})** for the least abundant species.

■ In Table 2.1, the mixing ratio of CO_2 is given as 368 ppm. Express this value as a number (in scientific notation), and then as a percentage.

▪ A value of 368 ppm means that in every million molecules of air, 368 will, on average, be molecules of CO_2. So 368 ppm is equivalent to $368/10^6 = 368 \times 10^{-6} = 3.68 \times 10^{-4}$ (in scientific notation). Multiplying by 100, this becomes 3.68×10^{-2}% or 0.0368%.

■ Now express the mixing ratio of CO_2 in ppb.

▪ If there are 368 molecules of CO_2 per million in total, there would be 368 000 per billion, so the answer is 368 000 ppb.

Thus, 1 ppm = 10^3 ppb, and similarly 1 ppb = 10^3 ppt.

Table 2.1   Recent (1998) average mixing ratios of some of the gases in (absolutely) dry air in the lower atmosphere – the region up to about 10 km, known as the troposphere (see Section 2.2.1).

Gas (and formula)	Mixing ratio
major constituents	
nitrogen (N_2)	0.78
oxygen (O_2)	0.21
argon (Ar)	0.0093
trace gases	
carbon dioxide (CO_2)	368 ppm
methane (CH_4)	1745 ppb
nitrous oxide (N_2O)	314 ppb
ozone (O_3)	10–100 ppb

■   Given the information in Table 2.1, how would you describe the bulk composition of the lower atmosphere?

▨   99% is nitrogen and oxygen (roughly in a 4 : 1 ratio), and most of the rest (0.93%) is argon.

■   Is any one of these major components a greenhouse gas?

▨   No. The chemically inert noble gas argon exists as individual atoms; nitrogen and oxygen molecules each consist of two atoms of the same element. None of them fulfils the criterion for being infrared-active (Box 2.2).

Note that the mixing ratios in Table 2.1 are for *dry* air. The contribution from water vapour is not included because the amount in the air is highly variable – from practically none at all up to about 4% (by volume). Part of the explanation is that air can 'hold' only a certain amount of water vapour: it has a 'saturation' limit, which depends mainly on temperature. The variable humidity of the air (a measure of its water vapour content) is part of our everyday experience: it affects the ability of sweat to evaporate, for example, and the drying of clothes on the line.

Averaged over time and around the globe, water vapour represents about 0.5% of the total atmospheric gas. This relatively high abundance makes water vapour the single most important natural greenhouse gas: it contributes about 60% of the surface warming attributed to the natural greenhouse effect. Carbon dioxide, the second most abundant, contributes a further 25% or so; most of the rest is due to the other three trace gases in Table 2.1, which have much lower atmospheric concentrations. (One further contribution is noted in Section 2.2.3.)

The fact that the Earth is not a frozen and lifeless rock shows that the *natural* greenhouse effect is not a 'bad thing'; indeed, it is a 'good thing'! As we implied in Chapter 1, it is the extra warming produced by an *enhanced* or amplified greenhouse effect, due to an increase in the atmospheric concentration of CO_2 (and indeed other greenhouse gases), that lies at the heart of current concerns. We shall sometimes refer to this as an increase in the atmospheric 'burden' of

CO_2 (or of greenhouse gases in general), since an increase in concentration necessarily implies an increase in the total amount (or number of molecules) of the gas in the atmosphere.

Question 2.2

Analogies are a useful aid to understanding, and can be a powerful means of communicating scientific ideas to a lay audience. However, they can be misleading. Look back at the quote from John Tyndall at the beginning of this section. In what way is the analogy used there a misleading one? Explain your reservations, making reference to the mechanism that actually creates the Earth's greenhouse effect.

2.2 Energy flows within the Earth–atmosphere system

Before we focus on the enhanced greenhouse effect, we need to refine the schematic representation in Figure 2.6 and draw in some of the other processes that influence the Earth's temperature – not only at the surface, but also at different levels within the atmosphere.

2.2.1 The vertical 'structure' of the atmosphere

The atmosphere is not a simple, uniform slab of absorbing material. On the contrary, it gets progressively 'thinner' or less dense with increasing altitude (height above mean sea level); i.e. the *total* number of molecules in a given volume of air is lower, and so is the pressure. About 80% of the total mass of the atmosphere is within some 10 km of the surface; 99.9% lies below 50 km.

The important corollary is that the key greenhouse gas molecules (H_2O and CO_2) are also more abundant close to ground level, and increasingly scarce at higher altitudes. So a better picture of radiation trapping in the real atmosphere is to imagine it happening in a series of stages. Outgoing longwave radiation is repeatedly absorbed and re-emitted as it 'works up' through the atmosphere; it is re-radiated to space only from levels high enough (i.e. thin enough) for absorption to have become weak. This suggests that the atmosphere should be warmer at ground level – close to the source of the outgoing radiation, and where the absorbing molecules are more abundant. Everyday experience confirms this expectation; it generally gets colder as you walk up a mountain, for example.

Figure 2.8 is a typical temperature profile of the atmosphere. It shows that air temperature does indeed fall with increasing altitude throughout the lower atmosphere or **troposphere**, reaching a minimum value (of about −55 °C) at the **tropopause**. This lies 8–15 km above the ground, depending mainly on latitude: it is higher (and colder) at the Equator than at the poles. No mountains rise above the troposphere; it is where we live and where almost all weather phenomena (rain, clouds, winds, etc.) occur. However, if you could travel higher up (without the protection of a jet aircraft), you would find that the temperature soon starts to increase again – and continues to do so up to the stratopause at the top of the **stratosphere**. Why is this?

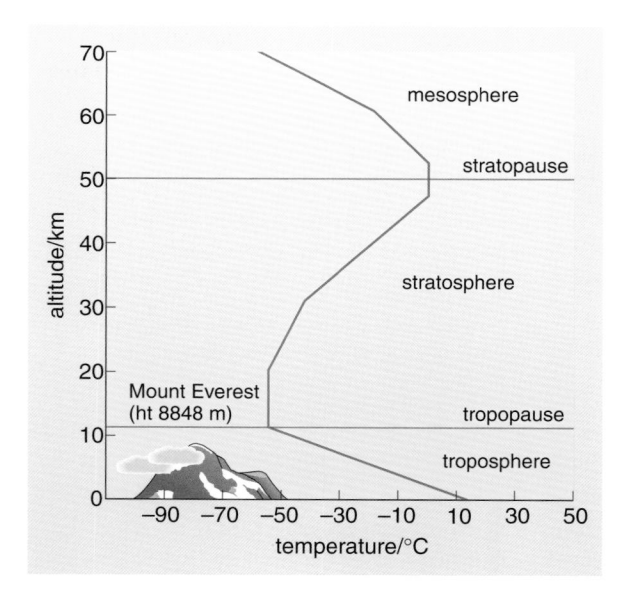

Figure 2.8   The characteristic temperature profile of the atmosphere produces a vertical structure like a series of concentric shells. The successive regions or 'spheres' are separated by 'pauses' where the change in temperature with altitude switches from decreasing to increasing, or vice versa. The outer more-rarefied reaches of the atmosphere (which extends up to 100 km or so) are not included.

2.2.2 The fate of incoming solar radiation

■ Look back at Figure 2.6. In this schematic representation, what is the fate of incoming solar radiation?

▨ It is either reflected back to space (31 units) or absorbed by the surface (69 units).

Some solar radiation is, in fact, absorbed as it travels down through the atmosphere. Mostly, this is radiation at wavelengths in the two 'tails' of the solar spectrum (Figure 2.4) – the ultraviolet and the near infrared.

Like water vapour and CO_2, the ozone in the troposphere acts as a greenhouse gas. Unlike those two gases, however, very little of the Earth's ozone is, in fact, in the lower atmosphere; the bulk of it (some 90%) is in the stratosphere, where it forms the so-called **ozone layer** (referred to in Section 1.3). In this more-rarefied region, ozone plays a different role because it also absorbs the shorter ultraviolet wavelengths in the solar spectrum – radiation that is lethal to many micro-organisms and can damage important biological molecules, leading to conditions such as skin cancer in humans. Fortunately for life on Earth, most of this radiation is absorbed by the ozone layer, preventing it from penetrating deeper into the atmosphere. More pertinent here, the absorption of incoming solar energy by stratospheric ozone heats this region of the atmosphere *directly*. In effect, the stratosphere is heated from *above*, whereas the troposphere is heated from *below*. This is why the highest temperatures are found at the top of the stratosphere, but at the bottom of the troposphere (as shown in Figure 2.8).

About half of the incoming near-infrared radiation is also absorbed, mainly by water vapour low down in the troposphere. In addition, the atmosphere contains a huge assortment of **aerosols** – fine solid particles and liquid droplets suspended in the air. Except in the aftermath of a major volcanic eruption (of which more in Section 2.4), aerosols are also most abundant in the lower atmosphere; natural sources include desert dust wafted into the air by wind, smoke and soot from wildfires, salt from sea-spray, and so on. Depending on their make-up, aerosols can absorb solar radiation – or (and this is usually more important) scatter some of it back to space. Globally, aerosols make a significant contribution to the Earth's albedo (included in the figure of 31% quoted earlier). They also play another important role. Many aerosols act as **cloud condensation nuclei**, providing surfaces that promote the condensation of water vapour to form the liquid droplets (or ice crystals, at higher and colder altitudes) suspended in clouds – a process that occurs less readily in 'clean' (i.e. aerosol-free) air.

2.2.3 The role of clouds

We have already identified one role that clouds play in the Earth's climate: they are highly reflective (Section 2.1.1). At any given time, about half of our planet is covered by clouds; the sunlight they reflect back to space accounts for about 55% of the total planetary albedo. However, clouds also absorb and re-emit *outgoing* longwave radiation; i.e. they contribute to the back radiation from the atmosphere, and hence to the natural greenhouse effect. This is why temperatures tend to be lower under clear night skies than on nights with extensive cloud cover.

Thus, clouds present something of a paradox: they both warm and cool the Earth. The balance between these two opposing effects is a delicate one – dependent on factors such as the type and thickness of the clouds, their altitude, whether they consist of water droplets or ice crystals, and so on (Figure 2.9). Averaged over time and around the world, satellite data indicate that the net effect of clouds in our current climate is a slight cooling of the surface. As you will see, predicting how the balance between warming and cooling might shift in a warmer world remains one of the biggest headaches for climate scientists.

Figure 2.9 Researchers are only beginning to understand the complex role clouds play in modulating the planet's temperature. The figure summarises some key points, stressing how different types of clouds affect the Earth's radiation balance differently. How these variations fit together to produce a global cooling effect, and how that might change in a warmer world, remains uncertain.

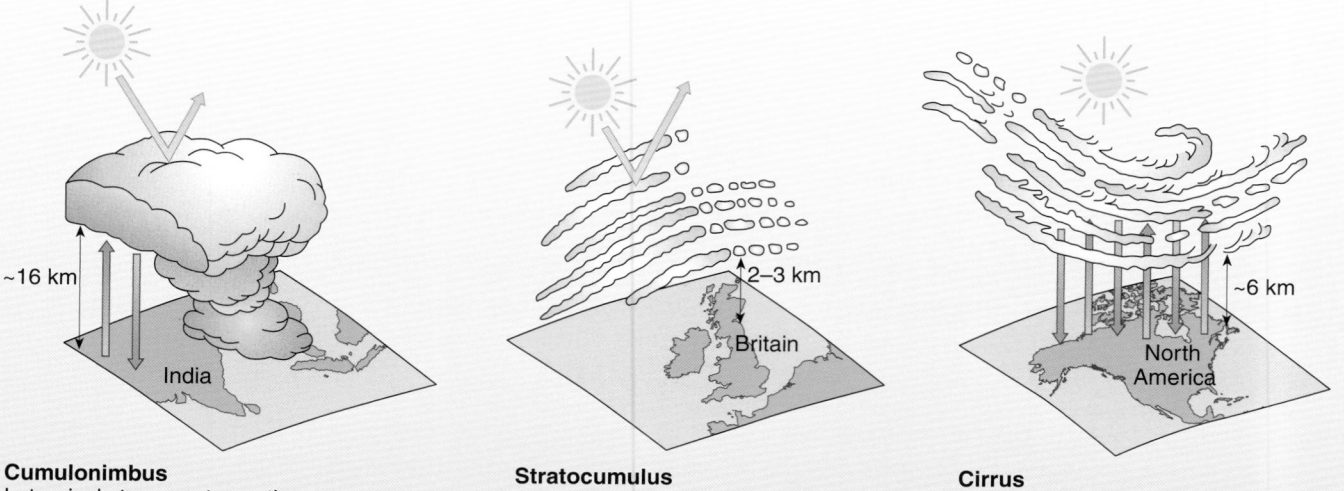

Cumulonimbus
In tropical storm systems, these thunderheads topped with high anvils trap three times as much heat as clouds trap on average, but reflect so much solar radiation back up that the warming effect is cancelled. Global warming might upset this delicate balance, but in which direction?

Stratocumulus
These fluffy clouds lie in vast low layers over oceans in temperate zones. The tops reflect a surprisingly large amount of solar radiation, for a net cooling effect. Global warming could shift them north or south, but would this intensify or moderate the warming?

Cirrus
These high wisps were believed to trap much heat below but reflect little back into space. They have recently been found to have an unexpectedly large number of tiny ice crystals. If these reflect more solar radiation than expected, it could counterbalance the heat-trapping effect.

2.2.4 The role of convection in the atmosphere

We come now to our final refinement to the simple picture in Figure 2.6. Recall that the troposphere is heated from below, with temperature then falling with increasing altitude. This situation sets the scene for the onset of convection – the bulk flow or circulation of a fluid driven by differences in temperature. Convection in the atmosphere plays a vital role in two further mechanisms – *quite apart from the emission of longwave radiation* – whereby energy is transferred from the Earth's surface to the atmosphere.

The first is the transfer of 'thermal' energy (often referred to rather loosely as 'heat') by a combination of conduction and convection. This is essentially the same mechanism that heats a saucepan of water on the stove; see Box 2.4. The situation in the atmosphere is more complicated, but the basic principle is the same. Warm air, heated by contact with the ground or a warm sea, rises upwards carrying heat transferred from the surface aloft. This allows more cool air to come into contact with the surface and be heated in its turn. Working together, conduction/convection drive a significant flow of heat across the boundary between the surface and the air.

Box 2.4 Heating water by conduction and convection

Anyone who tries to pick up a metal spoon left in contact with a hot pan quickly learns that metals are good conductors of heat. **Conduction** is the transfer of heat through matter by molecular activity; i.e. the energy is transferred through contact between individual molecules. By contrast, **convection** is the transfer of heat by bulk movement or circulation within a fluid (a liquid like water or a gas like the air).

In Figure 2.10, heat is transmitted from the electric element, through the pan to the water in contact with the base of the pan by conduction. As water in this layer warms up, it expands – this is called **thermal expansion** – and so becomes less dense than the water above. Because of this new buoyancy, the warm water begins to rise, to be replaced by cooler, denser water from above which is heated in its turn. On reaching the surface, the warmed water begins to lose heat to the air; it cools, becomes denser and sinks, then is heated again and rises, and so on. As long as the water is heated unequally (i.e. from the bottom up), the water will continue to 'turn over' in a convective circulation so that eventually all of it becomes warm.

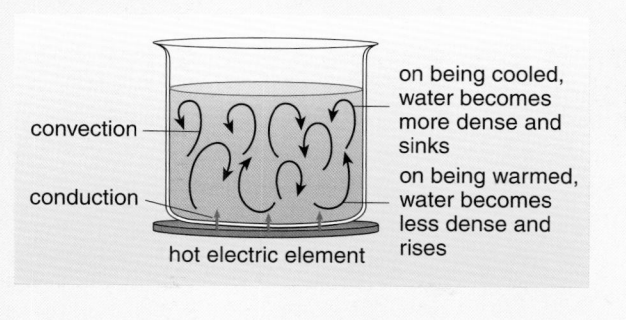

convection

conduction

hot electric element

on being cooled, water becomes more dense and sinks

on being warmed, water becomes less dense and rises

Figure 2.10 The circulatory pattern in a pan of water heated on an electric element.

The second form of energy transfer is indirect, but even more important on a global scale. It involves the evaporation of water – mainly from the oceans, but also from lakes and rivers, soils, rocks and vegetation on land. Evaporation requires energy, known as the **latent heat of vaporisation**, which is extracted from the surface involved. This is why the evaporation of sweat acts to cool the body. The latent heat of vaporisation of water, i.e. the amount of heat needed to convert 1 kg of liquid water to water vapour at the same temperature (and the amount of heat *released* to the surrounding environment when 1 kg of water vapour condenses) is 2.25×10^6 J kg^{-1} – higher than the value for any other substance.

■   How does convection in the overlying air help to promote the evaporation of water?

▨   Convection carries air containing water vapour upwards, so the air just above the surface does not become 'saturated' (Section 2.1.2), enabling more water to evaporate.

As we noted earlier, the saturation limit of air depends on temperature: *cool air can carry less water vapour than warm air*. As moisture-laden air is carried upwards, it cools and may become saturated. Continued rise and further cooling then results in the condensation of water vapour onto aerosols in the air: clouds form and latent heat is released to the atmosphere. Clouds, the turbulence of atmospheric convection and the winds that redistribute heat around the world (discussed in Chapter 4) are largely confined to the troposphere (*tropos* is Greek for 'turning').

■   Look back at Figure 2.8. It is often said that the tropopause acts like a lid, preventing convection in the lower atmosphere from reaching any higher. Can you suggest why?

▨   With (less dense) warm air lying above (more dense) cooler air, conditions in the stratosphere are not conducive to convection. (*Stratos* is Latin for 'layered'.)

Rapidly rising air can (and does) overshoot the tropopause, mostly in the updraught of violent storms over the tropics. And there are return routes as well, mainly at middle latitudes. In general, though, the circulation of air in the stratosphere does not interact strongly with the wind systems in the lower atmosphere. It is within the troposphere that the full drama of the Earth's weather occurs.

2.3 An overview of the global energy budget

Figure 2.11 incorporates the additional factors considered in Section 2.2, including the *non*-radiative energy transfers across the surface–air boundary (green arrow). Essentially a more detailed version of Figure 2.6, this figure gives quantified estimates of the globally averaged energy budget for the whole Earth–atmosphere system, and its component parts. Question 2.3 should help you to find your way around Figure 2.11, and to draw together many of the key points developed so far in this chapter. Make sure to try answering it before moving on.

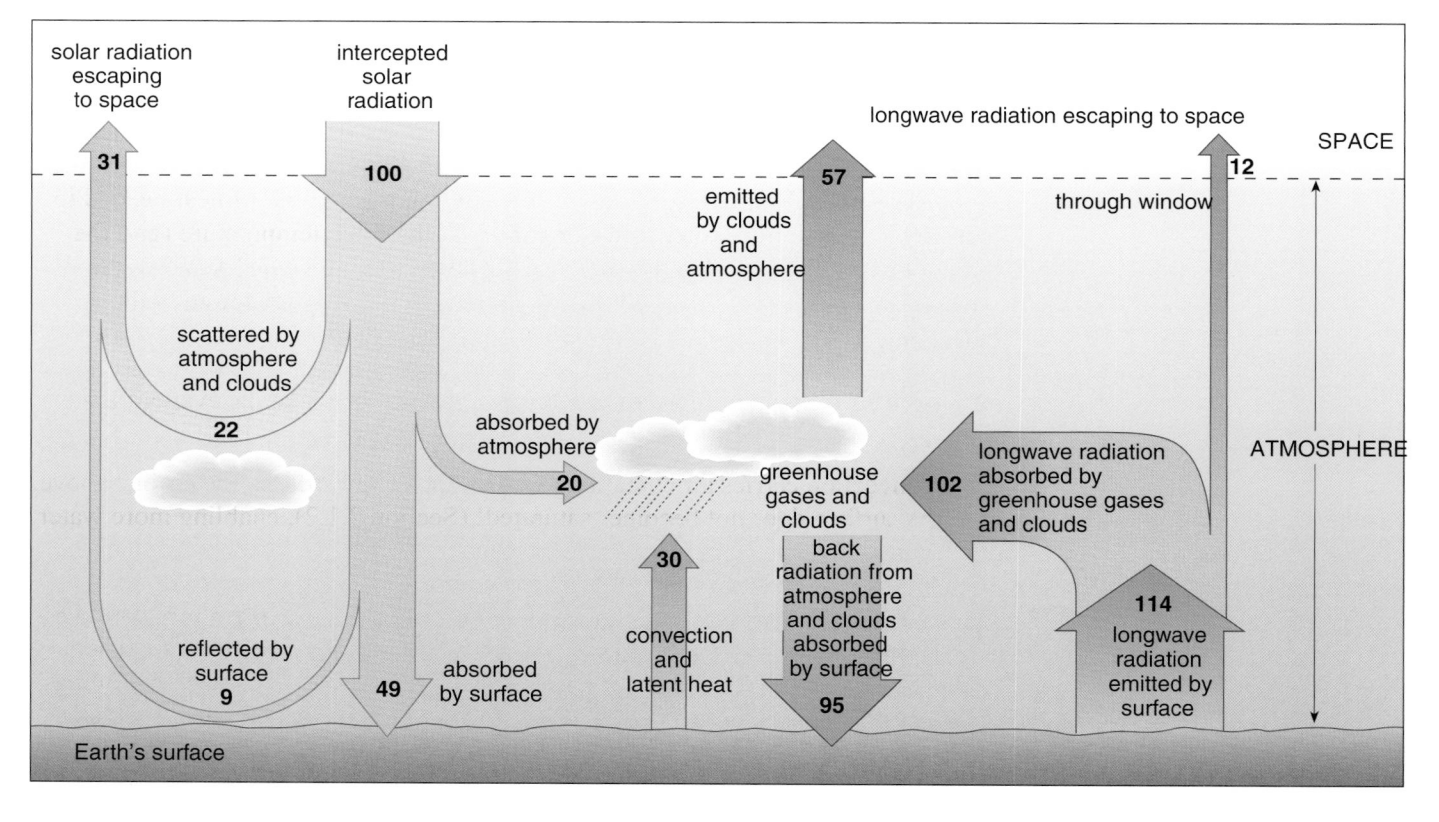

Figure 2.11 Schematic representation of the overall energy budget for the Earth and its atmosphere. Figures are global annual averages expressed as a percentage of the rate per unit area at which solar radiation is intercepted by the Earth; i.e. 100 units is equivalent to 342 W m^{-2}, as in Figure 2.3.

Question 2.3

With reference to Figure 2.11:

(a)   What proportion (as a percentage) of the Earth's planetary albedo is due to solar radiation reflected by the surface? Which regions of the world are likely to be mainly responsible for this contribution?

(b)   Calculate the difference between the rate of energy gain and the rate of loss for: (i) the Earth's surface; (ii) the atmosphere; and (iii) the whole Earth–atmosphere system (i.e. at the top of the atmosphere). What do you conclude about the Earth's GMST?

(c)   What proportion (as a percentage) of the longwave radiation emitted by the surface is absorbed by the atmosphere?

(d)   Translate the 114 units of longwave radiation emitted by the surface into a rate of energy transfer (in W m^{-2}). Explain why your answer is consistent with the fact that the Earth's GMST is higher than its effective radiating temperature ($-19\,^\circ$C).

To sum up: in Figure 2.11, the whole Earth–atmosphere system is in a dynamic **steady state** or equilibrium. Most (89%) of the outgoing longwave radiation is absorbed and recycled by the atmosphere, and ultimately re-emitted to space from higher, colder levels (Figure 2.8). As a result, energy circulates *within* the system at a higher rate than the rate of input or output at the top of the atmosphere: this is why the Earth's surface is warmer than it otherwise would be. But in a balanced state, there is no net accumulation of energy in any part of the system, and no net loss. In short, Figure 2.11 depicts a world where the GMST is not changing. So what might cause the Earth's GMST to change?

2.4 'Radiative forcing' as an agent of climate change

Since its first major report in 1990, the IPCC has used the concept of 'radiative forcing' as a simple measure of the importance of a potential climate change mechanism. The basic idea is straightforward. Any factor that disturbs the radiation balance *at the top of the atmosphere* has the potential to 'force' the global climate to change: it will either warm up or cool down until a balance is restored. The perturbation to the energy balance of the whole Earth–atmosphere system is called **radiative forcing**, and is given in the units W m^{-2}.

■ Look back at Figure 2.11. What three factors could disturb the radiation balance at the top of the atmosphere?

▨ A change in the Sun's output, and hence in the solar constant; a change in the Earth's albedo; and a change in the longwave emission to space.

Among the more enduring hypotheses to account for climate change are those based on the idea that the Sun is a variable star and that its output of energy varies through time. Indeed, this idea underlies the sceptical view that recent global warming has little to do with human activities; rather, the argument goes, solar variability is the main culprit. We shall come back to that issue in Chapter 3. For now, we use the possibility of solar variability to put some flesh on the notion of radiative forcing.

To that end, Figure 2.12 illustrates the effect of a 1% change (up or down) in the solar constant, and hence in the globally averaged solar radiation intercepted by the Earth (the 100 units in Figure 2.12a). Assuming that the planetary albedo is unchanged (at 31%), an increase in the solar constant (Figure 2.12b) produces a **positive radiative forcing**: the rate at which the Earth–atmosphere system absorbs solar radiation (69.69 units) is now greater than the rate at which it emits

Figure 2.12 (a) The globally averaged radiation balance at the top of the atmosphere from Figure 2.11 (i.e. 100 units is equivalent to 342 W m^{-2}). (b) and (c) The imbalance induced by a 1% increase or decrease, respectively, in the solar constant, assuming no change in the planetary albedo.

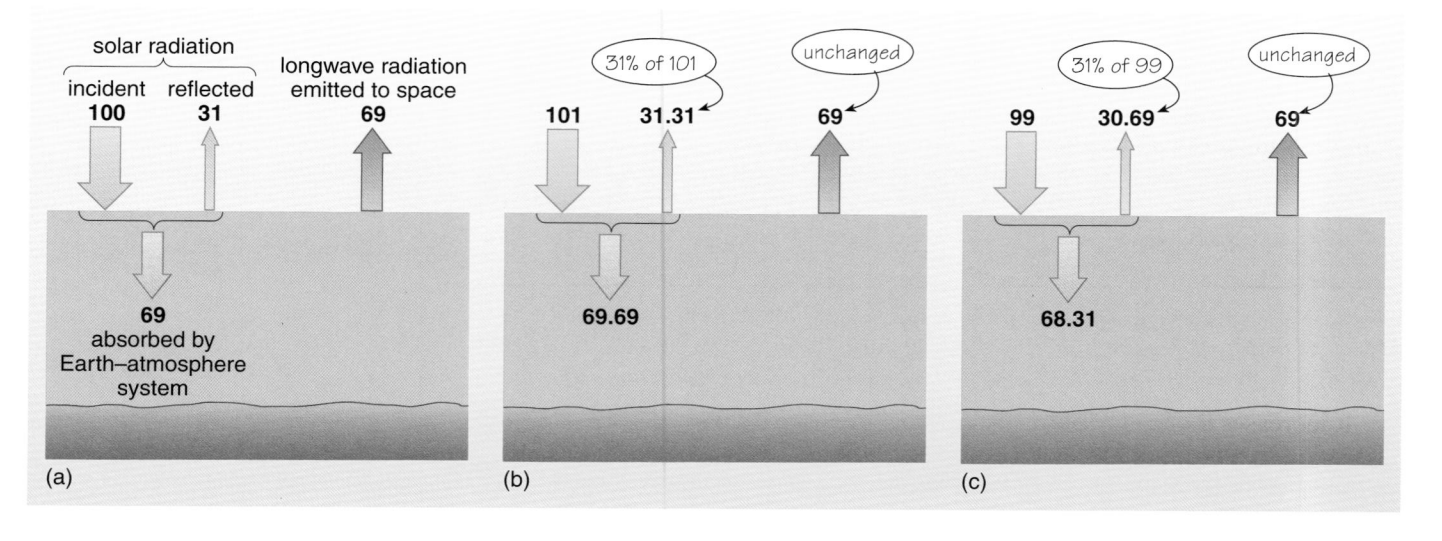

longwave radiation to space (69 units). This has a warming effect. Conversely, a reduction in the solar constant (Figure 2.12c) produces a **negative radiative forcing**, which has a cooling effect.

Question 2.4

According to Figure 2.12, what is the radiative forcing, in $W\ m^{-2}$, associated with a $\pm 1\%$ change in the solar constant?

Earlier in the course (in Topic 2, *Near-Earth objects and the impact hazard*), reference was made to another natural phenomenon that can lead to a radiative forcing of climate (though it was not expressed in these terms). Explosive volcanic eruptions spew vast quantities of gases and fine-grained debris (volcanic ash) into the atmosphere. The greatest eruptions are sufficiently powerful to inject material high into the stratosphere, where it gradually spreads around the world. The result can be a significant and widespread cooling effect on climate (see Box 2.5).

Box 2.5   1816: the 'year without a summer'

> The bright sun was extinguish'd, and the stars
> Did wander darkling in the eternal space,
> Rayless, and pathless, and the icy earth
> Swung blind and blackening in the moonless air;
> Morn came and went – and came, and brought no day,
> And men forgot their passions in the dread
> Of this their desolation.
>
> (Lord Byron, *Darkness*, 1816)

The largest volcanic event of modern times was the eruption of Mount Tambora in Indonesia in April 1815. Where records exist, they reveal a period of abnormally cold weather that prevailed during the spring and summer of 1816 in many parts of the Northern Hemisphere. The effects were especially severe in the northeastern United States, with average temperatures in New England up to 3.5 °C below normal in June, for instance, and unseasonal frosts and snowfalls. Europe was also badly affected, leading to crop failures and famine in England, France and Germany. The below-average temperatures lasted for about two years.

In the summer of 1816, there were also widespread reports of a dim Sun, or persistent haze that was not dispersed by surface wind or rain (since it was actually up in the stratosphere) – though few captured its effects as powerfully as Byron's poem.

■ Why might a major volcanic eruption be expected to have a cooling effect on climate at the Earth's surface?

▨ It increases the load of aerosols in the stratosphere, potentially increasing the absorption of incoming solar radiation in this region and/or scattering more of it back to space (Section 2.2.2). Both effects cause a cooling at the surface.

Figure 2.13 The explosive eruption of Mount Pinatubo in the Philippines in June 1991 devastated the surrounding area and sent about 25×10^9 kg of SO_2 into the stratosphere. Over the following year, the haze of sulfate aerosols travelled around the world and lowered the average surface temperature in the Northern Hemisphere by about 0.5 °C.

Although one of the more dramatic features of a major eruption (Figure 2.13), volcanic ash has little enduring impact on climate because it settles out of the stratosphere within a few months. Far more important is the amount of sulfur dioxide (SO_2), one of the volcanic gases, emitted during the eruption. Chemical reactions rapidly convert the gas to droplets of sulfuric acid, and these **sulfate aerosols** can remain in the stratosphere for several years (the persistent haze of Box 2.5). Their main effect is to increase the back-scattering of solar radiation.

■ With this in mind, how would you describe the climatic effects of a major volcanic eruption in terms of radiative forcing?

▨ The extra load of stratospheric aerosols effectively increases the planetary albedo (the second of the three factors identified at the beginning of this section), and this constitutes a *negative* radiative forcing. (The effect is analogous to a reduction in the solar input.)

The resulting cooling effect can be significant (as noted in connection with the Pinatubo eruption in Figure 2.13), but only on a relatively short-term basis – typically, 1–3 years at most. Air movements gradually carry the sulfate aerosols down into the troposphere, where they are usually washed out by rain within a few weeks.

But how does an increase in the atmospheric burden of greenhouse gases lead to a radiative forcing of climate? Again we use an illustrative example. Suppose the atmospheric concentration of CO_2 is doubled instantaneously (known as a **CO_2-doubling**), but everything else (the solar input, planetary albedo, concentrations of other greenhouse gases, etc.) remains the same. What would be the immediate effect? With more molecules of CO_2 in the atmosphere, a higher proportion of the outgoing longwave radiation would be absorbed, *reducing* the net emission to space. Complicated, but well-understood, calculations give a reduction by about 4 W m^{-2} (from 236 W m^{-2} to 232 W m^{-2}) for a CO_2-doubling.

■ Does this change represent a positive or negative radiative forcing?

▨ The forcing is positive. The effect is analogous to an increase in the solar constant (by rather more than 1%, according to Question 2.4).

There is no dispute about this central conclusion. Increasing the atmospheric concentration of CO_2, or any other greenhouse gas, *will* force the global climate to warm up; we shall often refer to this as '**greenhouse forcing**'. However, the weighty tomes issued by the IPCC bear witness to the fact that 'the devil is in the detail'! In particular, there is still major uncertainty about what is perhaps the most fundamental question in the whole climate change debate: how much will the Earth's GMST rise in response to a given amount of greenhouse forcing? We shall revisit this question many times as the topic unfolds. Here, we focus next on what is known about the amount of greenhouse forcing to date.

2.5 The human impact on the atmosphere: the coming of the industrial age

There is no doubt that CO_2 is accumulating in the atmosphere. The record from Mauna Loa (detailed in Figure 1.5) charts a continuing rise in CO_2 concentration since measurements began in 1958, when the level was 315 ppm; the value had reached about 370 ppm by the end of the 20th century, and hit more than 378 ppm in 2004. Important as changes in atmospheric CO_2 undoubtedly are (see below), we need to be aware that this is not the whole story of human-induced greenhouse forcing. In particular, monitoring programmes established during the 1980s reveal an upward trend in the levels of two other natural greenhouse gases as well – methane (CH_4) and nitrous oxide (N_2O). But how do we know that the build up of all three gases over recent decades is due to human intervention?

One strong line of evidence that it is comes from an unlikely source – the vast ice sheets of Greenland and Antarctica. As glacier ice is formed by compaction of successive layers of snow, small bubbles of air become trapped. When a sample of ice is drilled out (Figure 2.14), these air bubbles can be dated quite accurately, and when analysed, provide an archive of past atmospheric composition – including the levels of CO_2, CH_4 and N_2O. Figure 2.15 (adapted from IPCC, 2001a) sets the current situation in the context of ice-core data that trace variations in the atmospheric concentrations of these three gases over the past millennium.

Figure 2.14 Scientists at the US National Ice Core Laboratory examine an ice-core sample. Faint lines in the sample are annual dust layers (deposited in summer months), and counting these allows air bubbles trapped in successive layers to be dated.

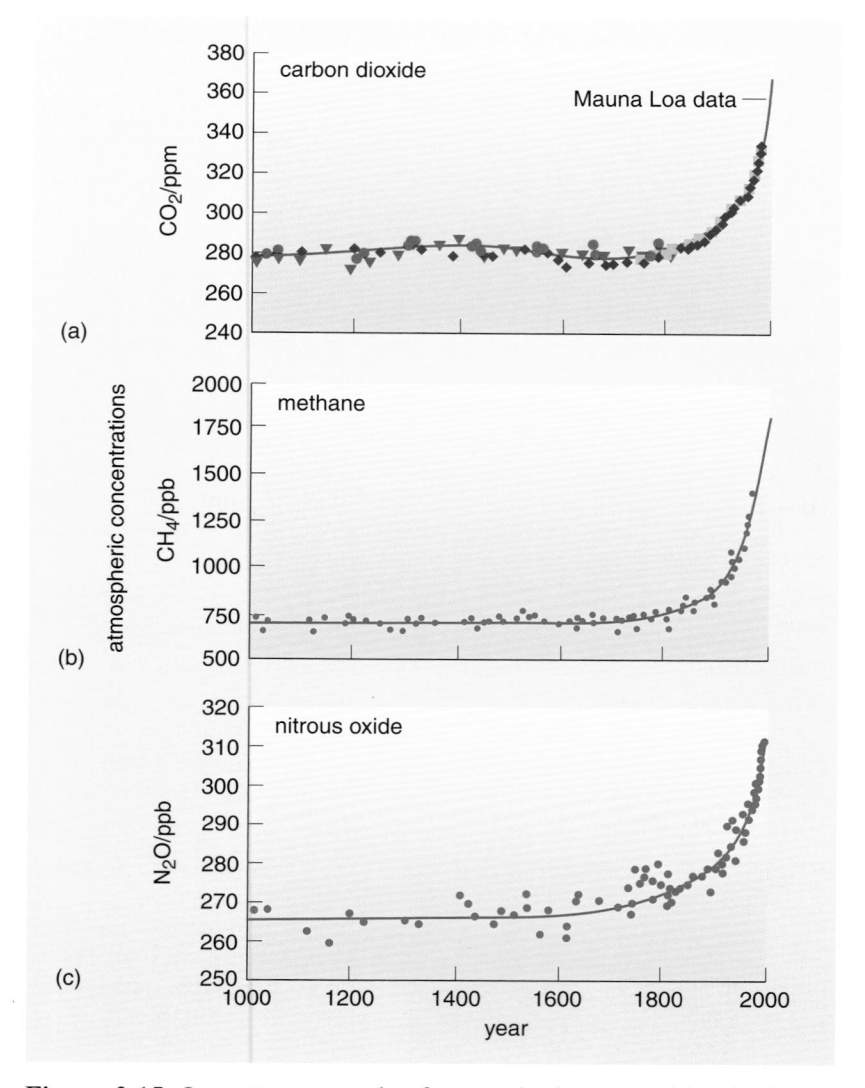

Figure 2.15 Long-term records of atmospheric composition in the past provide the context for the impact of human activities. The figure shows changes in the atmospheric concentration of (a) CO_2, (b) CH_4 and (c) N_2O over the past 1000 years. Ice-core data from several sites in Antarctica and Greenland (shown by different symbols in (a)) are supplemented with data from direct atmospheric measurements over recent decades – shown by the line for CO_2 (labelled the Mauna Loa data) and included in smoothed curves for CH_4 and N_2O.

■   With this longer-term perspective in mind, what does Figure 2.15a suggest about the change in atmospheric CO_2 during the period covered by the Mauna Loa record?

   It continues a rising trend that seems to have started towards the end of the 18th century. For some 800 years before that, the CO_2 level fluctuated little about a mean value close to 280 ppm.

Similar patterns are evident for both methane (Figure 2.15b) and nitrous oxide (Figure 2.15c). For each gas, the average level over the first 750 years of these ice-core records (i.e. up to 1750) is taken as a measure of its 'pre-industrial'

Table 2.2 Information on 'well-mixed' greenhouse gases influenced by human activities. (Source: IPCC, 2001a.)

Gas	Concentration Pre-industrial	1998	Atmospheric lifetime/years	Global Warming Potential
natural greenhouse gases				
CO_2	280 ppm	368 ppm	~ 100*	1
CH_4	700 ppb	1745 ppb	12	23
N_2O	270 ppb	314 ppb	114	296
synthetic halocarbons				
CFC-11 ($CFCl_3$)	0	268 ppt	45	4600
CFC-12 (CF_2Cl_2)	0	533 ppt	100	10 600
HCFC-22 (CHF_2Cl)	0	132 ppt	12	1700

* The significance of this value for CO_2 is discussed in detail in Chapter 5.

concentration; these values are collected in Table 2.2, along with some other pertinent information we shall come on to shortly.

■ Using the information in Table 2.2, calculate the percentage change in the atmospheric concentrations of (i) CO_2; (ii) CH_4; and (iii) N_2O since the pre-industrial period 1750 up to 1998.

▨ There has been an increase by (i) 31%; (ii) 149%; and (iii) 16%. For CO_2, for example, the concentration has increased by (368–280) ppm = 88 ppm, so the percentage increase has been (88/280) × 100% = 31%. Similar calculations for CH_4 and N_2O give the other values.

There is one further point to note about the plots in Figure 2.15. The increase in the atmospheric burden of these gases since pre-industrial times is not linear; rather it appears to be accelerating. For example, it took over 200 years for the level of CO_2 to rise from 280 to 330 ppm (1750 to around 1975; Figure 1.5); it has taken just 30 years for it to increase by the same amount, i.e. a further 50 ppm.

As indicated in the heading to Table 2.2, these three natural greenhouse gases are described as being 'well-mixed', which means that they are distributed fairly uniformly throughout the troposphere. This is because they persist in the atmosphere long enough to be moved around the world by large-scale air movements (discussed in Chapter 4) and 'mixed up' with other atmospheric constituents, so their concentrations do not vary much from place to place. Current estimates of the **atmospheric lifetimes** of CO_2, CH_4 and N_2O are also given in Table 2.2 – along with comparable information for some of the infrared-absorbing **halocarbons** that do not occur naturally, but are now found in trace amounts in the atmosphere (albeit at the level of only a few tens to hundreds of parts per *trillion*, ppt; Box 2.3) as a result of their manufacture and use for various purposes. As a group of compounds, halocarbons can be thought of as derived from hydrocarbons (methane, for the examples in Table 2.2), but with some or all of the hydrogen atoms in the molecule replaced by halogen atoms – usually some combination of fluorine (F) and chlorine (Cl), as in the **chlorofluorocarbons (CFCs)** and hydrochlorofluorocarbons (HCFCs).

Indicted for their role in stratospheric ozone loss (recall Figure 1.6d), the use of all CFCs has now been phased out under the evolving provisions of the Montreal Protocol on Substances that Deplete the Ozone Layer (first agreed in 1987). The two main CFCs are included in Table 2.2 for two reasons. First, these compounds are eventually destroyed by chemical reactions within the atmosphere, but this is a slow process – whence their long atmospheric lifetimes. It will take many decades to remove all trace of these compounds from the atmosphere (e.g. see Figure 2.16). Secondly, CFCs are also potent greenhouse gases – and so, unfortunately, are many of the other halocarbons (typified by HCFC-22 in Table 2.2) that have come on stream as CFC-substitutes in some key areas (e.g. refrigeration), and are now building up in the atmosphere. Basically, this can be traced back to the fact that halocarbons tend to absorb strongly at infrared wavelengths within the 'atmospheric window' (Section 2.1.2), where absorption by the natural greenhouse gases is weak.

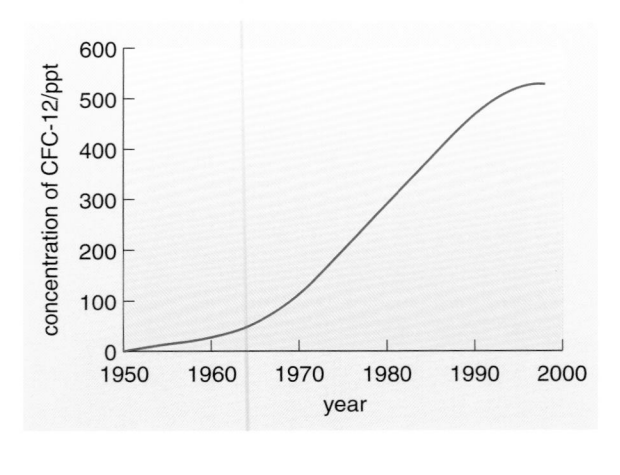

Figure 2.16 The trend in the atmospheric concentration of CFC-12 over the period 1950 to 1998. Thanks to the Montreal Protocol, the growth rate has slowed and then levelled off, but it will take many decades for natural processes to remove all of the CFC-12 already stored in the atmosphere.

This point is made more forcibly by the information collected under the heading 'Global Warming Potential' (GWP) in the final column of Table 2.2. This is a complicated index, designed mainly for use in a policy-making context. Put simply, it is a measure of the radiative forcing induced by adding to the atmosphere a given mass (1 kg, say) of a particular greenhouse gas *relative to* that induced by adding the *same* mass of carbon dioxide; this is why the entry for CO_2 is '1'. So we can think of the GWP value as a measure of the 'effectiveness' of a greenhouse gas as a climate change agent *relative to carbon dioxide* – but only on a mass-for-mass basis. This proviso is important. At first sight, the GWP values listed in Table 2.2 would suggest that CO_2 is a relatively weak greenhouse gas; certainly the halocarbons are a factor of at least 10^3 times more effective, when comparing the release of equal masses of the compounds. The reason CO_2 is given such prominence is that humans are responsible for generating so much more of this gas than any other.

■   How do the concentration data in Table 2.2 provide evidence to support this statement?

▨   In *absolute* terms (rather than the percentage terms noted above), the increase in atmospheric CO_2 has been much greater than that for any of the other greenhouse gases (natural or synthetic); it has risen by close to 100 ppm since pre-industrial times, while the CH_4 level, for example, has gone up by around 1000 ppb or just 1 ppm (Box 2.3).

The atmospheric content of purely synthetic compounds like the halocarbons can be wholly ascribed to human activities. But what about the greenhouse gases that do occur naturally? As you may recall from your earlier studies, atmospheric CO_2 is part of the global carbon cycle – and so too is the methane in the atmosphere, though this is probably a less familiar idea. Likewise, N_2O is part of the natural nitrogen cycle.

We shall examine the workings of the carbon cycle in detail in Chapter 5. The key point for now is that, for each of these gases, there are natural processes that release it into the atmosphere (**sources**), and other natural processes that remove it again (**sinks**). The relatively stable atmospheric concentrations that prevailed in the pre-industrial world tell us that these sources and sinks were in balance (more or less) at that time. Clearly, this natural balance has been disturbed over the past 200 years or so – a period marked by an explosive growth in the human population. At the end of the 18th century, there were fewer than 1 billion people on the planet; there are over 6.3 billion today, and official estimates suggest that the upward trend is likely to continue for some time to come (Figure 2.17).

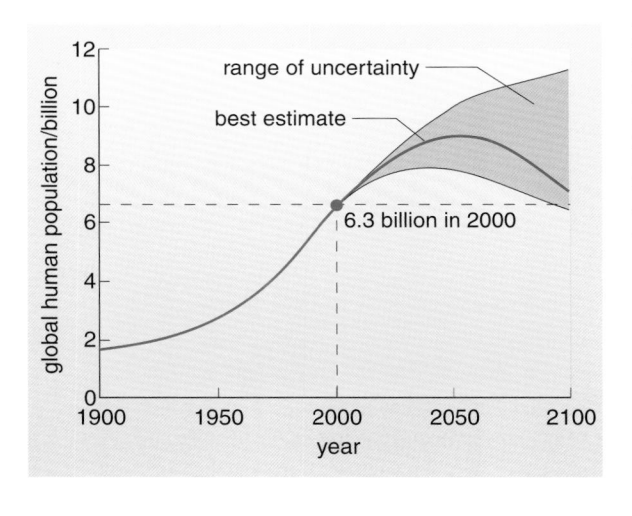

Figure 2.17 According to current best estimates, the human population is projected to peak at around nine billion by 2050, though some experts believe that it could go on increasing throughout the 21st century.

For the most part, the human impact on the atmospheric burden of natural greenhouse gases can be traced back to activities that effectively add a new source of the gas and/or increase natural emissions in various ways. Take CO_2, for example. Despite being the feature that characterises the industrial age, burning fossil fuels is not the only anthropogenic source of CO_2. For centuries, people have been clearing forests, burning the wood and turning vast tracts of land over to agricultural use in order to feed an ever-expanding population. As you will see in Chapter 5, the process of '**deforestation and land-use change**' also adds to the CO_2 content of the atmosphere. The range of human activities that have augmented natural emissions of CH_4 and N_2O are summarised in Box 2.6, along with a brief comment about another natural greenhouse gas – tropospheric ozone. Study the material in the box, and then work through the following questions.

Box 2.6 Sources of other greenhouse gases – the human connection

Methane is generated during the breakdown of organic matter by bacteria that thrive in *anaerobic* (i.e. oxygen-free) environments – principally in waterlogged soils (bogs, swamps and other wetlands, whence methane's common name of 'marsh gas') and in the guts of termites and grazing animals. But today, only some 30% of global CH_4 emissions come from natural sources, with natural wetlands accounting for about two-thirds of the total. Rice paddies, effectively artificial marshes, contribute a further 11%, and an astonishing 16% is due to the flatulence of grazing livestock (cattle, sheep, etc.)! While such sources are undoubtedly biogenic in origin, they also clearly have an anthropogenic element – closely linked to human food production, in this case.

Waste management (e.g. organic matter rotting in landfill sites) adds a further anthropogenic source of CH_4 (around 17% of global emissions). And since natural gas is mainly methane, so too does leakage from natural gas pipelines and the common practice of venting the gas to the atmosphere at oil production sites and from coal mines (a further 19%). Finally, burning vegetation can also generate CH_4, depending on the way it burns (i.e. smouldering as opposed to flaming).

Nitrous oxide is part of the natural nitrogen cycle; it is produced by the activities of micro-organisms in soils and sediments. Again, the increase in its atmospheric concentration is thought to result mainly from agricultural activities, such as the application of nitrogenous fertilisers to boost crop yields; some of the nitrogen ends up in the air as N_2O. In addition, the high-temperature combustion of fossil fuels (or indeed, any kind of vegetation) in air produces some N_2O (through reaction between N_2 and O_2 in the air), along with other nitrogen oxides (notably nitric oxide, NO).

Ozone is also a natural component of the lower atmosphere (due in part to transport down from the stratosphere), but the normal background level is low. However, enhanced concentrations of tropospheric ozone are now found in many polluted environments, especially over densely populated industrialised regions. Here, ozone is generated close to the surface by the action of sunlight on the mix of gaseous pollutants that is typically found in vehicle exhaust fumes – unburnt hydrocarbons, carbon monoxide (CO) and nitric oxide (NO). Ozone is one of the more noxious components of 'photochemical smog' (recall Figure 1.6b), since exposure to enhanced levels of the gas is harmful to both human health and plant growth.

Unfortunately, gains made in reducing vehicle emissions of the key ozone 'precursors' (by fitting catalytic converters) are being outweighed by the worldwide growth in car usage. And there are many other anthropogenic sources of these pollutants as well – including power stations, industrial processes, and the burning of vegetation.

- How does the extraction, distribution and burning of fossil fuels add to the atmospheric burden of other greenhouse gases, as well as CO_2?

- It does so both directly (e.g. N_2O formed during combustion; CH_4 released at fuel extraction sites and through leakage from gas pipelines) and indirectly (emissions of O_3 precursors from vehicles and power stations).

- What other activity that is fundamental to human welfare also seems to have played a major role?

- Food production. Agricultural activities increase emissions of both CH_4 (rice paddies and livestock) and N_2O (fertiliser use). Since burning vegetation often goes along with clearing land for agricultural use, we can add that in as well (a source of CH_4, N_2O and O_3 precursors, as well as CO_2).

Unlike the well-mixed greenhouse gases in Table 2.2, tropospheric ozone is relatively short-lived and there are marked regional variations in its concentration. This has made it difficult to track long-term changes in the *total* amount of ozone in the troposphere, though recent estimates (reported in the TAR) suggest a significant increase since pre-industrial times, by an estimated 36%.

Translating the build up of each of the greenhouse gases into an estimate of the corresponding positive radiative forcing gives the figures collected in Table 2.3; the relative contributions are shown in a more immediately striking form in the 'pie diagram' in Figure 2.18. Evidently, the dominant contribution to date has indeed come from the large increase in atmospheric CO_2. Nevertheless, the build up of the other gases, coupled with their greenhouse efficiency, means that they too are now playing a significant role as climate change agents; together they account for nearly 50% of the historical greenhouse forcing. This is why the Kyoto Protocol does, in fact, cover a 'basket' of greenhouse gases (including CH_4, N_2O and halocarbons not included in the Montreal Protocol) as well as CO_2. In later discussions focusing chiefly on carbon dioxide, it is important not to forget the additional contributions of the other greenhouse gases.

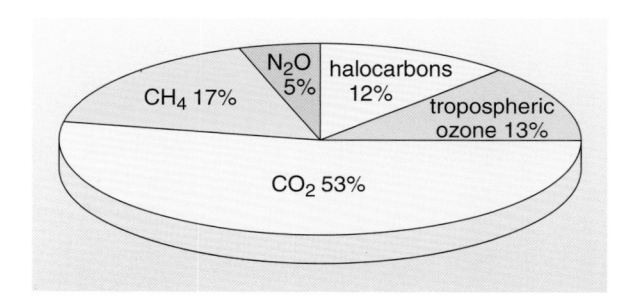

Figure 2.18 Relative contributions of various gases to the total greenhouse forcing of climate over the period 1750 to 2000.

Table 2.3 Estimated contributions to the greenhouse forcing of climate over the period 1750 to 2000 (IPCC, 2001a).

Gas	Radiative forcing/W m^{-2}	% Contribution
long-lived		
CO_2	1.46	53
CH_4	0.48	17
N_2O	0.15	5
halocarbons	0.34	12
short-lived		
tropospheric O_3	0.35	13
total	2.78	100

- What other natural greenhouse gas has not been mentioned in this section?

- Water vapour, the most important of all (Section 2.1.2).

As noted earlier, the water vapour content of the air depends on temperature, and on very little else. The total amount of water vapour in the atmosphere is not directly affected by human actions. However, it can be affected *indirectly* – and in a way that has important implications for the global climatic response to the build up of other greenhouse gases. This is an issue we shall address directly in Chapter 4, but you might like to think about it in the meantime.

There is also something else to think about in the context of 'the human impact on the atmosphere'. Since the dawn of the industrial age, human activities have been pumping a cocktail of particulate matter, as well as greenhouse gases, into the lower atmosphere. In particular, coal often has a high sulfur content, released as SO_2 when the fuel burns (in a power station, industrial process, fireplace, etc.). The 'unpolluted' troposphere naturally contains a certain background level of sulfate aerosols derived from various sulfur-containing gases of both volcanic and biogenic origin. Anthropogenic emissions of SO_2 add to the background aerosol load, and that has the same direct radiative effect as the episodic injection of volcanic aerosols into the stratosphere: it increases the back-scattering of solar radiation.

The 'urban haze' typical of many industrialised regions with a high traffic density (recall Figure 1.6b) also contains 'carbon-based' particulate matter derived from fossil-fuel combustion – including droplets of organic compounds, together with varying amounts of black graphitic and tarry carbon particles (collectively known as '**black carbon**'). Similar '**carbonaceous**' **aerosols** are found in the dense smoke plumes generated by the large-scale burning of vegetation that occurs on a regular basis in many parts of the world. In some regions, natural wildfires (ignited by a lightning strike) are supplemented by fires set deliberately for forest clearance (e.g. in Amazonia and parts of southeast Asia), or as part of the annual agricultural cycle (e.g. to stimulate a flush of new grass for livestock in the savannah grasslands of southern Africa). Data from satellite-borne instruments (Figure 2.19) are helping researchers to map the distribution of fine aerosols (whether sulfates or carbonaceous material) typical of anthropogenic sources (Figure 2.19a) – and to distinguish these from the coarser particles (dust and salt-spray) that have largely natural origins (Figure 2.19b).

The radiative forcing produced by the build up of well-mixed greenhouse gases is both positive (i.e. it has a warming effect) and occurs everywhere around the globe. The climatic effects of an increased load of tropospheric aerosols are different in three important ways.

1   Like sulfates, most aerosols are highly reflective, so they effectively increase the planet's albedo, producing a *negative* forcing (i.e. they cool the surface). Black carbon is an exception to this general rule: it strongly absorbs both incoming sunlight *and* outgoing longwave radiation, and it is thought that this has a warming effect at the surface.

2   Anthropogenic aerosols are short-lived in the lower atmosphere (sulfates return to the surface as 'acid rain'; recall Figure 1.6c), so concentrations vary considerably by region (a pattern evident in Figure 2.19a) and over time. The radiative effects of an increased load of tropospheric aerosols therefore act on a regional, rather than a truly global, scale.

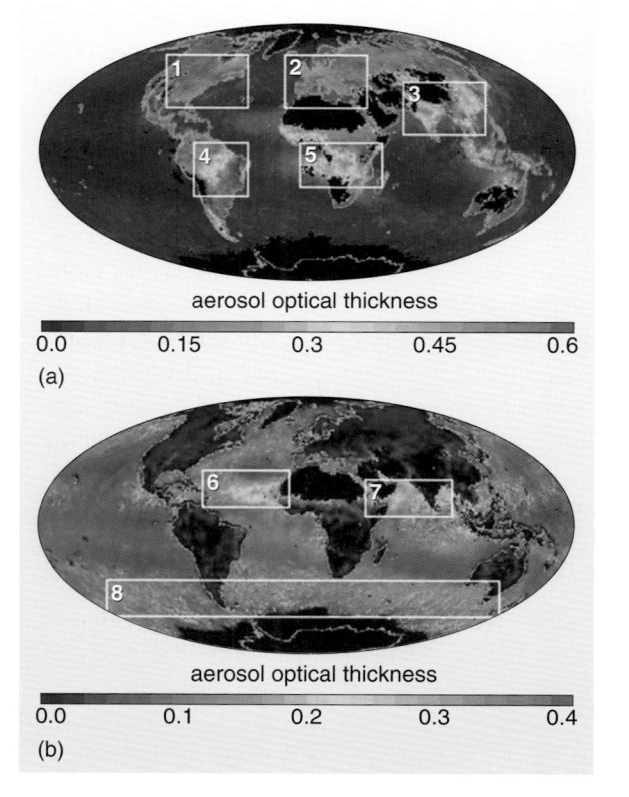

Figure 2.19 Distribution of (a) fine and (b) coarse aerosols from measurements taken by the NASA Terra satellite for September 2000. The aerosol optical thickness is a measure of the total aerosol load (in each size group) in the lower atmosphere, and is represented by the colour scale. White boxes indicate regions with high aerosol concentrations. (a) The image shows fine particles in pollution from North America, Europe and south and east Asia (regions 1, 2 and 3), and in dense plumes downwind from vegetation fires in South America and southern Africa (regions 4 and 5). (b) The image shows coarse dust from Africa (region 6), salt particles generated in the windy conditions of the Southern Ocean (region 8) and desert dust (region 7).

3   Anthropogenic aerosols (especially sulfates) also have a potentially important *indirect* effect on the Earth's radiation balance, linked to their role as cloud condensation nuclei (Section 2.2.2). In polluted regions, the numerous aerosol particles share the condensed water during cloud formation, producing a higher number of small liquid droplets; such clouds are more reflective (i.e. they have a higher albedo), which makes for an additional cooling effect at the surface. This is known as the **indirect aerosol effect**.

The cooling influence (both direct and indirect) of sulfate aerosols in the troposphere has been appreciated for over a decade: it featured in the first IPCC report in 1990, for example. Research since then has begun to unravel the climatic effects of other anthropogenic aerosols, but the extraordinary diversity of these particles (in size, chemical composition, radiative properties, etc.) means that this is turning out to be another complicated and uncertain part of the climate change puzzle. The general view is that tropospheric aerosols mostly produce negative forcing, but there is little confidence in the ability to quantify the *total* human-related effect, and the way it has evolved over time during the industrial age.

■   Given the fundamental question we highlighted at the end of Section 2.4, why is this an important issue?

▨   The cooling influence of most anthropogenic aerosols could have acted to mask (i.e. partially offset) the full warming effect of the build up of greenhouse gases since pre-industrial times.

We shall come back to this issue towards the end of Chapter 3, once we have examined the evidence that the Earth really is warming up.

Summary of Chapter 2

1   Figure 2.11 summarises the ways in which the Earth's surface and atmosphere gain and lose energy. The main points are as follows:

- A proportion (the planetary albedo) of the incoming shortwave radiation from the Sun is reflected (or scattered) directly back to space, mainly by clouds and the Earth's surface (especially snow and ice cover), but also by aerosols (e.g. dust, salt particles, etc.). Most of the rest is absorbed by the surface, thereby warming it.

- Outgoing longwave (infrared) radiation from the Earth's surface is repeatedly absorbed and re-emitted by greenhouse gases naturally present in the atmosphere (mainly water vapour and CO_2, but also methane, nitrous oxide and ozone); this warms the lower atmosphere (or troposphere). Some of the re-emitted radiation ultimately goes out to space, maintaining an overall radiation balance at the top of the atmosphere. But back radiation from the atmosphere keeps the Earth's surface over 30 °C warmer than it otherwise would be – the natural greenhouse effect.

- Clouds both cool the surface (by reflecting solar radiation) and warm it (by absorbing and re-emitting outgoing longwave radiation). Globally, the net effect is a slight cooling of the planet.

- Energy is also transferred from the surface to the atmosphere as heat (through conduction and convection) and through the evaporation/ condensation of water (latent heat transfer).

2   The troposphere is heated from below whereas the stratosphere is heated from above, mainly by the absorption of incoming uv radiation from the Sun by the ozone layer. This produces the characteristic variation of temperature with altitude from the surface up to the stratopause (Figure 2.8).

3   Radiative forcing is an imbalance between the solar radiation absorbed by the Earth–atmosphere system and the longwave radiation emitted to space. It can be either positive (which has a warming effect) or negative (which has a cooling effect). Natural sources of radiative forcing include variations in the solar constant (either up or down) and episodic injections of large amounts of volcanic sulfate aerosols into the stratosphere (which has a short-term cooling effect at the surface).

4   Various human activities (including the extraction, distribution and burning of fossil fuels; industry; burning vegetation and land-use change; agriculture; waste management, etc.) have increased emissions of natural greenhouse gases (or their precursors in the case of tropospheric ozone). As a result, the atmospheric concentrations of these gases have increased since pre-industrial times, by about 31% for CO_2, 149% for CH_4, 16% for N_2O and 36% for O_3. The use of entirely synthetic compounds (halocarbons, e.g. CFCs) has also added new (and potent) greenhouse gases to the atmosphere. This has produced a positive radiative forcing (greenhouse forcing) of climate, which is expected to lead to global warming.

5   Human activities also increase the tropospheric load of sulfate aerosols (due to SO_2 emissions) and various carbonaceous particles (from fossil fuel and

vegetation burning). Anthropogenic aerosols mostly produce negative forcing, both directly (by back-scattering solar radiation) and indirectly (through their influence on cloud albedo).

6   Long-lived gases (CO_2, CH_4, N_2O and halocarbons) are well-mixed in the troposphere. By contrast, the concentrations of relatively short-lived species (e.g. ozone and aerosols) are variable in both space and time.

Questions for Chapter 2

Question 2.5

Information on the different albedos of various types of surface was given in Section 2.1.1. Given that information:

(a) Explain how a cover of snow or ice is likely to affect the amount of incident solar radiation *absorbed* by land or sea.

(b) According to the TAR, there has been a 20% decrease in global forest area since 1850. If we assume that dark forest cover (with an average albedo of 10 – 20%) has been replaced by farmland and pasture with an albedo similar to that of grassland (say, 35%), why might this have contributed to the radiative forcing of climate over the past 150 years? Would the forcing be positive or negative?

Question 2.6

One suggested strategy for reducing anthropogenic emissions of methane is to capture the gas generated in landfill sites, and pipe this away for use as a fuel (for local domestic needs, say). But burning methane produces CO_2. Why might this still be a sensible option if the overall aim is to reduce the *total* greenhouse forcing of climate in future?

Question 2.7

Draw a simple annotated diagram to illustrate the radiative effects (both direct and indirect) of tropospheric sulfate aerosols. Include in your diagram the link with human activities.

Chapter 3

What do we know about recent climate change?

Here are some quotes from the 'Summary for Policymakers' (SPM) included in the report from the scientific working group (Working Group I; Box 1.2) in the IPCC TAR (IPCC, 2001a):

- The Earth's climate system has demonstrably changed on both global and regional scales since the pre-industrial era, with some of these changes attributable to human activities.

- Globally, it is very likely that the 1990s was the warmest decade and 1998 the warmest year in the instrumental record [1861–2000].

- New analyses of proxy data for the Northern Hemisphere indicate that the increase in temperature in the 20th century is likely to have been the largest of any century during the past 1000 years. It is also likely that [...] the 1990s was the warmest decade and 1998 the warmest year [of the millennium].

- In the light of new evidence and taking into account the remaining uncertainties, most of the observed warming over the last 50 years is likely to have been due to the increase in greenhouse gas concentrations.

The overall aim of this chapter is to review the scientific evidence supporting these conclusions. For example, how sure are scientists that the Earth really is warming up? Specifically, what do terms such as 'very likely' and 'likely' actually mean? And how do we know that the record warmth of recent decades is not just some naturally occurring fluctuation in the Earth's temperature that has little, if anything, to do with human activities?

As you will see, the 'background noise' of natural variability makes establishing the existence of a 'significant' global warming trend – one that *could* be due to rising levels of greenhouse gases in the atmosphere – not only difficult, but also highly contentious. Work that challenges the mainstream view on this issue, embodied in the IPCC consensus, is commonly cited by those who remain sceptical about the link between climate change and human activity. We look at one recent example, set in the political context of the day, later on in the chapter. First, we focus on what is known about variations in the Earth's temperature over a range of past time-scales.

3.1 Records of the Earth's temperature

To put the temperature records reported by the IPCC in context, we start with a longer-term geological perspective on the Earth's GMST.

3.1.1 Long-term rhythms in the climate

The instrumental record referred to above is based on direct temperature measurements (using thermometers), and extends back only 150 years or so. Temperatures further back in time are reconstructed from a variety of **proxy data**. These include historical documents, together with natural archives of climate-sensitive phenomena, such as the growth or retreat of glaciers, tree rings, corals, sediments and ice cores (see Box 3.1). In general, the proxy data record becomes more sparse and more imprecise the further back in time we go. Nevertheless, it has proved possible to produce a reasonably reliable reconstruction of how global temperature has varied throughout most of the Earth's history; this is known as the **palaeoclimate** record (from the Greek *palaios* for 'ancient').

Box 3.1 Proxy data: ways to reconstruct past climates (Stokstad, 2001)

People have recorded the vicissitudes of climate and their impact on human affairs for centuries, so archaeological inscriptions and historical documents (diaries, ship's logs, etc.) are a valuable, if somewhat anecdotal, source of climate information. In addition, a variety of techniques – ranging from counting pollen types in lake sediments to analysis of isotope ratios in ancient ice (recall Figure 2.14) – yields rich, if sometimes ambiguous, climate information from many natural sources.

For example, *dendroclimatology* depends on the fact that trees in many parts of the world experience an annual growth cycle (Figure 3.1). Each year's growth (the thickness and/or density of a ring) depends on the local temperature and moisture conditions, creating a unique record that can then be matched with overlapping records from other trees to produce longer time series. Annual records typically go back 500 to 700 years. In a few cases, the preservation of fossil trees has allowed continuous records from 11 000 years ago to the present to be constructed.

In a similar way, cyclical responses lead to annual banding in corals, which can provide information about sea-surface temperatures, sea level and other ocean conditions – typically back to some 400 years ago.

Layered sediments on lake and ocean floors are another rich source. The types of pollen trapped in lake sediments reveal shifting patterns of vegetation, and thus indirect information about temperature and moisture conditions. Records can go back some 100 000 years. In marine sediments, analysis of microfossils can provide data on seawater temperature and salinity (salt content), atmospheric CO_2 and ocean circulation. Less common deposits of coarse debris can point to the break up of ice sheets and the release of detritus from melting icebergs. Marine sediments provide information from time periods ranging from 20 000 years to 180 million years ago.

Finally, long ice cores drilled out of the Greenland and Antarctic ice sheets yield a wealth of information. For example, past temperatures can be determined by *oxygen isotope analysis*. 99% of the oxygen on Earth is the isotope ^{16}O; most of the rest is ^{18}O. Because water molecules containing the different isotopes (i.e. $H_2^{16}O$ and $H_2^{18}O$) have slightly different physical properties, it turns out that the $^{18}O/^{16}O$ ratio in ice locked up on land is affected by the ambient temperature at the time when the ice formed. Thus, fluctuations in the oxygen isotope ratio in an ice core provide a proxy for temperature changes back through time (see Figure 3.2). The cores also include atmospheric fallout such as wind-blown dust, volcanic ash, pollen, etc. – along with trapped air bubbles (as discussed in Section 2.5).

Figure 3.1   Unlocking the secrets of past climates. Each year, a growing tree produces a layer of new cells beneath the bark. If the tree is felled and the trunk examined (or if a core is taken), the growth pattern from year to year appears as a series of rings.

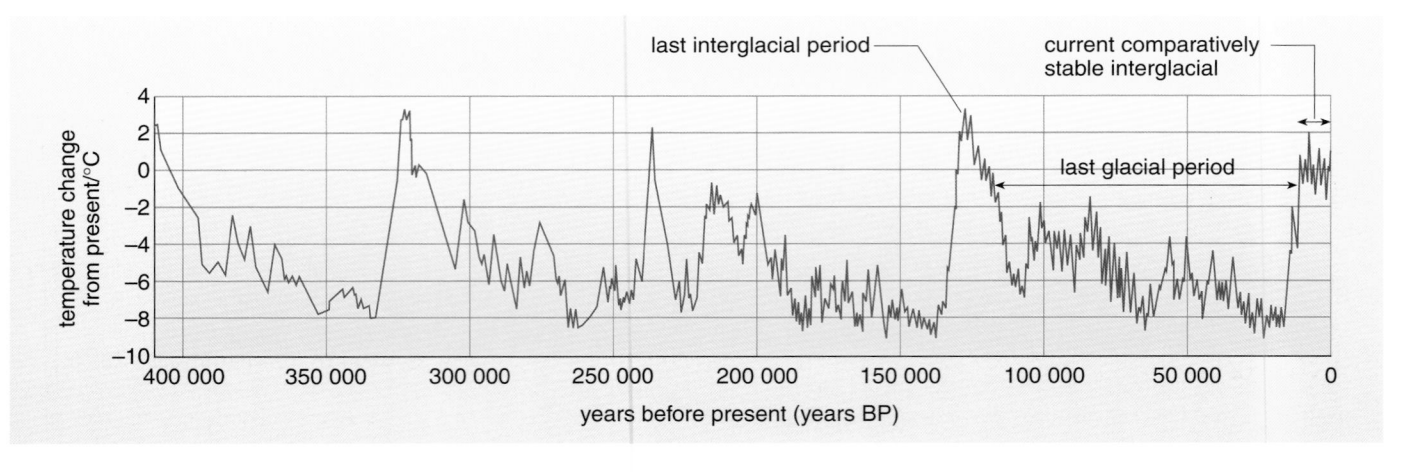

Figure 3.2 Temperature changes over the past 400 000 years reconstructed from the Vostok ice core, the longest continuous ice-core record to date.

This record tells us, for example, that the Earth entered into the most recent comparatively cold period of its history (known as the Pleistocene Ice Age) around 2.6 million years ago. On a geological time-scale, these Ice Ages are relatively rare, covering only 2–3% of the history of our planet. The characteristic feature of the current one (and there is no reason to suppose that it is finished) is evident in Figure 3.2. Drilled in Antarctica, the Vostok ice core provides a temperature record that goes back several hundreds of thousands of years. Beyond about 10 000 years ago, it tells a story of an unstable climate oscillating between short warm **interglacial periods** and longer cold **glacial periods** about every 100 000 years – with global temperatures varying by as much as 5 to 8 °C – interspersed by many more short-term fluctuations.

By contrast, global temperatures over the last 10 000 years or so seem to have been much less variable, fluctuating by little more than one or two degrees. In short, the interglacial period in which we live, known as the **Holocene**, appears (on available evidence) to have provided the longest period of relatively stable global climate for at least 400 000 years. It is almost certainly no coincidence that this is also when many human societies developed agriculture and when the beginnings of modern civilisations occurred. We now shift the focus to the more recent past – the period during which human population growth and the coming of the industrial age began to make their mark on the composition of the atmosphere.

3.1.2 Temperature changes over the past millennium

One of the most striking images in the IPCC TAR is reproduced (in adapted form) in Figure 3.3. Together, these two temperature records tell a compelling story, crystallised in our earlier quotes from the SPM. So let's just pause to take a closer look at each of them.

The instrumental record of the Earth's GMST

Immediately striking in Figure 3.3a are the marked fluctuations in global temperature from year to year. Equally, the averaging that produced the smoothed curve brings out considerable variability over periods of a decade or so as well. Set against this 'background noise' however, there clearly has been a general warming over the past 140 years.

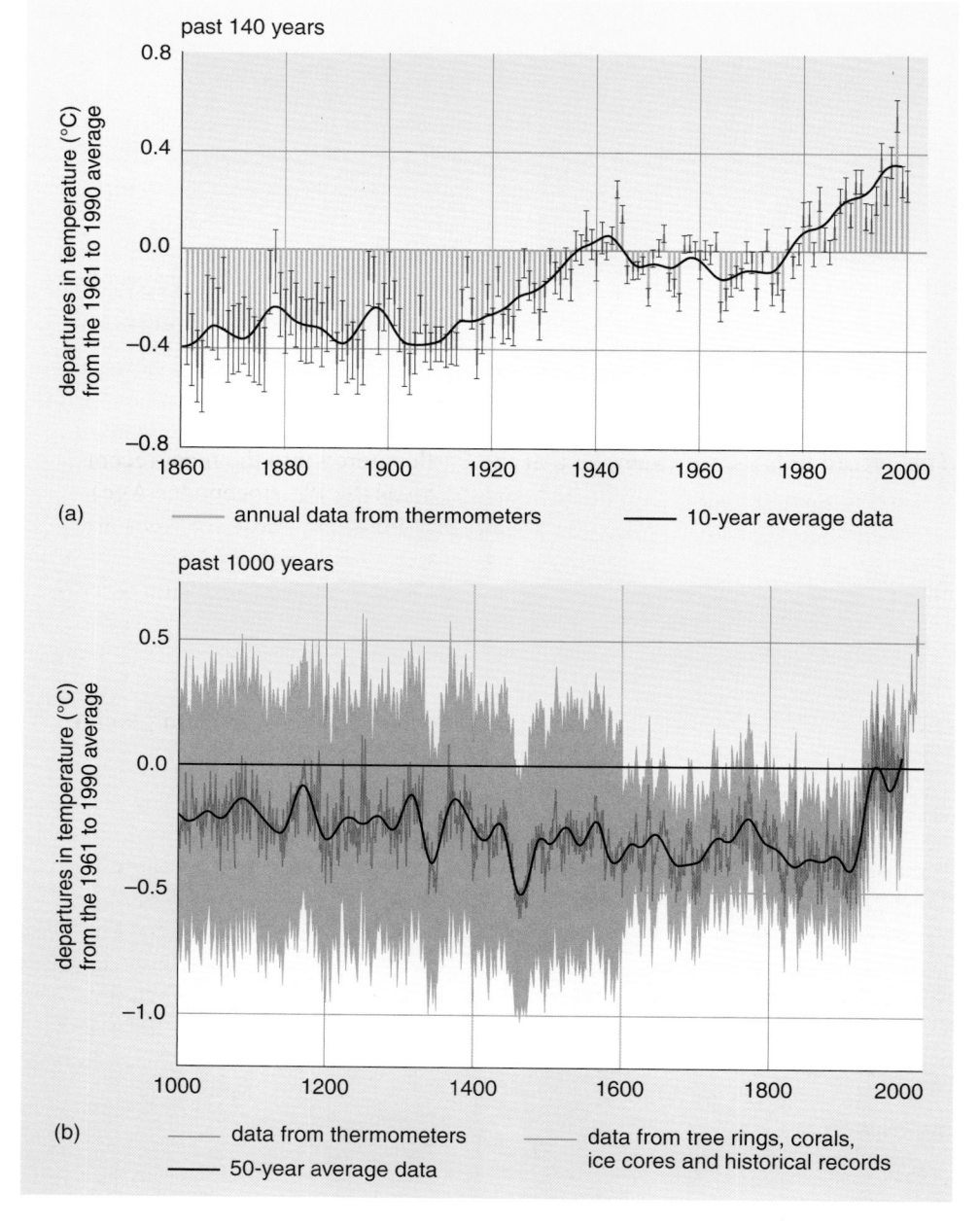

Figure 3.3 Variations of the mean surface temperature: (a) globally over the period 1860–2000; (b) in the Northern Hemisphere over the past 1000 years. In both cases, data are plotted as 'deviations' from the mean value, or *climatological average*, for a particular 30-year period (here 1961–1990). This is a convention widely used by climatologists. In (a), error bars are attached to values for each individual year and don't always overlap with the 'smoothed' curve (black line). (Source: IPCC, 2001a.)

■ Use the smoothed curve in Figure 3.3a to estimate the overall warming.

▨ The curve starts about 0.40 °C below the climatological average, and ends up about 0.35 °C above it. So the overall warming amounts to some {0.35 − (−0.40)} °C = 0.75 °C.

Before engaging further with the details of that trend, it is pertinent to ask about the uncertainties in the instrumental record, indicated by the error bars attached to the annual data. In practice, it is a complex and time-consuming business to 'aggregate' weather observations (be they on land or at sea) from around the world into global averages (recall Section 1.2), and hence construct the kind of climatological time series shown in Figure 3.3a. Uncertainty can arise for various reasons, collected here under two broad headings.

1   *Sampling errors*   Even today, land-based weather stations tend to be concentrated in heavily populated regions of the industrialised world (Figure 3.4). More remote areas and large parts of the ocean are often poorly monitored – and this was even more true in the past. For example, until fairly recently most marine observations were made by 'ships of opportunity'. An uneven spatial coverage effectively 'samples' the Earth's temperature non-uniformly. And as the spatial coverage changes over time, spurious trends and biases can become embedded in the historical record.

2   *Data reliability*   Apparent jumps or trends in the record from a particular station may be an artefact of some local effect. Changes in instrumentation or observing times, or in precise location or the local environment, can all affect the reliability of the data. An important example here is the spurious warming associated with the growth of towns and cities around (or near) a weather station – the so-called 'urban heat island effect'.

Figure 3.4   Today, the WMO (World Meteorological Organisation; Section 1.3) oversees the free international exchange of meteorological data, as well as promoting properly taken observations from a worldwide network of land and marine monitoring stations, including moored buoys and fixed platforms at sea (e.g. oil rigs). The map shows the distribution of these various surface stations.

Figure 3.3a is the result of a painstaking effort to screen the available records (both land-based and marine) – applying corrections where possible or simply rejecting unreliable data – and then to estimate and quantify the uncertainty in the final global averages. Thus, the top (or bottom) of each little orange bar represents the central or 'best' estimate for each year's reconstructed temperature. The error bars represent the 95% confidence interval or range; i.e. there is a 95% probability that the 'true' value lies within this range (see Box 3.2).

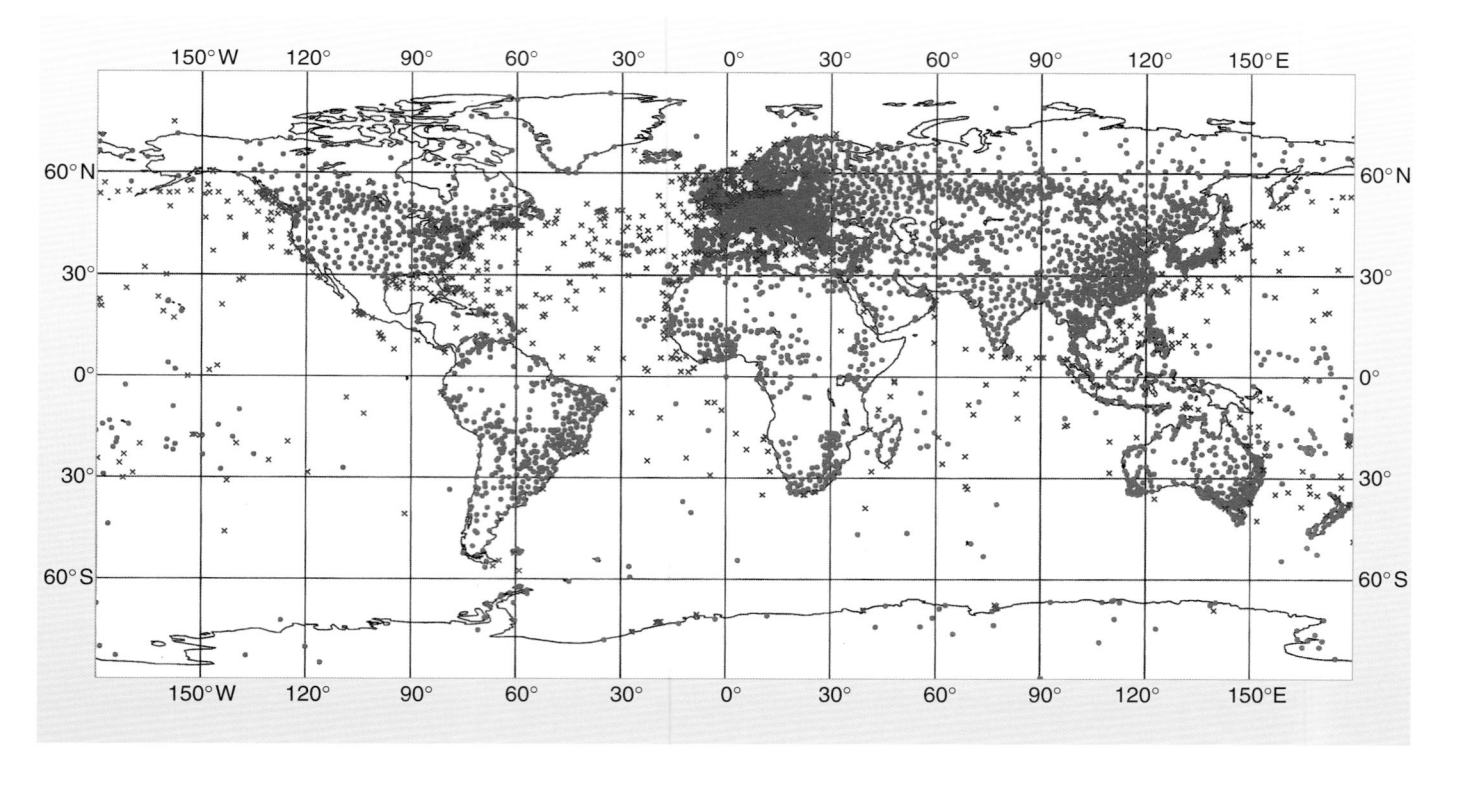

Box 3.2 Measures of uncertainty

Probabilistic statements based on a 'formal' statistical analysis of observational data (e.g. the temperature measurements that feed into estimates of GMST) were introduced earlier in the course (Topic 1 *BSE/vCJD*; Box 1.7). Where IPCC scientists were unable to estimate and quantify the uncertainties in their conclusions in this way, they adopted a 'likelihood' language, originally proposed by Moss and Schneider (Figure 1.18). This was intended to convey their level of confidence in the validity of a conclusion, based on their collective *subjective* judgement. This is fairly unfamiliar territory for most scientists, but reflects the 'policy relevant' context in which the IPCC operates. In other words, if the expert community does not attempt to make such judgements, then someone else will! The translation is as follows:

virtually certain: greater than 99% probability that a conclusion or finding is valid

very likely: 90–99% probability

likely: 66–90% probability

medium likelihood: 33–66% probability

unlikely: 10–33% probability

very unlikely: 1–10% probability

exceptionally unlikely: less than 1% probability.

By applying a standard statistical technique (rather than the rough-and-ready judgement 'by eye' that you used above), the IPCC concluded (IPCC, 2001a): 'Over the 20th century, the increase [in GMST] has been 0.6 ± 0.2 °C'.

■ The 95% confidence level applies to this statement as well. Describe in your own words what this means.

■ The central (or best) estimate of the temperature rise is 0.6 °C; there is a 95% probability that it lies between 0.4 °C and 0.8 °C, and only a 5% probability that it is less than 0.4 °C or greater than 0.8 °C.

Averaged over the whole century, this estimate translates into a *rate* of warming of 0.06 °C per decade. However, the smoothed curve in Figure 3.3a makes it abundantly clear that there were two periods of sustained warming and two periods when the GMST fluctuated without any overall warming or cooling trend. Deciding where the fluctuations end and the warming begins is open to debate. The IPCC's verdict? Most of the warming occurred in the periods 1910 to 1945 and since 1976. The rate of warming for both periods is about 0.15 °C per decade, more than twice the century-long average.

On a regional scale, the most recent warming has been almost global in extent (i.e. it has been happening almost everywhere), but is most marked over the continental landmasses at mid- and high latitudes in the Northern Hemisphere.

And there are some notable 'hot spots', especially in the coldest regions of the far northern Arctic fringe. For the past few decades, parts of Siberia, Alaska and Canada have been warming much faster than the global average rate. In Point Barrow, Alaska (Figure 1.3b), for instance, the annual mean temperature has gone up by 2.3 °C over the past 30 years. Meanwhile, at the other end of the planet, the Antarctic peninsula (the long finger of land that sticks up towards the southern tip of South America in Figure 3.4) has experienced a warming of about 2.5 °C since 1950; average *winter* temperatures are up by nearly 5 °C.

■   Now have another look at the second bullet point in our opening remarks to this chapter. Given the 'likelihood' language adopted in the TAR (Box 3.2) and the information in Figure 3.3a, does this seem a reasonable conclusion?

▨   Yes. It does indeed seem 'very likely' (90–99% probability) that the 1990s was the warmest decade (and 1998 the warmest year) in the instrumental record.

In the early years of the 21st century, there is no immediate sign that global temperatures have taken a downturn. At the time of writing (2006), 2002, 2003 and 2004 stand as the second, third and fourth warmest years, respectively, in the instrumental record. Indeed, the top ten warmest years have all occurred since 1990.

Question 3.1

In its second major report (published in 1996), the IPCC assessed the instrumental record up to (and including) 1994. At that stage, the Panel's best estimate of the increase in GMST since the late 19th century was 0.45 °C – the same as its original estimate (in 1990). How does this compare with the more recent estimate in the TAR, and what is likely to be the main reason for the difference?

The proxy data record for the past millennium

To establish whether 20th century warming is unusual, we need to place it in the context of longer-term climate variability during the Holocene. Because of the scarcity of proxy data from the Southern Hemisphere, the IPCC TAR focused on reviewing a number of reconstructions of the average surface temperature for the Northern Hemisphere, not the whole globe. Figure 3.3b is the record they endorsed as the most reliable guide to how temperatures averaged across the whole hemisphere changed during the course of the last 1000 years. Like the instrumental record (shown in red), the proxy record includes annual data and a smoothed curve that brings out variability on a time-scale of several decades. The grey region is the 95% confidence range in the annual data. Note that the uncertainty is much greater than for the period covered by the instrumental record, and increases further back in time.

■   How would you summarise, in a sentence, the overall long-term trend brought out by the smoothed curve in Figure 3.3b?

▨   There is no one 'correct' answer to a question like this, and if you get a chance to discuss the figure with other students, don't be surprised if you come up with slightly different descriptions.

Here is the formulation the IPCC came up with (IPCC, 2001a):

> The long-term hemispheric trend is best described as a modest and
> irregular cooling from AD 1000 to around 1850–1900, followed by an
> abrupt 20th century warming.

This description and the record it is based on challenge a widely held belief.
Conventional wisdom has it that the Northern Hemisphere experienced a
'Medieval Warm Period' (roughly the 11th to 14th centuries) – when vineyards
flourished in southern Britain and the Vikings colonised Greenland, for example –
followed by a 'Little Ice Age' that lasted well into the 19th century (Figure 3.5);
icebergs became common off Norway, ice fairs were sometimes held in London
on the frozen River Thames in winter, and advancing mountain glaciers crushed
entire villages in the Alps.

Figure 3.5   'Hunters in the snow', an imaginary landscape painted by Peter Bruegel
the Elder in February 1565, during the first of the great winters of the next 200 years.
This seems to have been the most severe period of the Little Ice Age in Europe.

There is no doubt that the landmasses bordering the northern North Atlantic (NE
America, Iceland, Greenland and NW Europe) did experience more genial climes
during the Middle Ages, followed by several centuries of a generally colder
regime than now. These climate changes were often pronounced, but they did not
always occur at the *same* time in different regions. As a result, when conditions
are averaged over the whole hemisphere, the changes no longer appear
exceptional. In other words, current evidence does not support hemisphere-wide
synchronous periods of anomalous warmth or cold over this timeframe. Such
periods appear to have been mainly a regional phenomenon, and are thought to
have been associated with changes in the state of the atmosphere–ocean system
centred on the northern North Atlantic. Natural fluctuations such as this occur on
almost all time-scales (see Chapter 4). They can have a profound effect on

climate on local or regional scales, but are greatly diminished in their influence on hemispheric or global mean temperatures.

The shape marked out by the smoothed curve in Figure 3.3b has seen this reconstruction dubbed the 'hockey stick', especially in the US (think of the graph turned through 90°). Its significance is that the warmth of the last few decades appears to be *unprecedented* in this 1000-year period; i.e. it rises above the range of natural variability, and exceeds the uncertainty in the proxy data record (at the 95% confidence level).

- ■ Now look back at the third bullet point at the beginning of the chapter. What do you make of the language used there?

- ■ It is more cautious. Use of the word 'likely' implies a 66–90% probability (Box 3.2) that the statements are true (i.e. a greater than 2 in 3 probability), based on the collective judgement of the IPCC scientists. Presumably this acknowledges residual concerns about the very large uncertainty associated with proxy data records.

Bearing in mind that every dot and comma in the SPM is pored over (Chapter 1), this is still a pretty strong conclusion – the more so, since it was the first time the IPCC had put the warmth of the late 20th century in the context of changes over a millennial time-scale. *Detection* of a warming 'signal' above the 'noise' of natural variability does not prove that human activity is the probable cause (the question of *attribution* is taken up in Section 3.5), but it is an important first step in that process. As a consequence, it is fraught with political significance.

3.2 Contested science: a case study

For complex issues such as global climate change, there are many opportunities for scientists to take issue with the findings of their colleagues. They can disagree about the procedures for gathering data, the completeness or coverage of the data, how the data are analysed and interpreted, and then finally the conclusions. The assumptions that shape a particular piece of research and inform the kind of questions that will be asked can be no less contentious than the quality of the data gathered.

Such contention is not unique to climate science, of course. Fuelled in part by very human concerns such as a desire to protect one's reputation, competition for funding, etc., vigorous debate is the lifeblood of science; it helps to drive further investigation and innovation. In scientific areas where society has pressing concerns, however, influences beyond the normal cut and thrust of scientific debate come into play. Scientists are typically aware of the potential policy implications of their research, and may shape their work accordingly. Often, such research is stimulated or funded by organisations with an interest in the outcome of the policy debate. In turn, interest groups and policy makers tend to adopt a 'pick n'mix' approach to the available scientific evidence, promoting research that reinforces their existing arguments and beliefs, and neglecting or criticising more uncomfortable findings. Equally, the influence of individual scientists sometimes owes more to their access to decision makers or the media than to the reliability of their knowledge.

In short, the science associated with policy-sensitive areas like climate change is almost bound to be hotly contested, with disputes within the scientific community being extensively reported by the media. In the early years of this century, the 'hockey stick' reconstruction (Figure 3.3b, first published by Professor Michael Mann and colleagues in *Nature* in 1998) became the target for a sustained (and at times, vitriolic) attack that had a high public profile in the US. This is not altogether surprising. It is a potent image – and has become, for some, an icon of what we are doing to the climate. Equally, we should bear in mind the political circumstances of the day. Shortly after he took office in 2001, President George W. Bush withdrew the US from the Kyoto Protocol (Chapter 1) on the grounds that it would harm the US economy. Given the link between fossil fuels, CO_2 emissions and economic activity, this is a legitimate concern; it may well be shared (privately) by other world leaders. Nevertheless, rejection of this landmark agreement to curb CO_2 emissions from industrialised countries set the tone for the Bush Administration. It was widely seen as hostile to any mandatory cutbacks in CO_2 emissions, and open to the influence of sceptical scientific opinion on global warming – either directly (Figure 3.6) or through the activities of various business-backed lobby groups.

Figure 3.6   In September 2003, *The Observer* reported allegations that White House officials had sought to interfere with a report from the US Environmental Protection Agency (EPA) in order to play down the message that climate change is a serious problem.

With this background in mind, you should now tackle Activity 3.1. At its heart is a scientific challenge to the 'hockey stick' reconstruction, and the key conclusion based on it (i.e. that the warmth of the last few decades has been extraordinary), in a paper by Sallie Baliunas and Willie Soon of the Harvard–Smithsonian Centre for Astrophysics, published in the scientific journal *Climate Research* in 2003. At the time, the authors were two of the more visible scientific sceptics of the link between climate change and human activities (in the US, at least). The controversy generated by this challenge is a good example of how the science and the politics of climate change have become inextricably interlinked, and the implications that has for communicating the range of thinking on this issue. The Activity should get you thinking about the points raised earlier in this section (and in Chapter 1). It also serves to identify some themes and questions that are taken up later on.

Activity 3.1

Allow about two hours

This Activity is based around the first part of the BBC Radio 4 mini-series 'Climate Wars' broadcast in the UK in January 2004. The programme charts the genesis and fate of the research referred to above, how it became a *cause célèbre* in Washington, and the highly inflamed debate that followed. It gives you a chance to hear some of the scientists involved talk about their own work, together with some of the more influential sceptical voices in the climate debate in the US at the time. The programme can be found on the S250 DVD by going to Topic 5 and following the link to 'Climate wars'.

Have Figure 3.3 to hand while you listen to the programme, and be ready to take notes that will help you to jot down your thoughts on the following questions at the end.

1 How did Baliunas and Soon go about their research? What questions did they ask of the proxy data records? And what was their main conclusion?

2 What were the main points in Mann's rebuttal of the paper by Baliunas and Soon? What issues were raised about the publication of this paper?

3 Why did the work by Baliunas and Soon have such a big political impact in Washington?

4 William O'Keefe is president of the George C. Marshall Institute, a Washington-based think tank. What appears to be the main agenda of this organisation in the climate change context?

5 What was the main point at issue in the row over the report from the EPA referred to in Figure 3.6?

6 The *National Assessment on Climate Change* was a US government-sponsored report that assessed (among other things) the impacts of climate change for different regions across the country. What criticisms were levelled at this report? What was particularly disturbing about attempts to have the report withdrawn?

7 Myron Ebell is one of the directors of the Competitive Enterprise Institute in the US – a business-backed lobbying organisation dedicated to the principles of free enterprise and limited government. How would you characterise his stance on the global warming issue?

3.3 The meaning of 'consensus': peer review and the IPCC process

At the time of writing (2006), debate about the 'hockey stick' reconstruction continues to rumble on. In this and other controversial areas, it is natural that scientists who are not part of the IPCC process should scrutinise its assessments and continue to ask probing questions about its conclusions. At the same time, however, it's important to keep claims that run counter to the mainstream view in perspective – and to bear in mind that there may well be a political agenda behind the *selective* promotion of such claims. In the US, for example, Congress had already refused to ratify the Kyoto Protocol before the Bush Administration took office. A sustained campaign, stressing the uncertainties in the science, by the notorious and now largely defunct Global Climate Coalition (a business NGO comprising several large multinational fossil fuel companies) is credited with having played an important role in that decision.

As pointed out in Chapter 1, the IPCC's remit is to analyse and evaluate the existing peer-reviewed literature, pertinent to the many scientific, technical and socioeconomic aspects of human-induced climate change. This huge interdisciplinary task depends on the work of thousands of collaborating natural and social scientists – a significant proportion of the academic community engaged in climate change-related research. To put the sensitivity of the IPCC's role into sharper focus (Edwards and Schneider, 2001):

> As a hybrid science-policy body, the IPCC must maintain credibility and trust *vis-à-vis* two rather different communities: the scientists who make up its primary membership, and the global climate policy community to which it provides input […] The IPCC's rules of procedure spell out a variety of methods designed to ensure its reports include the best available scientific knowledge and that they represent this knowledge fairly and accurately. Chief among these is the principle of peer review, traditionally one of the most important safeguards against bias and error in science.

As far as the scientific literature is concerned, the basic elements of the **peer review** procedure were touched on in the *Introduction to the Course*, and revisited in Activity 3.1. Scientists write articles (papers) and submit them to a journal. The journal editor sends the paper to several referees, all of them experts in the authors' field (i.e. their 'peers'). Referees can typically chose one of three recommendations: acceptance, rejection or acceptance after certain specified changes are made. The third option ('revise and resubmit') is by far the most common. The process usually goes back and forth a few times, with several rounds of revisions, until an acceptable compromise is achieved.

■ So, did the peer review process 'fail' in the case of the Baliunas and Soon paper at the heart of Activity 3.1?

▨ It's difficult to say. We know that one referee was unhappy (noting that the conclusions didn't follow from the way the data were analysed), but other referees must presumably have recommended publication.

This highlights one of the perceived problems with peer review; different referees can come up with radically different conclusions about the merits of a particular piece of work. Some commentators see this as a fundamental weakness of the whole system. Others have concluded that most reviewer differences probably result from 'real and legitimate differences of opinion among experts about what good science is or should be'.

As we said earlier, disagreement is healthy; it moves science on. But, as Edwards and Schneider go on to say:

> if expert judgement varies too widely to provide a quasi-mechanical means of winnowing out bad science from good, why is peer review important? […] We maintain that peer review ought to be regarded as a [sometimes fallible] human process whose primary functions are to improve the quality of scientific work, to maintain accountability both inside and outside the scientific community, and to build a scientific community that shares core principles and beliefs even when it does not agree in detail.

This perspective on what peer review is 'for' bears directly on its role in the IPCC process. Recall that IPCC reports are not primary science, but assessments of the state of the field based on a critical evaluation of existing work. Nevertheless, draft chapters and other IPCC documents are subjected to their own peer review process. This is more open, extensive and inclusive than most, involving non-specialists (government advisers, business lobby groups, etc.) as well as expert scientific reviewers. Typically, hundreds or even thousands of changes are made as each document goes through several drafts.

This exhaustive process has played a major role in building a broad-based scientific consensus on the causes and implications of recent climate change, and in establishing the credibility of IPCC reports for policy purposes. These days, most of the world's leading climate researchers are involved in one way or another – as authors or reviewers, or because their work is used and cited. Over the years, some of the more outspoken scientific sceptics have been drawn in as well, so their views are now represented in the process that produces eventual consensus on the 'current state of knowledge'. In effect, then, the IPCC has become the voice of the expert climate science community, and is now regarded as an authority by most (if not all!) governments around the world. As we stressed in Chapter 1, its assessments are a major driving force behind international climate policy.

Yet there are critics who charge that the very notion of 'consensus science' is a nonsense, commonly citing those giants of the past (e.g. Galileo, Einstein) who have challenged and revolutionised the scientific dogma of the day. If controversy and robust debate is the lifeblood of science, the argument goes, then 'consensus' must surely be its death knell, and deeply anti-scientific.

The counter argument is that the IPCC consensus is not some unassailable 'truth'; it is simply a fair representation of the expert scientific community's current general opinion, based on the available evidence and subject to revision. Behind the public, government-negotiated and carefully crafted face of this consensus (in the SPMs) is a lot of messy and uncertain science. The highly technical bulk of each report (Figure 1.8) documents limitations of current understanding, areas of disagreement, caveats about uncertainties, etc. There is no point pretending this is not the case. As stated at the outset, in a field as complex as climate change, uncertainty is unavoidable. Moreover, ongoing research may help to reduce uncertainties in some areas while at the same time uncover new sources of uncertainty elsewhere. We have already encountered one example – growing awareness of the complicated climatic effects of tropospheric aerosols – and doubtless many more will come to light in the years ahead.

To return to the original focus of this chapter, few researchers base their underlying concern about the build up of atmospheric CO_2 on the Earth's recent temperature history. Rather, it is rooted in what might be termed the 'relentless logic' of the physics of the greenhouse effect (Section 2.4), and fuelled by the dramatic rise in greenhouse gas concentrations over the past 200 years or so (Figure 2.15). On the other hand, there is little doubt that the record-breaking warmth of the 1980s and 1990s has lent warnings about the 'greenhouse problem' a popular credibility they previously lacked. Activity 3.2 invites you to ponder on that popular perception.

Activity 3.2

Allow 15–20 minutes

The theory that we were heading into another 'ice age' was quite topical and scientifically respectable in the 1970s. Indeed, this was one of the concerns on the agenda at the first World Climate Conference (in 1979; Box 1.1), along with the prospect of greenhouse warming. Here are a couple of quotes, which give you a feel for how the issue was presented at the time:

> The threat of a new ice age must now stand alongside nuclear war as a likely source of wholesale death and misery for mankind.
>
> (Nigel Calder, *International Wildlife*, July 1975)

> This cooling has already killed hundreds of thousands of people. If it continues and no strong action is taken, it will cause world famine, world chaos and world war, and this could all come about before the year 2000.
>
> (Lowell Ponte, *The Cooling*, 1976)

(a) Look back at Figure 3.3a. Can you suggest why the idea that the world was headed for a cooler regime might have gained credence at the time?

(b) What devices are used in the quotes above in order to communicate the implications of 'global cooling'?

(c) In the 1970s, some scientists argued that the cooling was due to expanding industrial activity. What do you think was the basis for this suggestion?

(d) What salutary lessons can be drawn from this episode that are relevant to the current debate about global warming?

3.4 A 'collective picture of a warming world'

The observed increase in GMST may be the key global indicator of greenhouse warming, but it is far from being the only tangible sign of climate change during the 20th century. This brings us back to the first bullet point at the beginning of the chapter. Just what is meant by the Earth's 'climate system', and how it produces the rich diversity of climatic regimes around the world, are questions we examine in more detail in Chapter 4. Here, we take a brief look at the growing body of evidence that many different climate variables, as well as physical and biological systems around the world, have been affected by recent

Box 3.3 'Global warming: early warning signs' (UCS, 2004)

1 The Himalaya The Khumbu Glacier (on a popular climbing route to the summit of Mount Everest) has retreated by over 5 km since 1953. In the central and eastern Himalaya, glaciers are contracting at an average rate of 15 m per year, and could be gone by 2035 if this trend continues – with serious implications for populations who depend on glacial meltwater for drinking supplies, etc. Meanwhile, glacial lakes are swelling in Bhutan, increasing the risk of catastrophic flooding downstream.

2 Alaska, USA Most of the state is underlain by **permafrost** (permanently frozen soil). Thawing permafrost is causing the ground to subside (by 4–10 m in some places), undermining buildings, roads and other infrastructure. In some coastal areas, wave action is undermining cliffs softened by permafrost melt, increasing the risk of flooding for native communities. In the interior, forests of spruce and birch are taking on a 'drunken' appearance

Figure 3.7   A 'drunken' forest on ground softened by melting permafrost, outside Fairbanks, Alaska.

(Figure 3.7) on softening ground, and trees are dying as they succumb to waterlogged conditions.

3 Chokoria Sundarbans, Bangladesh Rising sea levels have flooded about 7500 hectares of coastal mangrove forest during the past three decades. Global sea-level rise is aggravated by substantial deltaic subsidence in the area due mainly to human activities, such as reduced sediment supply following dam construction upstream for irrigation schemes, and the over-extraction of groundwater (Chapter 1).

4 United Kingdom The average flowering date of 385 British plant species has advanced by 4½ days during the 1990s compared with the previous four decades; 16% of the species flowered 15 days earlier on average. Over a 20-year period (between 1968–72 and 1988–91), many bird species have extended the northern margins of their breeding ranges in the UK by an average of 19 km.

5 Monteverde Cloud Forest, Costa Rica A reduction in dry-season mists due to warmer Pacific Ocean temperatures has been linked to the disappearance of 20 species of frogs and toads, upward shifts in the ranges of mountain birds, and declines in lizard populations.

6 Antarctic peninsula Adélie penguin populations have shrunk by 33% over the past 25 years in response to declines in their winter sea-ice habitat. Adélies depend on sea ice as a resting and feeding platform. They are being replaced by gentoo penguins (a sub-Antarctic species that has begun to migrate towards the pole) which thrive in open water.

climate warming. The examples collected in Box 3.3 will give you a flavour of the sorts of reports that are now emerging from research programmes, though for the most part we focus on the overall picture summarised in the TAR.

3.4.1 Physical and weather-related indicators

The indicators collected in Table 3.1 have been observed to change over large regions of the Earth during the 20th century. According to the TAR, there is now a good level of confidence that what is being recorded is the result of long-term change rather than short-term natural fluctuations. As we noted earlier (Section 3.1.2), the most recent period of warming has been almost global in extent, but particularly marked at high latitudes. So are the changes in Table 3.1 consistent with rising temperatures on both a regional and global scale?

Table 3.1 Twentieth century changes in the Earth's climate system.

Weather indicators	Observed changes*
hot days/heat index†	increased (*likely*)
cold/frost days	decreased over most land areas during 20th century (*very likely*)
continental precipitation	increased by 5–10% over 20th century in Northern Hemisphere (*very likely*), although it has decreased in some regions (e.g. N and W Africa and parts of Mediterranean)
heavy precipitation events	increased at mid- and high northern latitudes (*likely*)
frequency and severity of drought	increased summer drying and associated incidence of drought in a few areas (*likely*); in recent decades, frequency and intensity of droughts have increased in parts of Asia and Africa

Physical indicators	Observed changes*
global-mean sea level	increased at average annual rate of 1–2 mm during 20th century
duration of ice cover on rivers and lakes	in mid- and high latitudes of Northern Hemisphere, decreased by 2 weeks during 20th century (*very likely*); many lakes now freeze later in autumn and thaw earlier in spring than in 19th century
Arctic sea-ice extent and thickness	thinned by 40% in recent decades in late summer (*likely*), and decreased in extent by 10–15% since 1950s in spring and summer
non-polar glaciers	widespread retreat during 20th century
snow cover	decreased in area by 10% since satellite observations began in 1960s (*very likely*)
permafrost	thawed, warmed and degraded in parts of polar and sub-polar regions

* Levels of confidence (Box 3.2) where available are given in italics.

† Heat index is a measure of how humidity acts along with high temperature to reduce the body's ability to cool itself.

Question 3.2

(a)   Figure 3.8 is a schematic representation of the distribution of daily temperatures (for a fictional location), scattered around the mean value according to a bell-shaped curve (a 'normal' distribution). At the tail ends of the distribution, the shaded areas represent the frequency of occurrence of unusually cold (left) and unusually hot (right) days. Suppose now that the mean temperature increases, but the distribution of temperatures around the mean (i.e. the shape of the curve) is unchanged. Sketch a second curve on Figure 3.8 to represent this 'new' climate, and use it to explain the first two weather-related entries in Table 3.1.

(b)   In the examples of potential impacts of climate change in Figure 1.13 (Section 1.5), the box labelled 'HEALTH' includes 'weather-related deaths'. Drawing on your own experience, how might the shifts you identified in part (a) be expected to affect the human death-toll due to temperature extremes?

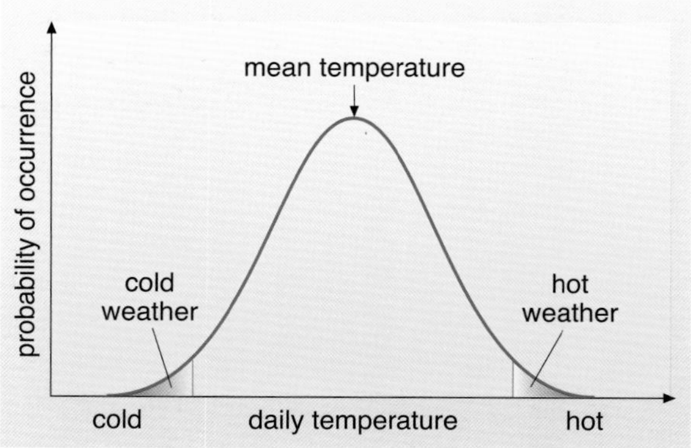

Figure 3.8   The distribution of daily temperatures around the mean value for a fictional location; see Question 3.2.

The remaining weather indicators in Table 3.1 (changes to precipitation and droughts) are less easy to link directly with a rise in GMST. However, they do bear directly on one of the major reasons for concern about regional climate change (Chapter 1) – a possible increase in extreme events – and we shall come back to them, in that context, in Chapter 7.

■ What about the changes in physical systems collected in Table 3.1? How might these be explained by rising temperatures?

▢ The thinning and reduced extent of snow and ice cover over land and sea, and the melting of permafrost (Box 3.3), are all consistent with a warming of the climate. We might also expect that this warming has, in turn, contributed to the observed sea-level rise, both through direct warming and thermal expansion of seawater (Box 2.4; Section 2.2.4), and because the widespread melting of glaciers has added more water to the oceans (the two causes we hope you identified in Activity 1.3).

Sea-level rise is one of the most feared aspects of global warming for island nations like Tuvalu, and for inhabitants of other low-lying parts of the planet (Chapter 1). Yet keeping tabs on *global mean* sea level (the indicator included in Table 3.1) is, if anything, an even more complicated problem than monitoring the Earth's temperature – and again provides scope for disagreement and controversy among scientists.

Today, sea-levels are recorded by coastal tide gauges *relative* to a fixed benchmark on land. Averaged over a period of time (a year, say, to remove short-term effects due to waves, tides, weather conditions, etc.), the result is the local 'mean sea level'. The difficulty in interpreting changes in mean sea level at a particular locality is that the land moves up and down as well. These vertical land movements can result from human activities (of the kind noted in connection with Bangladesh in Box 3.3), or more generally from natural causes – including tectonic processes (e.g. earthquakes) and very slow adjustments to major changes in ice-loading. For instance, the UK is still adjusting to the melting of ice at the end of the last glacial period; Scotland is rising a few mm a year and the south of England is sinking at a similar rate.

With this in mind, you can begin to see why it might be difficult to establish how global mean sea level (sea level averaged across the globe) has varied over the past century due solely to changes in the total *volume* of water in the oceans. It is this so-called 'eustatic' sea-level change that is linked to the climate-related factors identified above: thermal expansion of seawater and melting of land ice. All the historical records from tide gauges around the world measure only relative sea level. Not only is the spatial distribution of high-quality long-term records decidedly patchy, but individual records must also be adjusted for local land movements. This is a major source of uncertainty in the IPCC estimate included in Table 3.1.

■ What does this estimate imply about the total sea-level rise over the 20th century?

▢ A rate of increase of 1–2 mm per year translates into a rise of 10–20 cm in the past 100 years.

But is this linked to 20th century climate warming? There is no independent evidence of this. All scientists can do is to *estimate* the contributions due to the observed warming, and see whether this matches the *observed* sea-level rise. The IPCC TAR estimates of the various temperature-linked contributions are collected in Table 3.2. Some background information on these estimates is given in Box 3.4. Read through that material, and then try Question 3.3.

Table 3.2 Estimated contributions to mean rate of sea-level rise (in mm y^{-1}) from thermal expansion and land-ice change, averaged over the period 1910–1990. See Box 3.4 for significance of negative values, and entry for 'long-term ice sheet adjustment'. Estimates for the *observed* rate of increase are included for comparison. (Source: IPCC, 2001a.)

	Low	**Central estimate**	**High**
effects due to 20th century warming:			
thermal expansion	0.3	0.5	0.7
glaciers	0.2	0.3	0.4
Greenland ice sheet	0.0	0.05	0.1
Antarctic ice sheet	−0.2	−0.1	0.0
long-term ice-sheet adjustment	0.0	0.25	0.5
total estimated	0.3	1.0	1.7
observed	1.0	1.5	2.0

Box 3.4 Glaciers and ice sheets: how do they respond to climate warming?

The ice stored on land is usually carved up into two broad categories:

1 **Glaciers** (and small ice caps) in mountainous areas (such as the Alps, Andes, Himalayas, etc.) and at high latitudes (in places like Iceland, Alaska, the Canadian Arctic and Scandinavia).

2 The vast **ice sheets** in Greenland and Antarctica.

A glacier or ice sheet gains mass by *accumulation* of snow (which is gradually transformed to ice) and loses mass (known as *ablation*) mainly by melting at the surface or base, with subsequent runoff or evaporation of the meltwater. Bodies of ice have their own internal dynamics as well. Ice is deformed and flows within them – down a mountain for example, or in vast slow-moving 'ice streams' within the major ice sheets. Where a glacier or ice stream meets the sea, ice may be removed by the calving of icebergs or by discharge into a floating ice shelf (Figure 3.9), from which it is lost by basal melting and calving of icebergs.

Figure 3.9   Virtually all ice shelves appear as huge walls of ice towering up to 40 m above the ocean. During the 'heroic age' of Antarctic exploration, the Ross Ice Shelf (the largest on the fringes of the continent) was known as the 'Great Ice Barrier'.

How climate warming affects the total mass of an individual glacier or ice sheet depends on how the balance between accumulation (through snowfall) and ablation (through melting and discharge) responds to rising temperatures. On the face of it, this is a simple task of relating climate to accumulation and loss rates. In practice, numerous factors conspire to complicate this simple picture – not least the internal dynamics of the ice body.

Nevertheless, estimates of glacier and ice-sheet sensitivity to climate change have been made. On the basis of such estimates, a warmer climate is judged to result in a shrinkage of glaciers and the Greenland ice sheet, due to increased ablation. By contrast, Antarctic temperatures are currently so low that modest warming is expected to *increase* the overall mass of ice, due to increased accumulation accompanying a warmer atmosphere with increased moisture availability.

One final, very important complicating factor: the mass balance of a body of ice is essentially always attempting to catch up with climate. There is a time lag between climate change and the corresponding effect on a glacier or ice sheet, known as the response time.

In general, glaciers are not only pretty sensitive to climate change, they also have relatively short response times – typically 50 years or so, though the actual value varies depending on surface area, ice thickness and other factors. By contrast, changes in ice discharge from ice sheets have response times of 1000 years or more. Hence, it is likely that the Greenland and Antarctic ice sheets are still adjusting to their past history, especially the last glacial/interglacial transition. Table 3.2 includes an estimate of the contribution this long-term adjustment has made to 20th century sea-level rise.

Question 3.3

(a)   Using the central estimates in Table 3.2, work out the percentage contribution each factor has made to the mean rate of sea-level rise during the 20th century. Which of these factors appears to have made the major contribution?

(b)   In broad terms, are the estimated contributions from glaciers and the major ice sheets (due to 20th century warming) consistent with the background information in Box 3.4?

Clearly, there are large uncertainties associated with the estimates collected in Table 3.2. This reflects a lack of sufficient observational data, inadequate understanding of the complex processes involved and shortcomings in the models used to produce some of these estimates. For instance, there is abundant evidence that the 20th century saw widespread glacier retreat across the globe: from the Arctic to Peru and New Zealand, from Switzerland to the Himalaya (Box 3.3) and the famed snows of Mount Kilimanjaro (Figure 3.10), vast ice fields and glaciers are shrinking. Yet it is still a difficult and uncertain business to quantify the loss of ice and assess its impact on the total volume of water in the world's oceans.

Meanwhile, the sheer physical size and inaccessibility of the ice sheets, the extreme climates and the occurrence of long periods of polar darkness have long rendered the acquisition of representative measurements extremely difficult. For example, the lack of suitable long-term data means there is no *direct* evidence that the whole Greenland ice sheet did actually shrink during the last 100 years; the estimate in Table 3.2 is based entirely on modelling studies driven by the observed warming over the ice sheet. However, satellite surveillance has been in

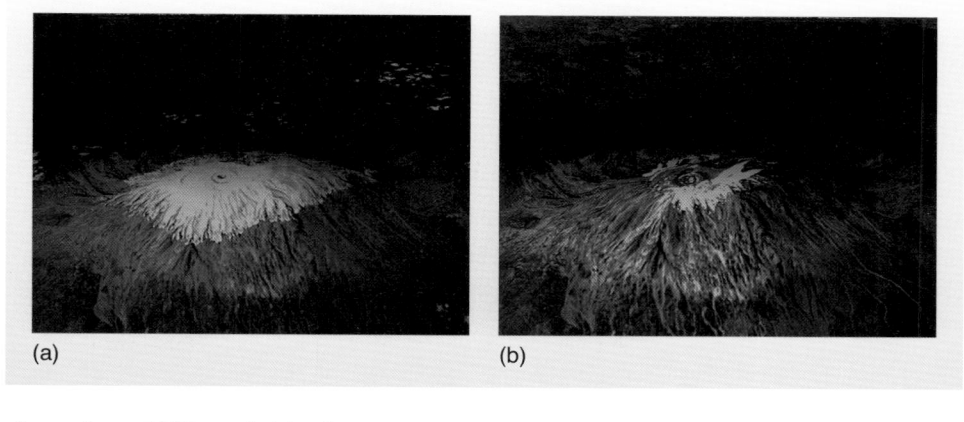

Figure 3.10 Satellite images of Mount Kilimanjaro, Tanzania, in (a) February 1993 and (b) February 2000. Around 82% of the snow and ice on the summit has disappeared since 1912, with about one-third melting since 1990. At current rates, scientists believe the ice cap could be gone by 2015, with important implications for tourism in Tanzania.

place since 1990, and this short-term record does indicate a rapid thinning of the edges of the ice sheet.

Summaries of available data for the whole of Antarctica have tended to find small positive net mass balances overall (in line with the estimate in Table 3.2), though with high degrees of uncertainty. But once again, there are signs that dramatic change is underway in some parts of the continent – not least the recent rapid collapse of several ice shelves around the Antarctic peninsula (Figure 3.11). Despite the newspaper headlines that accompany such an event, bear in mind that disintegration of a *floating* ice shelf does not, by itself, contribute to sea-level rise. (If you want to prove this for yourself, try floating ice cubes in a tumbler brimful of water to see if it overflows as they melt.) However, there is concern that, without ice shelves to act as dams, the continent's ice streams and glaciers might migrate faster towards the coast, ultimately contributing to sea-level rise. There are early indications that this may be happening in some parts of western Antarctica.

■ Now have another look at the estimates in Table 3.2. Taken together, do they tell the whole story of sea-level rise during the 20th century?

▨ Probably not. The uncertainties are large, but (based on the central estimates) these climate-related contributions make up only some 67% of the observed rate of increase. However, the high estimate does account for the observed rise.

The IPCC identified the influence of some additional factors (*not* directly related to climate change, such as the extraction of groundwater), but were still left with a discrepancy between the estimated and observed rate of sea-level rise. Given the uncertainties that pervade this issue on all fronts, this is not altogether surprising. Nevertheless, the TAR concluded that 'it is very likely [90–99% probability; Box 3.2] that the 20th century warming has contributed significantly to the observed sea-level rise'.

3.4.2 Environmental indicators

The notion of a link between climatic conditions and the behaviour of plants and animals (e.g. the growth of trees or coral) and the composition of natural communities or ecosystems (the type of vegetation in a given area, say) is

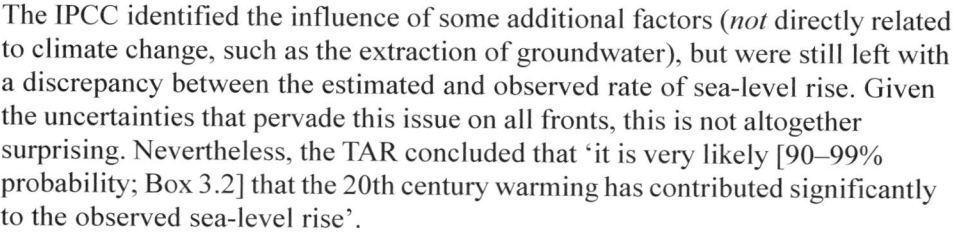

5th Mar 2002
17th Feb 2002
31st Jan 2002
1995

Figure 3.11 Satellite images tracking the spectacular collapse of part of the Larsen-B ice shelf on the eastern side of the Antarctic peninsula. In 2002, a huge area (about 3200 km²) of ice disintegrated in just 35 days. This was the largest collapse event of the last 30 years, bringing the total loss of ice extent from seven ice shelves to 17 500 km² since 1974. The ice retreat is attributed to the region's strong warming trend (Section 3.1.2).

fundamental to the use of proxy data to reconstruct past climates. Some examples of biological responses to recent climate change were included in Box 3.3. Here we should be wary of jumping to conclusions. Such changes involve complex living systems that can respond in complicated ways to a great variety of other pressures. Particular caution is necessary wherever records are of short duration, which in this context means less than a few decades.

Well aware of this stricture, and having conducted a literature survey of papers documenting biological and ecosystem changes on this sort of time-scale, the IPCC concluded (with high confidence) that the following observations are related to recent climate change:

- earlier flowering of plants, budding of trees, emergence of insects and egg-laying in birds and amphibians
- lengthening of the growing season in mid- to high latitudes
- shifts of plant and animal ranges to higher latitudes and higher altitudes
- decline of some plant and animal populations.

You may well have noticed the kind of 'phenological' changes referred to in the first two points – shifts in the timing of life cycle events in plants and animals. Many biological phenomena (e.g. leaf bud burst and flowering in plants) cannot proceed until a minimum temperature has been reached over an adequate length of time. Changes in the timing of such events are easy to observe and monitor, and can provide sensitive indicators of climate change. Studies from various regions and ecosystem types tell a consistent story. For example, from Scandinavia to the Mediterranean and across North America, the growing season (Chapter 1) for plants has increased by 1–4 weeks over the past 50 years; spring comes earlier, but leaf fall in deciduous plants is delayed. Many animal life cycles also depend on temperature; in the UK, for instance, it seems that aphids now appear on average a week earlier than 25 years ago.

Migrating animals, especially butterflies and birds, benefit from keeping pace with the changes by arriving earlier in their summer habitat, so that food such as pollen and insects is available at the right time. Many are responding in just such a manner. However, there are signs that, in some cases, important inter-dependencies may be slipping 'out of sync' as the species involved respond to changed conditions in different ways; one example is included in Figure 3.12.

Other plants and animals are adapting by extending their ranges – an example of the type of response referred to in the third bullet point above. Put simply, the underlying principle here is the one we invoked in connection with warming-related shifts in optimal crop zones in Chapter 1: the geographical limits of many plants and animals are determined very largely by temperature. In the Northern Hemisphere, for instance, it may be too cold for some species further north (or at higher altitudes), and too warm for other species further south (or at lower altitudes; alpine plants come to mind). Either way, shifts of the kind that appear to be underway (Box 3.3, points 4–6) are broadly consistent with a warmer climate.

Natural communities of plants and animals are in a constant state of change, and their composition is often strongly influenced by climatic factors. In a warmer climate, crucial interactions in the complicated dynamics of natural systems can be disrupted; some species will fare better than others. Those that are

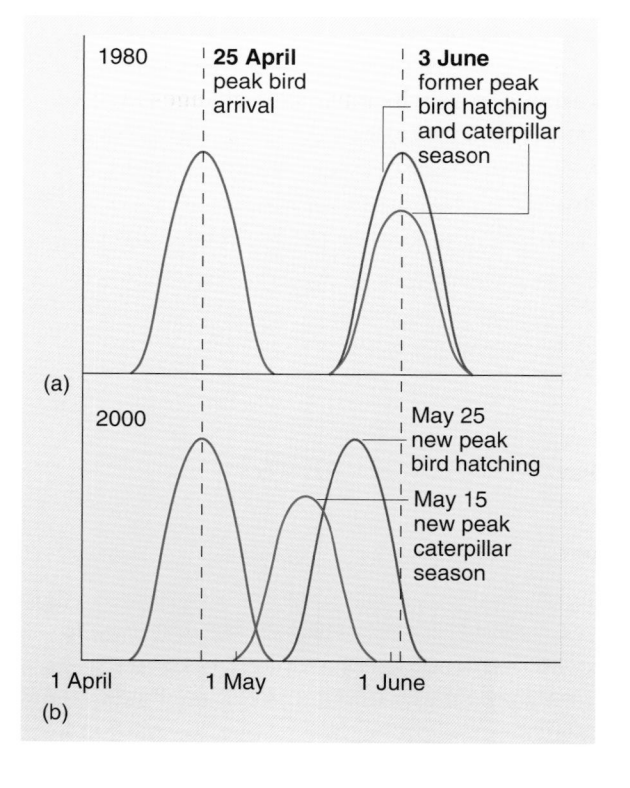

Figure 3.12 An example of emerging 'desynchrony' between bird behaviour (in migrating flycatchers) and insects (moth caterpillars), an important food source for their nestlings. Flycatchers that migrate from Africa to The Netherlands to breed still arrived at the same time (on average) in 2000 (b) as they did 20 years earlier (a). Because of higher temperatures, however, the caterpillars now emerge about 2 weeks earlier than before. The birds' peak egg-hatching date has also shifted, but not enough. So nestlings now miss peak caterpillar emergence, and may go hungry. (In each part of the figure, the curves are schematic representations of the distribution of dates for each of the key events.)

particularly sensitive to environmental change and/or unable to adapt in various ways (e.g. by colonising new areas) may suffer a decline in population (the final bullet point above), or be lost altogether (Box 3.3, point 5).

To sum up: the IPCC TAR is confident that a large proportion (over 80%) of the observed changes in these environmental indicators are in the direction consistent with well-established temperature relationships. In other words, there is a negligible probability that they happened by chance, given what is known about the various mechanisms of change in biological systems. Taken together with all the other indicators reviewed earlier in the chapter, they do indeed add up to a 'collective picture of a warming world' (IPCC, 2001a). At the same time, they serve as a portent of the kinds of changes that could lie ahead.

The threat of mass extinctions and loss of biodiversity regularly hits the headlines (Figure 1.1). We shall not attempt to grapple with the complexities of this issue – another potent and contested area of the climate change debate. Bear in mind, though, that ecological systems around the world are already under siege from countless other pressures linked with human activities: loss or fragmentation of habitat due to deforestation, urban and industrial development, demand for agricultural land, etc.; air and water pollution; overfishing and marine pollution; and so on. While some species may increase in abundance or range, climate change is likely to increase existing threats to other more vulnerable species, and some may literally have nowhere to go as the world warms up. Examples include plants and animals that thrive only in the coldest parts of the planet – at high latitudes and/or high altitudes. Like the Adélie penguins of Antarctica (Box 3.3), the polar bears, walrus and ringed seals of the far north all depend on Arctic sea ice in one way or another.

3.5 An evolving consensus on attribution

The fact that the Earth really is warming up now commands near-universal support. However, it is one thing to detect a global warming trend that appears to be unprecedented in the past millennium (Section 3.1.2), and quite another to establish with a given level of confidence that it has been *caused* by (i.e. can be attributed to) human activity – specifically, the increase in greenhouse gas concentrations and associated radiative forcing since pre-industrial times (reviewed in Section 2.5). Establishing 'cause-and-effect' relationships in the behaviour of complex natural systems is always difficult, and often controversial. With such high stakes in the present context, the 'question of attribution' is probably *the* most sensitive area of the IPCC's remit. Certainly, it is an area where the Panel has always exercised particular caution over its pronouncements, well aware that these will make headline news around the world. As scientists involved in the IPCC process have put it (Allen *et al.*, 2001):

> We should recall that the IPCC was under considerable pressure in 1990 to make a statement attributing observed climate changes to human influence 'because if they don't, someone else will' (and indeed, did). The IPCC is a cautious body, and if the evidence is not available in the peer-reviewed literature to support a statement, it will not make it, no matter how great the interest in that statement might be. In the end, this caution resulted in the attribution statement made in the Second Assessment Report [in 1996] having much more impact than if it had been made prematurely.

The reference here is to the much-quoted statement cited in Chapter 1: 'The balance of evidence suggests that there is a discernible human influence on global climate'. Even this decidedly equivocal language was sufficient to trigger charges that the IPCC process had been 'corrupted', and a high-profile campaign (again, especially in the US) aimed at discrediting the Panel's conclusions. Just five years later, however, the TAR pointed to humans as the culprits in more robust terms: it is 'likely' (66–90% probability; Box 3.2) that 'most of the warming over the last 50 years' is attributable to 'the increase in greenhouse gas concentrations' – the final bullet point at the beginning of this chapter.

Before we take a closer look at the evidence behind this statement, it is worth pausing to consider why there might be grounds for scepticism about there being a causal link between 20th century climate change and human activity – a stance that a few scientists continue to maintain. With this in mind, try Question 3.4 before moving on.

Question 3.4

(a) Figure 3.13 shows how the greenhouse forcing of climate (summarised in Table 2.2, Section 2.5) has evolved over time since 1750. Compare the pattern of change in this figure with that marked out by the smoothed curve in the instrumental record of the Earth's GMST, Figure 3.3a. Why might this comparison raise doubts about attributing the development of global warming to the build up of greenhouse gases in the atmosphere?

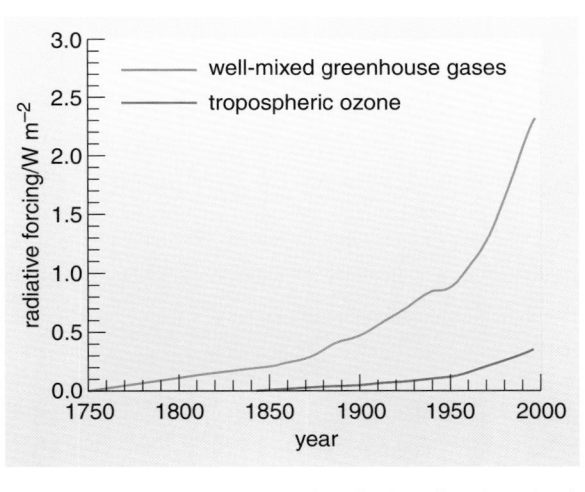

Figure 3.13 Time evolution of the radiative forcing during the industrial age, due to rising levels of well-mixed greenhouse gases (CO$_2$, CH$_4$, N$_2$O and halocarbons) and tropospheric ozone.

(b)   What other sources of radiative forcing, both natural and anthropogenic, could also have influenced global temperature over the past century? In each case, indicate whether the forcing would be positive or negative, or whether it could act either way.

3.5.1   Weighing up the evidence: the full cast of suspects

Figure 3.14 (again adapted from the TAR) takes your thoughts on Question 3.4 on a stage. It gives estimates of the cumulative effect since pre-industrial times of the various climate change agents, with the contributions expressed in terms of radiative forcing. Note that the figure also includes yet another device for communicating the IPCC's confidence in a particular finding – an indication of the 'level of scientific understanding' that accompanies each estimate. This reflects the authors' subjective judgement about the reliability of the forcing estimate, based on what is known about the factors that determine the forcing, the assumptions involved, and so on. Of the anthropogenic factors included in Figure 3.14, it is not surprising that there are large uncertainties, and generally

Figure 3.14 Estimated contributions to the radiative forcing of climate between 1750 and 2000, due to various anthropogenic factors (greenhouse gases, aerosols and land-use change) and to solar variability. Vertical lines represent subjective judgements of the uncertainty range in each estimate. They are not error bars (e.g. 95% confidence limits) in a conventional statistical sense. Note that it is not yet possible to give a 'best guess' estimate for the *indirect* cooling effect of aerosols (due to their influence on cloud albedo; Section 2.5). Note that 'organic carbon' refers to carbonaceous aerosols from fossil fuel burning, other than black carbon.

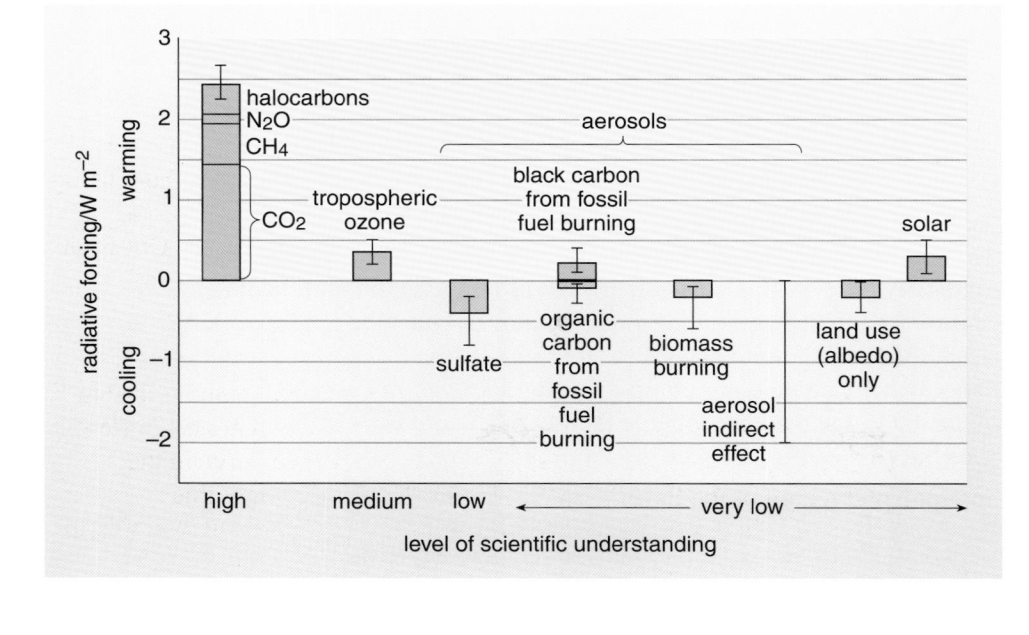

very low confidence, in the estimates for various aerosols, given the difficulties touched on in Section 2.5. Clearly, this goes for the impact on surface albedo of historical changes in land use (e.g. deforestation; Question 2.5) as well. Only for the well-mixed greenhouse gases is confidence high.

But what about the issue we flagged up earlier (Section 2.4) – the claim by some scientists that variations in the Sun's output (and hence the solar constant), and not higher levels of greenhouse gases, have been the main driving force behind 20th century global warming? This is a complicated and controversial area, and we do not have the space to go into it in any detail. However, it's important to be aware that the estimate of **solar forcing** included in Figure 3.14 is not based on direct measurements of variations in the solar constant. Such measurements became available only with the advent of satellite-borne radiation sensors in the late 1970s. These data reveal that the solar 'constant' does, in fact, vary slightly, fluctuating up and down (by about 0.08%) on an 11-year cycle. Unfortunately, the sensors degrade over time, and it is not yet clear whether these small rapid fluctuations (which are thought to have little effect on the Earth's climate) are superimposed on an underlying trend in the *average* value of the solar constant (given as 1368 W m^{-2} in Section 2.1.1) since the measurements began.

Reconstructions of what might have been happening to the solar constant further back in time rely on various proxy indicators of changes in solar activity (such as variations in the number of sunspots), and the relationship between such proxies and possible trends in the output of *energy* from the Sun (the key issue) is only poorly understood. Marked differences between the available reconstructions, together with uncertainties about the satellite record, account for the very low confidence in the 'best guess' estimate of historical solar forcing in Figure 3.14.

■   Given the information in Figure 3.14, why is it difficult to sustain an argument that the observed global warming is *entirely* due to solar variability?

▪   Although solar variability appears to have made a positive contribution to climate forcing during the industrial age, the 'best guess' estimate is 0.3 W m^{-2} – only a small fraction of that contributed by the well-mixed greenhouse gases alone (2.4 W m^{-2}); i.e. not counting the additional contribution from tropospheric ozone. It is inconsistent to argue that the Earth's GMST has been highly sensitive to very modest radiative forcing by the Sun, yet unaffected by substantial greenhouse forcing.

In short, the estimates in Figure 3.14 strongly implicate the chief 'suspect' for recent global warming – the enhanced greenhouse effect. But that does not, by itself, explain the bumpy rise in global temperature evident in Figure 3.3a, especially the puzzling pause in the upward trend in the middle of the 20th century (identified as a major inconsistency in Question 3.4). To address this issue, the starting point is a set of 'forcing histories' (i.e. reconstructions of the *time-evolving* change in radiative forcing like that in Figure 3.13) – one for each of the natural and anthropogenic factors that could have influenced global climate over the past century or so.

■   Since the aim is to construct a history of the *total* radiative forcing of climate, what other natural factor needs to be included in the analysis?

■ It should also include the history of **volcanic forcing**; i.e. the significant, though episodic and transient, negative forcing (cooling effect) from major volcanic eruptions.

In fact, volcanic activity was particularly strong at the end of the 19th century (e.g. the Krakatau eruption in 1883), and again since 1963 (culminating in the Pinatubo eruption in 1991; Figure 2.13, Section 2.4). By contrast, the first half of the 20th century was a quiet period for the major events that inject large amounts of volcanic aerosol into the stratosphere.

■ Look back at Figure 3.3a. Does the influence of the Pinatubo eruption show up in that record?

■ The annual values do indeed show a downturn in GMST in the years following this eruption (especially 1992 and 1993), so it is tempting to answer with a resounding 'yes'.

Here, detailed analysis has confirmed this conclusion. In general, though, we should again be wary of jumping to conclusions. When it comes to the detailed interpretation of the Earth's recent temperature history, we need to be mindful of the influence of yet another natural factor. Even in the absence of an external 'push' provided by radiative forcing, the GMST would not remain constant year after year. Interactions *within* the climate system (a major focus of Chapter 4) generate spontaneous, and inherently unpredictable, fluctuations in global temperature on a variety of time-scales, especially from year-to-year and over periods of a decade or so. This **internally generated natural variability** is a major source of the 'background noise' we referred to earlier (Section 3.1.2), and will always be superimposed on the global temperature response to any particular pattern of radiative forcing.

So, how do climate scientists assess *in a quantitative way* how the GMST might have responded to the history of radiative forcing over the past century – and thus gain a deeper insight into the underlying causes of the observed temperature changes? This is where climate modelling studies come into the picture.

3.5.2 The role of modelling studies

You will learn more about climate models in Chapter 6 – how they are put together and used; their strengths and limitations; and so on. For now, it is enough to know that state-of-the-art models are designed to simulate the workings of the climate system (in so far as this is currently understood), and include the 'internal' interactions that generate short-term natural variability in the real world. They provide modellers with a means of carrying out 'virtual' experiments on the climate system. In the present context, an important aim of these experiments is to identify the 'signal' of a human influence on climate, so studies typically involve 'feeding' into a model the time-evolving history of radiative forcing due to:

• natural factors (solar variations and volcanic activity) alone

• anthropogenic factors (usually just greenhouse gases and aerosols) alone, and

• both natural and anthropogenic factors combined.

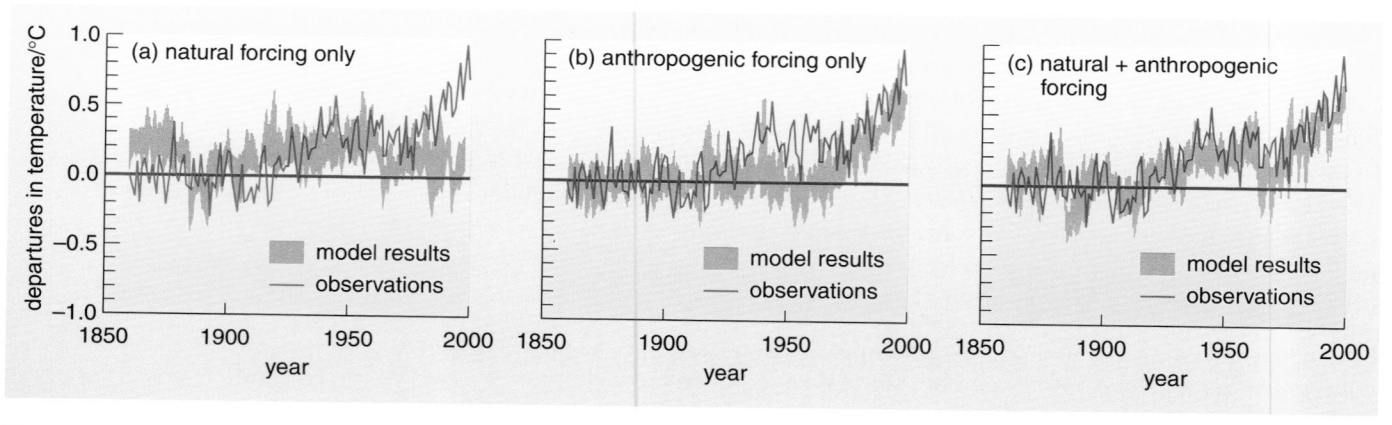

Figure 3.15 Complex climate models (see Chapter 6) have been used to simulate the Earth's temperature variations over the past 140 years in response to both natural and anthropogenic forcings. The figure shows comparisons between the observed changes and the results of model simulations done with: (a) natural forcing (solar variations and volcanic activity) only; (b) anthropogenic forcing (greenhouse gases and sulfate aerosols) only; and (c) both combined. In each case, the grey band encompasses the results of several model runs and gives an idea of the uncertainty in the simulated response (including that in the 'internal' variability generated by the model). The simulations in (b) and (c) include estimates of the direct and indirect effects of sulfate aerosols. Note that temperature changes are given relative to (i.e. as 'departures from') the climatological average for 1880–1920, not 1961–1990 as in Figure 3.3a. (Source: IPCC, 2001d.)

In each case, the model simulates the time-evolving change in GMST in response to that particular history of radiative forcing, and this is then compared with the observed temperature record (i.e. Figure 3.3a). The results of modelling studies of this kind reported in the IPCC TAR are shown in Figure 3.15. Study the figure and its caption carefully, and then work through the following questions.

■ What does the comparison in Figure 3.15a suggest about the influence of natural forcings during the course of the 20th century?

▨ The *net* effect of solar variations and volcanic activity seems to have produced a positive forcing of climate during the first half of the century, and probably contributed to the observed warming at that time. However, natural factors alone would have resulted in a slight cooling of the planet thereafter (i.e. the net forcing was negative).

In other words, natural factors cannot explain the observed warming over the last 50 years.

■ How does the comparison in Figure 3.15b support the IPCC's conclusion that most of this warming was due to human activities?

▨ The model-simulated response to anthropogenic forcing shows a persistent upward trend in GMST from around 1950 (when the greenhouse forcing accelerated; Figure 3.13). Further, the rate and magnitude of the simulated warming over recent decades is broadly consistent with the observed changes.

Note that the 'compensating' cooling effect (both direct and indirect) of the tropospheric load of sulfate aerosols, which increased throughout this period, is included in the study in Figure 3.15b. In experiments done with greenhouse forcing alone, the simulated warming over recent decades is typically larger than that observed in the real world.

Finally, Figure 3.15c shows that the best match with observations over the whole century is obtained in simulations that include both natural and anthropogenic forcings. This suggests that these forcings are sufficient to explain the major features of the Earth's recent temperature history. And that, in turn, adds weight to the case for an identifiable greenhouse warming signal over the past 50 years. The inconsistencies noted earlier (Question 3.4) then come down to the way this warming effect has been offset to some extent by the cooling influence of natural factors (especially around the middle of the century, evident in Figure 3.15a) and sulfate aerosols, together with the noise of internally generated natural variability.

Still, a word of caution is in order. For example, the simulations in Figure 3.15 do not include the influence of non-sulfate aerosols or past land-use changes. Bear in mind too the considerable uncertainty about the natural and anthropogenic forcings that *are* included – for all bar the contribution from increased greenhouse gas concentrations (Figure 3.14). Equally, it is pertinent to ask probing questions about the climate models used in studies like this (as we shall in Chapter 6): how confident should we be about the simulated response to radiative forcing?

The IPCC is well aware of these concerns – a major reason for caution over its pronouncements on the attribution question. The relevant chapter in the TAR documents the sophisticated statistical techniques that have been brought to bear on the significance of the similarities (or indeed, differences) between model simulated and observed changes – not only in the GMST, but also in other climate variables around the world (e.g. those included in Table 3.1). According to the IPCC, these more detailed studies 'consistently find evidence for an anthropogenic signal in the climate record of the last 35 to 50 years', even when uncertainties of the kind noted above are taken into account. Put this together with a longer and more closely scrutinised temperature record (Question 3.1), and the unprecedented warmth of recent decades (Section 3.1.2), and you can begin to see why the Panel finally felt able to endorse a less equivocal attribution statement. In the words that appeared in countless press reports when the TAR came out in 2001 (taken from one of the headings in the SPM): 'There is new and stronger evidence that most of the warming observed over the last 50 years is attributable to human activities'.

The IPCC is not alone in its conclusions. As one recent article in the journal *Science* put it (Oreskes, 2004):

> In recent years, all major scientific bodies in the United States whose members' expertise bears directly on the matter have issued similar statements […] concluding that the evidence for human modification of climate is compelling.

In short, the overwhelming scientific consensus is that the human impact on the atmospheric burden of greenhouse gases has made a significant contribution to recent climate warming – and hence, by implication, to the observed changes in other climate variables, and in physical and biological systems reviewed in Section 3.4. But what of the future? What further climate changes might lie ahead in a future that could see an extra three billion people on the planet by 2050 (Figure 2.17, Section 2.5)?

Just as simulations with climate models have provided insight into the human influence on climate in the past, so they are fundamental to projections of future human-induced climate change. A climate model is just what the name implies: a 'model' of the 'climate system'. But what do we actually mean by the Earth's climate system? This question has been lurking in the background in this and earlier chapters; it is time to address it directly.

Summary of Chapter 3

1   Reconstructions based on direct temperature measurements (back to 1860) and proxy data (Box 3.1) reveal that the Earth's GMST varies naturally on many different time-scales: from year-to-year, over periods of several decades and, in the longer term, according to the roughly 100 000-year rhythm of glacial/ interglacial cycles. The past 10 000 years has been marked by the relatively stable global climate of the present interglacial (the Holocene).

2   This chapter has revisited some of the themes identified in Chapter 1 in the context of one of the most politically sensitive issues in the IPCC's remit: the detection of an unusual global warming 'signal' above the 'background noise' of natural variability, and its attribution (in whole or in part) to human activities. The Panel's pronouncements on this issue gain authority from the exhaustive peer review process that underpins the production of its reports, together with the caution implicit in formulating consensus statements that are a fair representation of the collective 'expert judgement' of the climate science community. In the TAR, the IPCC used various devices (notably the 'likelihood' language in Box 3.2) in order to communicate levels of confidence in its conclusions (e.g. the bullet points at the beginning of this chapter).

3   From the instrumental record (Figure 3.3a), GMST is estimated to have risen by 0.6 ± 0.2 °C over the past century. The upward trend has been irregular, with most of the warming during two periods: 1910 to 1945 and since 1976. During recent decades, the local warming rate has been greatest at high latitudes, where it has been accompanied by the thinning and reduced extent of snow and ice cover over land and sea, and the thawing of permafrost (Table 3.1 and Box 3.3).

4   Based on the proxy data record for the Northern Hemisphere in the IPCC TAR (the 'hockey stick' reconstruction, Figure 3.3b), 20th century warming and the record temperatures of recent decades appear (66–90% probability) to have been unprecedented during the past millennium.

5   There is mounting evidence that many different climate variables (Table 3.1), as well as physical and biological systems around the world (Table 3.1 and Box 3.3), have been affected by 20th century climate warming. It is judged to have contributed significantly to the observed sea-level rise over the past 100 years (in the range 10–20 cm), mainly due to the thermal expansion of seawater and the widespread retreat of glaciers. Most of the observed changes in various environmental indicators (phenological changes, shifts in plant and animal ranges, population declines, etc.) are broadly consistent with a warmer climate, and are harbingers of the kinds of changes that could lie ahead.

6   Successive IPCC reports trace an evolving consensus on the 'question of attribution', culminating in the statement in the TAR: 'There is new and stronger evidence that most of the warming observed over the last 50 years is attributable to human activities'. Along with the evidence summarised in points 3–5 above, this statement is supported by critical appraisal of climate modelling studies that can reproduce the bumpy rise in GMST over the past century, in response to estimates of the historical radiative forcing from both natural factors (solar variability and volcanic activity) and anthropogenic factors (greenhouse gases and aerosols).

7   Although the IPCC process has led to a growing scientific consensus on the causes of recent climate change, the complexity and uncertainties in the science provide plenty of opportunities for sceptics to challenge some of the Panel's findings. Some scientific voices dispute the IPCC's interpretation of the proxy data record (the subject of Activity 3.1); a few continue to put forward various alternative theories (notably solar variability) to explain 20th century global warming. Robust debate and disputes over interpretation are the lifeblood of science, but it is important to bear in mind that there is often a political agenda behind the selective promotion of claims that run counter to the mainstream view.

Question for Chapter 3

Question 3.5

So how *does* 'switching on a kettle' make sea level rise? Write down the various steps in the chain of cause and effects as a set of bullet points. Now compare your notes with those you made at the end of Chapter 1 (Activity 1.3). Do you now feel more confident that you could cover all the links, if asked by a friend or colleague, say?

Chapter 4   What do we mean by the Earth's climate system?

Most of the weather statistics that make up the 'climate' characteristic of different regions around the world are manifestations of atmospheric behaviour – air temperatures, rainfall or snowfall, cloudiness, prevailing winds, etc., and their variation through the year. However, atmospheric processes are influenced by a multitude of interactions between the atmosphere and the underlying surface, be it land, sea or ice. Recall, for example, that the bulk of the solar input to the global energy budget is absorbed *first* by the surface of the planet (Figure 2.11): it becomes 'available' to the atmosphere only through the transfer of energy across the surface–air boundary. The evaporation of water is an important part of that energy transfer, supplying the atmosphere with water vapour (the most important natural greenhouse gas) as well as latent heat (when the water vapour condenses).

In short, the Earth's **climate system** is not just the atmosphere. As suggested by the wider perspective on recent climate change in Section 3.4, the climate system takes in the oceans, the parts of the Earth covered in snow and ice (known as the cryosphere), land surface and, ultimately, all forms of life (collectively, the **biosphere**). These other 'components' of the climate system are apparent in Figure 4.1. The cloud cover, which obscures so much of the Earth's surface shown in the Frontispiece, has been removed. Immediately obvious are bright areas of ice cover, the enormous expanse of ocean in the Southern Hemisphere, and the green of forests and crops.

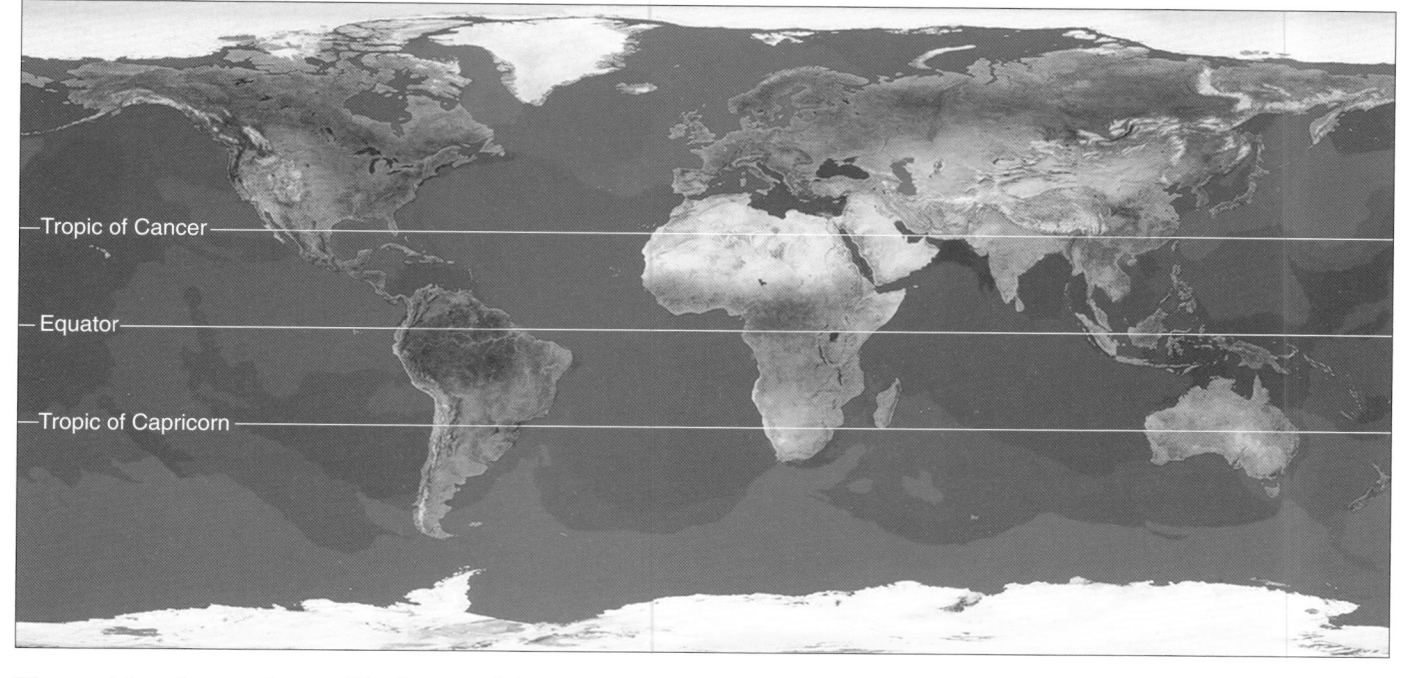

Figure 4.1   Composite satellite image of the Earth's surface. Green areas are forests and crops; pale yellow-brown areas are grassland, semi-arid scrub and desert; and brown areas at high northern latitudes are tundra (where plant life consists mainly of mosses and low shrubs). [Ignore the slight coloration of the areas of ice at high latitudes.]

Any comprehensive description of climate, which is needed to model climate change and its impacts, must take the workings of this complex, interconnected system into account. This chapter provides most of the background needed to understand the task faced by climate modellers, although the account is (of necessity) much abridged. We start with the climate system's external power source: energy from the Sun.

4.1   How the Sun drives the global weather machine

In Chapter 2, we concluded that the climate system takes in solar energy at a rate of 236 watts per square metre (W m^{-2}). But this is an average figure – averaged around the globe and over a year. In reality, the Sun's energy does not fall evenly on the Earth's surface: the input varies with latitude (because of the curvature of the Earth; Figure 4.2) and, at a given latitude, with the seasons.

■   Look at Figure 4.2. Can you suggest why the input of solar energy, and hence the surface temperature, is generally lower at high latitudes than at low latitudes?

■   At high latitudes, the Sun's rays strike the surface at a more glancing angle, so the incident solar radiation is effectively 'spread' over a wider area than at low latitudes.

Seasons occur because the Earth's axis of rotation is tilted (currently at an angle of 23.4°) to the plane of its orbit around the Sun. This means that the Northern Hemisphere is tilted towards the Sun for half of the year (from the spring equinox, 21 March, to the autumn equinox, 21 September, in the north), and away from the Sun for the other half of the year. As a result, the poles are in darkness for alternate six-monthly periods, and the zone that receives the maximum input of solar energy migrates north and south of the Equator with the seasons – between the Tropics of Cancer (23.4° N) and Capricorn (23.4° S), and back again.

The differential heating of the Earth's surface drives a huge, worldwide circulation of air, which acts to redistribute heat from hot equatorial regions towards the frigid poles – partly through the movement of warm air masses into cooler regions, and partly by transporting the latent heat 'locked up' in water vapour. As part of this **general circulation of the atmosphere**, air moves both vertically and horizontally, generating the large-scale pattern of surface pressure conditions and prevailing winds seen across the globe. An idealised representation of the main semi-permanent features is given in Figure 4.3 (overleaf). The aim here is just to point out how some of these features relate to one another; we shall not attempt to explain them in detail.

■   With this in mind, how do *surface* wind directions relate to regions of high and low surface pressure?

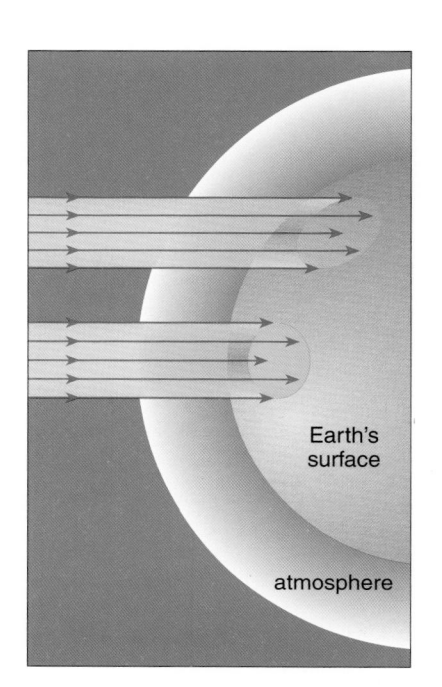

Figure 4.2   Two identical beams of sunlight reaching the Earth's surface at different latitudes.

Figure 4.3   Schematic representation of the major surface winds and semi-permanent high-pressure and low-pressure zones across the globe. Note that winds are named for the direction *from* which they are blowing. Vertical air movements (which occur all around the globe) are indicated on the left-hand side of the diagram; characteristic patterns of precipitation at the surface are given on the right-hand side. See text for significance of the ITCZ.

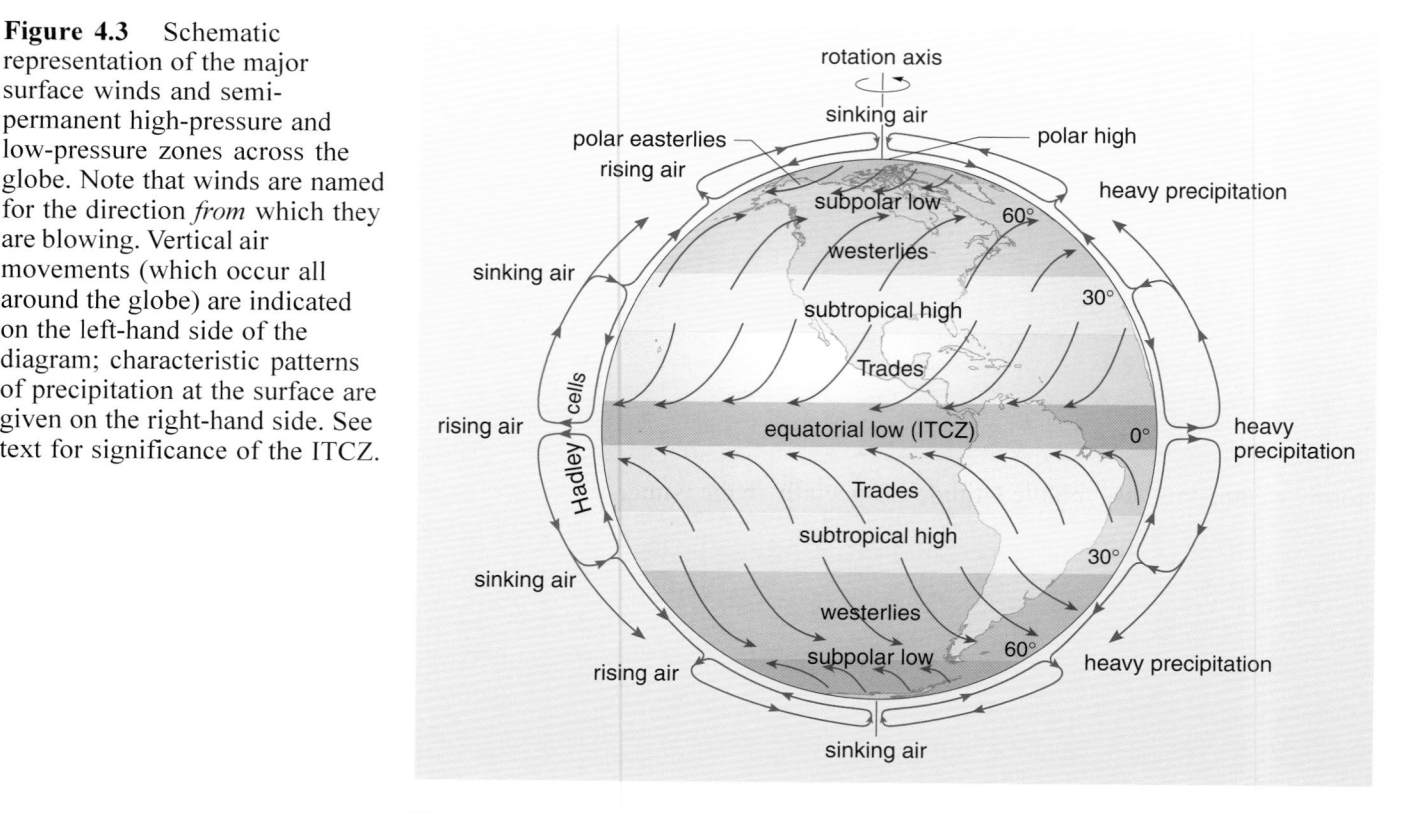

In Figure 4.3, surface winds blow from regions of high pressure to regions of low pressure; for example, the trade winds blow from the zones labelled 'subtropical high' towards the zone of low surface pressure along the Equator.

■   How do vertical air movements relate to regions of high and low surface pressure?

In regions of high pressure (e.g. the subtropical highs), air is sinking; in regions of low pressure (e.g. along the Equator), air is rising.

At low latitudes, these patterns of air movement are associated with a large-scale convective circulation to either side of the Equator: this is known as the Hadley circulation, or *Hadley cells* (identified in Figure 4.3). Fuelled by the high input of solar energy, warm air rises near the Equator and heads polewards aloft before sinking again over the subtropical highs. Some of the air heads back towards the Equator as the easterly trade winds (completing the Hadley circulation), and some flows towards the zones labelled 'subpolar lows' in Figure 4.3 as the prevailing westerlies of middle latitudes (roughly 40° to 60° north and south of the Equator).

But why does the high-level air sink again near 30° latitude, and not simply carry on to the poles? And why do the surface winds that originate and go their separate ways from the subtropical highs at these latitudes not blow directly in a north–south direction? The answer to both questions lies with the rotation of the Earth. Air masses moving over the surface of the Earth are bound to it by friction extremely weakly, and as they move, the Earth turns beneath them (from west to east). The effect, known as the *Coriolis effect*, is to deflect winds relative to the surface of the Earth: air moving towards the Equator is deflected to the west (i.e. into a more *easterly* flow); air moving towards the poles is deflected to the east (i.e. into a more *westerly* flow). Put another way, moving air is deflected to the *right* in the Northern Hemisphere and to the *left* in the Southern Hemisphere. Take a moment to convince yourself that these two descriptions are equivalent.

The Coriolis effect also restricts the poleward movement of air in the high-level branch of the Hadley cells. In general, the air aloft piles up faster than it subsides and flows out at the surface. As a result, the subtropical highs are a semi-permanent feature of the general atmospheric circulation. The circulation at higher latitudes is more complicated, and we shall not pursue the details. However, it's worth noting that Britain lies close to the zone where the mid-latitude westerlies and polar easterlies meet (or converge). The clash between warm air (from lower latitudes) and cold polar air is responsible for much of the stormy weather at these middle latitudes, especially in the winter.

Question 4.1

According to the information in Figure 4.3, is high precipitation associated with rising air or sinking air? Explain why this association seems reasonable.

The most dramatic manifestations of rising warm, moist air are the towering cumulonimbus clouds (Figure 2.9) that often mark the equatorial low or **Intertropical Convergence Zone (ITCZ)**, so called because this is where the trade wind systems of the two hemispheres meet (Figure 4.3). The ITCZ is visible in the Frontispiece as a band of clouds across equatorial Africa. There, and on other continents, the warmth and abundant rainfall associated with the ITCZ sustains the world's tropical rainforests. By contrast, air sinking from above is generally dry. Many of the world's great deserts lie at latitudes influenced by the general subsidence of air associated with the subtropical highs.

4.2 Bringing in the oceans, land surface and cryosphere

Figure 4.4 (overleaf) shows maps of mean surface temperatures across the world for the seasonally extreme months of January and July. Take a moment to study them.

■ Are the broad features of these temperature maps consistent with the variations in solar heating outlined above?

■ Yes. In both maps, there is a general decrease in temperature from the Equator to the poles. Comparing the maps shows how the band of highest temperatures shifts with the seasons: the 'hot spots' (with temperatures over 30 °C) are mostly south of the Equator in January, but north of it in July.

However, it is also abundantly clear that the isotherms in these maps do not run simply east–west.

■ With what are the most extreme departures from a simple east–west trend associated?

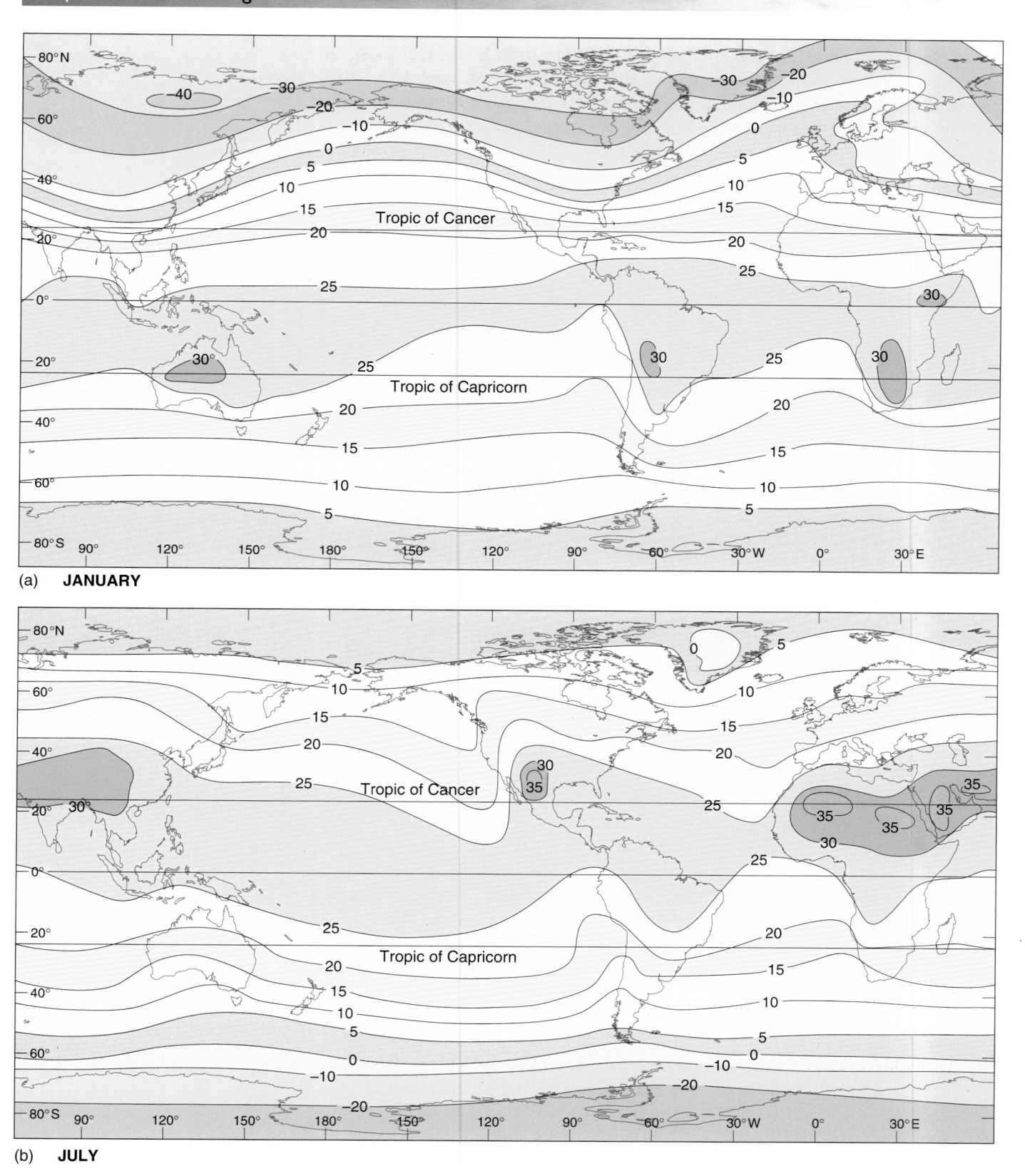

(a)   **JANUARY**

(b)   **JULY**

Figure 4.4   Mean sea-level temperatures across the world for (a) January and (b) July. The lines (temperatures in °C) between the different shades of colour are isotherms – contours of equal temperature. The temperatures have been adjusted to the equivalent at sea level to remove the influence of differences in altitude.

■ With the distribution of continents and oceans. The distortions are most apparent in the Northern Hemisphere, where there is more land. Note how the contours bend northward over the continents in summer (July), and southward in winter (January): the landmasses are generally warmer than the adjacent ocean in summer, and colder in winter.

The contrast in seasonal temperature changes between land and sea is due, in part, to the high **specific heat** of water – the amount of heat required to raise the temperature of 1 kg of water by 1 °C. On average, it takes about three times more heat to raise the temperature of a body of water by the same amount as an equal quantity of continental rock or soil. The resulting **thermal inertia** of the ocean – the fact that it effectively 'stores' heat and warms up (or cools down) only slowly – exerts a strong influence on climate, at both the regional and global scale. For example, onshore winds that have passed over ocean waters which are relatively warm in winter (and cool in summer) help to moderate the extremes of temperature experienced by coastal regions. Locations deep inside the continents typically endure hotter summers and colder winters.

On a global scale, the differential heating of the oceans and landmasses affects the general circulation of the atmosphere. In particular, it disrupts the idealised zonal pattern of equatorial low/subtropical high/subpolar low/polar high in Figure 4.3. In the real world, the continuous pressure belts shown there are replaced by more localised 'cells' of high and low pressure. These remain as more or less permanent features of the large-scale circulation, but they vary in strength and/or location through the year. And that, in turn, affects the wind systems experienced by different parts of the world.

To take just one example, the ITCZ tends to be located over the warmest parts of the Earth's surface, and migrates north and south of the Equator in response to the seasonal cycle of solar heating (Figure 4.4). These shifts bring **monsoons**, winds that reverse direction between winter and summer, to many low-latitude regions and result in an extreme seasonal variation in rainfall. In India, for instance, the summer rains account for 75–90% of the annual total: they are fed by southwesterly winds that bring warm, moisture-laden air from the Indian Ocean. By contrast, the wintertime circulation over southern and southeast Asia is dominated by northeasterly winds, bringing cool, *dry* air from the interior of the Asian landmass. Regions that experience a monsoon climate are highly vulnerable to slight shifts in the pattern and intensity of the seasonal rainfall. Failure of the rains can bring human suffering through drought, but so too can the floods and mudslides caused by excessive monsoon rainfall.

■ Jumping to the other climatic extreme, which parts of the Earth are likely to experience a seasonal snow cover of significant duration?

■ The coldest parts of the Earth – at high latitudes in winter, and at lower latitudes where there are mountains (evident as snow-covered peaks in Figure 4.1).

■ How does seasonal snow cover help to explain the extremely low temperatures across the northern continental landmasses evident in Figure 4.4a?

■ The very high albedo (up to 90%) of snow-covered surfaces means that little of the incident solar radiation (itself at a low level in winter) is actually absorbed.

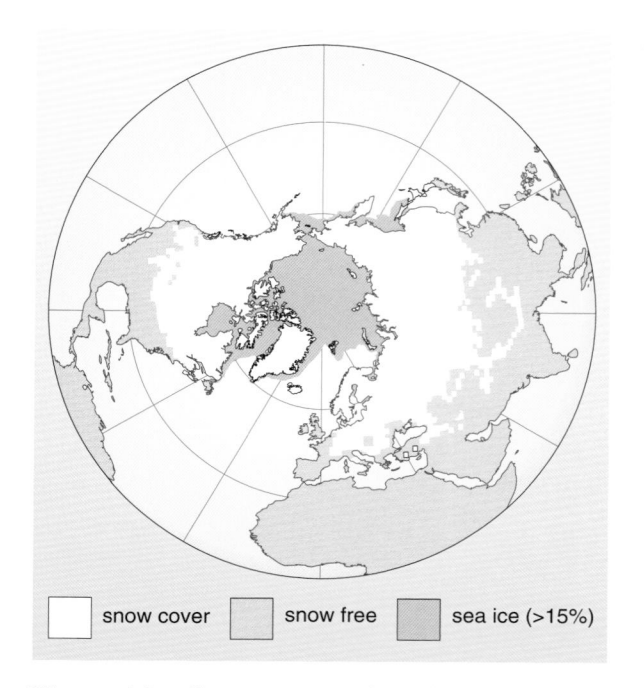

Figure 4.5   Snow cover and sea-ice extent for the Northern Hemisphere during January 1995. The central Arctic Ocean retains a permanent, multiyear ice cover, even though the extent of this perennial cover has decreased significantly in recent decades (Chapter 3). The area of sea ice expands out to cover large portions of other peripheral seas during the winter.

Large parts of the world (Figure 4.5) are strongly influenced by the presence of seasonal and perennial snow, glaciers and ice sheets, sea ice and permafrost (Box 3.3); collectively, these regions comprise the Earth's **cryosphere**. Although snow or ice cover has a major impact on the effectiveness of solar heating, we should bear in mind that, even without it, not all land surfaces are equivalent in this respect – a point we emphasised in connection with the radiative effects of land-use change in Chapter 3.

Working together, the factors outlined above determine the broad pattern of '**climate zones**' across the globe, shown in Figure 4.6 for the Northern Hemisphere. These zones are characterised by the seasonal march of temperature, rainfall (or snowfall) and moisture availability. Together with the availability of sunlight for photosynthesis (Chapter 5), these climatic conditions are, in turn, the main influence over the natural vegetation, or 'ecosystem type' (also included in Figure 4.6) that would – in the absence of human intervention – dominate each zone. Don't worry about the detailed classification of ecosystems. Note simply that there is a broad distinction between forests and the (largely non-woody) vegetation characteristic of grasslands (steppe and savannah), Mediterranean scrublands and deserts.

■   According to the information in Figure 4.6, what is the main factor underlying this distinction?

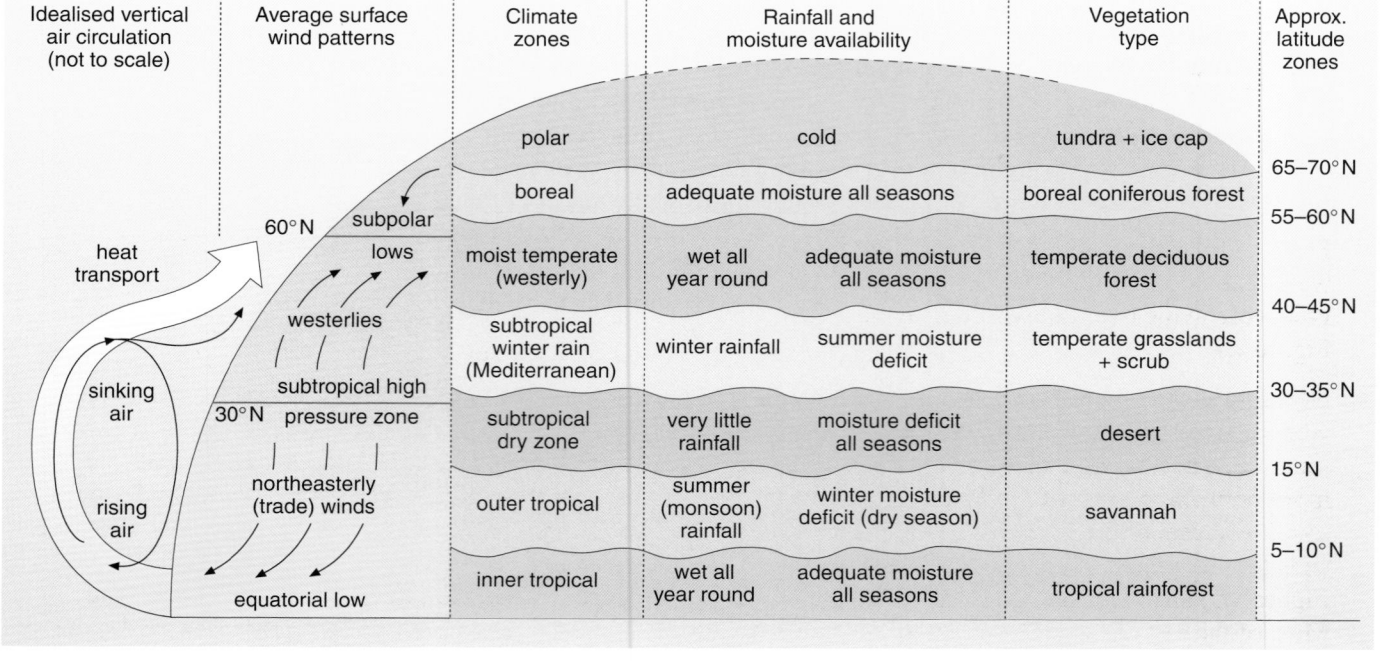

Figure 4.6   A simplified classification (by latitude bands) of climate zones and vegetation types, shown here for the Northern Hemisphere.

■   The availability of moisture. The zones that do not support forest all experience a moisture deficit for at least part of the year: the vegetation in these zones is adapted to survive the more or less arid conditions.

Figure 4.6 gives only a broad-brush account of the distribution of climatic conditions across the world. The detailed picture is complicated, not only by the contrast between land and sea, but also by the shape, or *topography*, of the landmasses. We know that temperature falls with increasing altitude, for example. But high ground affects the flow of air over the surface as well, and that can trigger precipitation, by forcing moisture-laden air to rise and cool. This can result in contrasting conditions to either side of a mountain range, with windward slopes that are wet and well-vegetated, while a more arid environment lies in the 'rain shadow' to the lee of the mountains.

The importance of moisture for plant growth is a reminder of one all-pervasive link between the atmosphere and the *whole* planetary surface: the global **hydrological cycle** – the overall storage and movement of water around the world. The main features of this global cycle are reviewed in Box 4.1: take a moment to study that material, and then try Question 4.2.

Box 4.1   The global hydrological cycle

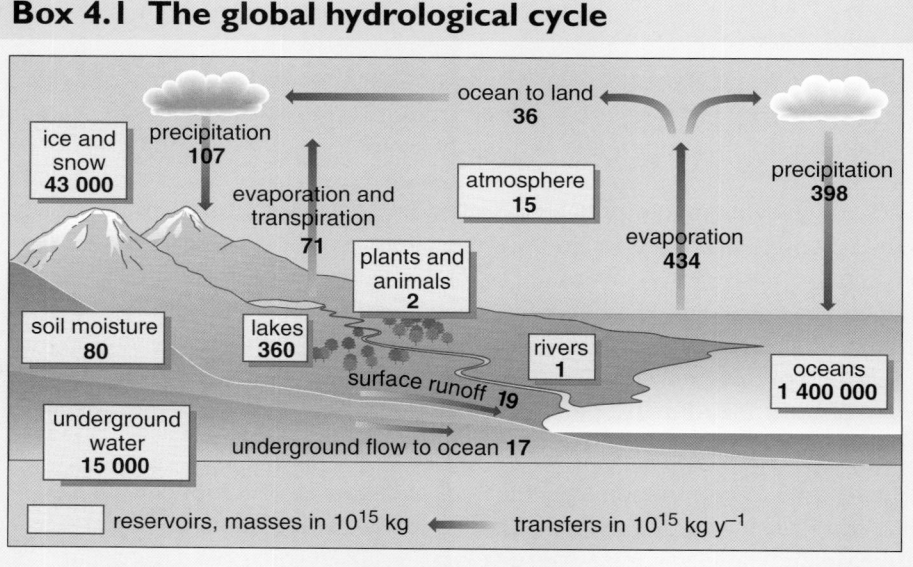

Figure 4.7   The global hydrological cycle with estimates of the amount of water stored in each reservoir, and the annual movements (averaged over several years) of water through the cycle. *All* of the figures recorded here are subject to large uncertainties, so you may find different values given elsewhere.

From a global perspective, each major repository of water can be regarded as a 'compartment' or **reservoir** in the overall hydrological cycle, as shown in Figure 4.7.

Not surprisingly, the overwhelming majority of the world's water (some 96%) is in the oceans. Of the remainder, nearly three-quarters is locked up in the more permanent parts of the Earth's cryosphere: the vast ice-sheets of Greenland and Antarctica, smaller ice caps (e.g. in places like Iceland and northern Canada; Figure 4.5) and mountain glaciers across the world. Most of the rest of the global inventory is underground (water in the subsoil and in rocks). Only a tiny fraction

of all freshwater is held on the surface (in lakes and rivers), and there is even less in the soil, as 'soil moisture' – the water available for plant growth.

Notice that Figure 4.7 incorporates the active part that vegetation plays in the water cycle. A broad-leaved forest, for example, is an important source of atmospheric moisture, both through simple evaporation of rain intercepted by the leaf canopy and through *transpiration*, whereby water drawn from the soil by plant roots escapes through tiny pores, called **stomata**, on the underside of the leaves. Together, these two processes are known as **evapotranspiration**.

Question 4.2

Given the estimates collected in Figure 4.7:

(a) Does the *total* amount of water entering and leaving the atmosphere each year balance? What would happen were this not the case?

(b) Does the overall balance hold *separately* over the oceans and over the land surface? How is the overall balance maintained?

In a *steady-state* cycle like the one depicted in Figure 4.7, none of the reservoirs involved either grows or diminishes. Yet all the evidence (reviewed in Chapter 3) points to a very different conclusion: we are now witnessing significant *changes* to some of the reservoirs in Figure 4.7 – the widespread retreat of mountain glaciers, for example. We shall come back to the implications of such changes later (Section 4.5). Here, we want to emphasise a particular perspective: *the hydrological cycle is a central part of the overall climate system*, intimately linked to the dynamics of the atmosphere and the global energy budget. For a start, the cycle is driven by evaporation.

■   From what parts of the world would you expect transfer of latent heat to the atmosphere to be greatest?

▨   From the tropical oceans, where conditions are conducive to high evaporation (Section 4.1), and from areas of tropical rainforest, where the lush vegetation supplies water vapour to the air through evapotranspiration (Box 4.1)

Winds carry water vapour (and hence latent heat) around. Cloud formation is bound up with vertical motion in the atmosphere – in the rising branch of a convective circulation (as over the ITCZ), for example, or in the ascent over a mountain barrier. And clouds (however ephemeral) play a crucial role in the Earth's radiation budget – both globally and regionally, through the geographical distribution of different types of cloud cover and the way that varies through the year (Section 2.2.3). Finally, precipitation returns the 'lifeblood of the biosphere' to the surface as rain, or snow if temperatures are low enough.

Virtually all the precipitation over maritime and monsoon regions does indeed come from ocean sources, in line with the globally averaged picture in Figure 4.7. Further inland, however, terrestrial evaporation (from soils, lakes, etc.) and especially evapotranspiration by vegetation can be equally, or even more, important. For example, it has been estimated that the tropical forest in the Amazon basin traps and recycles about half of the annual rainfall. Furthermore, the roots of trees and other vegetation bind the soil together, and help to stop it being washed away.

In conclusion, the characteristics of the continental landscape – its topography, albedo, soil type, snow or ice cover, and the type of vegetation it carries – are an important influence over the flow of air, the energy balance at the surface (and hence temperature) and the local or regional 'water budget': the balance between precipitation, evaporation, seasonal snow melt (where relevant), storage of water in the ground and surface runoff. That, in turn, is critical to plant growth (whether natural or cultivated) and to freshwater resources in general. The processes and characteristics of the land surface that are central to its role in the climate system are summarised in Figure 4.8.

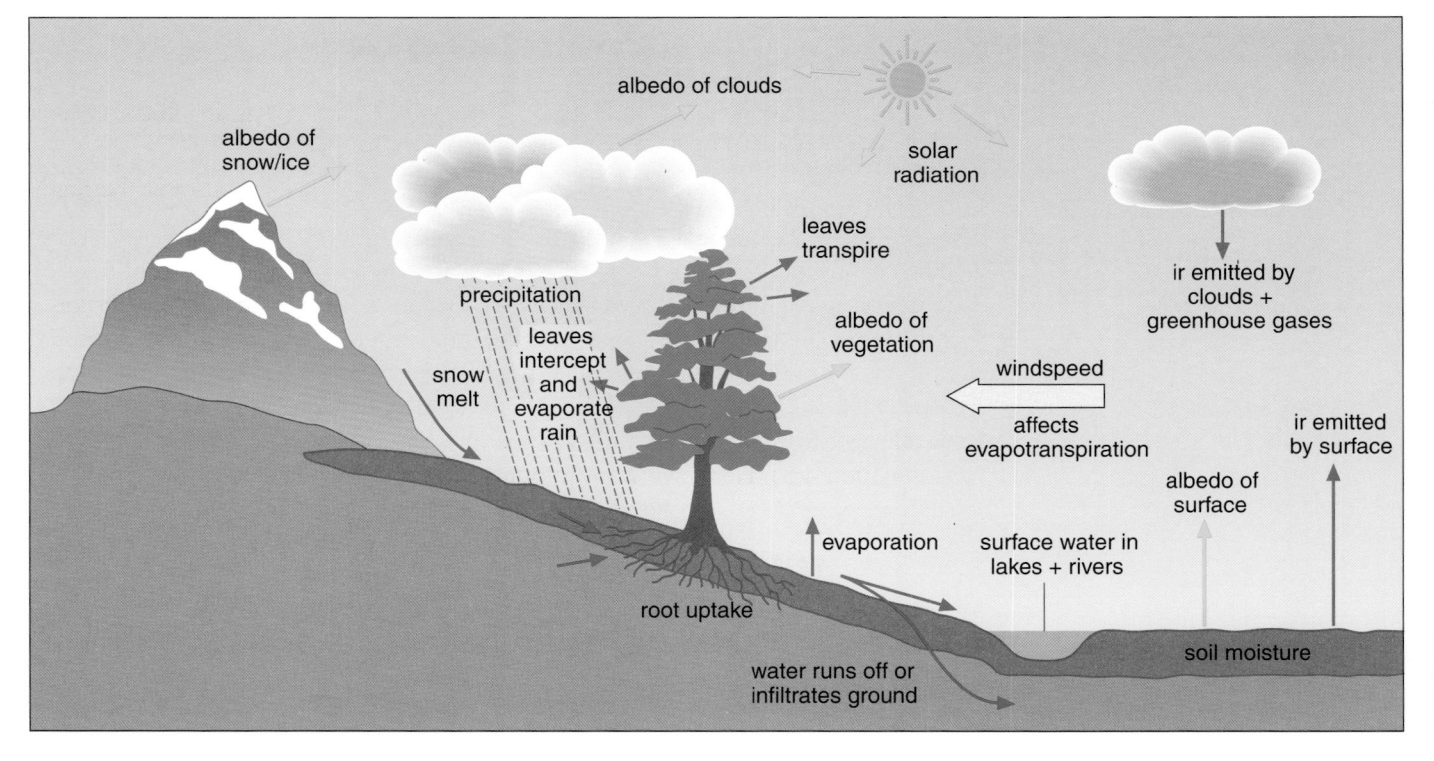

We now move on to take a closer look at the role of the ocean in the overall climate system. As a prelude to that, try Question 4.3.

Figure 4.8   Schematic representation of the processes and features that influence the energy balance at the land surface (and hence temperature), and the local or regional water budget.

Question 4.3

On the basis of the discussion so far, give two ways in which the ocean plays an important role in the climate system.

4.3 A closer look at the role of the ocean: ocean circulation

To emphasise the ocean's role in climate, we should bear in mind its sheer size: it covers 71% of the globe, so most of the solar radiation received at the surface goes into the ocean and warms the surface waters. Together with the high specific heat of water, the upshot is that the top 3 m of the ocean stores as much heat as the *entire* atmosphere. But ocean waters do not just store the solar energy they absorb; ocean currents redistribute heat before releasing it to the atmosphere, mainly via evaporation. In this way, they contribute to the polewards transport of heat from equatorial regions, and exert a major influence over regional climates. There are two interconnected circulatory systems in the ocean:

- a wind-driven surface current system, which is mostly confined to the uppermost wind-mixed layer of the ocean (see Box 4.2), and

- a deep circulation system, driven primarily by cooling at the surface in high latitudes.

Box 4.2 Surface ocean versus deep ocean

On average, the oceans are 3–5 km deep. The surface ocean is the layer that receives some solar radiation and is mixed by wind and wave action, usually the top 100–200 m or so: as a result, it is fairly warm. Below the surface ocean, the temperature drops steeply, through a zone known as the *thermocline*. By around 1 km deep, the water is at a fairly uniform temperature of −1 °C to +4 °C throughout the ocean (note that the freezing temperature of seawater is below 0 °C). Because the warmest, least dense water is at the top of the ocean, and the coldest, most dense water is at the bottom, the thermocline acts as an effective barrier to the *large-scale* mixing of surface and deep water. However, some localised exchange of water does occur, with profound implications for climate as we shall see.

Here, we look briefly at the main features of these two systems, and the connection between them.

4.3.1 Heat transport by the ocean: the surface current system

Winds blowing steadily across the ocean surface transfer 'momentum' (through friction) to the water, and cause the surface layer to move. A highly simplified version of the resulting surface current system is given in Figure 4.9 (ignore the areas marked out by coloured tones for now). The most conspicuous features are the more or less closed circulatory systems, or **gyres**, in each of the major ocean basins (the North and South Atlantic and the North and South Pacific).

The ocean currents that make up these gyres derive their energy principally from the wind systems associated with the subtropical highs – the easterly trade winds and the mid-latitude westerlies (recall Figure 4.3). Together with the influence of the Coriolis effect (which deflects currents from a strictly downwind direction) and the constraints imposed by the landmasses that border the ocean basins, the result is a nearly circular circulation pattern – moving in a clockwise sense in the Northern Hemisphere, and anticlockwise in the Southern Hemisphere. In the Southern Ocean, where there is no land barrier, the westerly winds drive the Antarctic Circumpolar Current (once known as the West Wind Drift) eastwards around the globe.

Water warmed at low latitudes is carried polewards in the western 'limbs' of the gyres, and constitutes an efficient system for transporting heat to higher latitudes. One specific, and important, example is the **Gulf Stream**. As this moves north along the east coast of the United States, it is strengthened by the prevailing westerlies and deflected (to the right since this is the Northern Hemisphere) into a northeastwards flow that eventually becomes the North Atlantic Drift.

■ Look back at Figure 4.4. Is there any evidence there of the way this warm current affects sea-surface temperatures?

▪ Yes. Especially in winter (Figure 4.4a), the shape of the isotherms in the North Atlantic tracks the northeastward flow of the Gulf Stream.

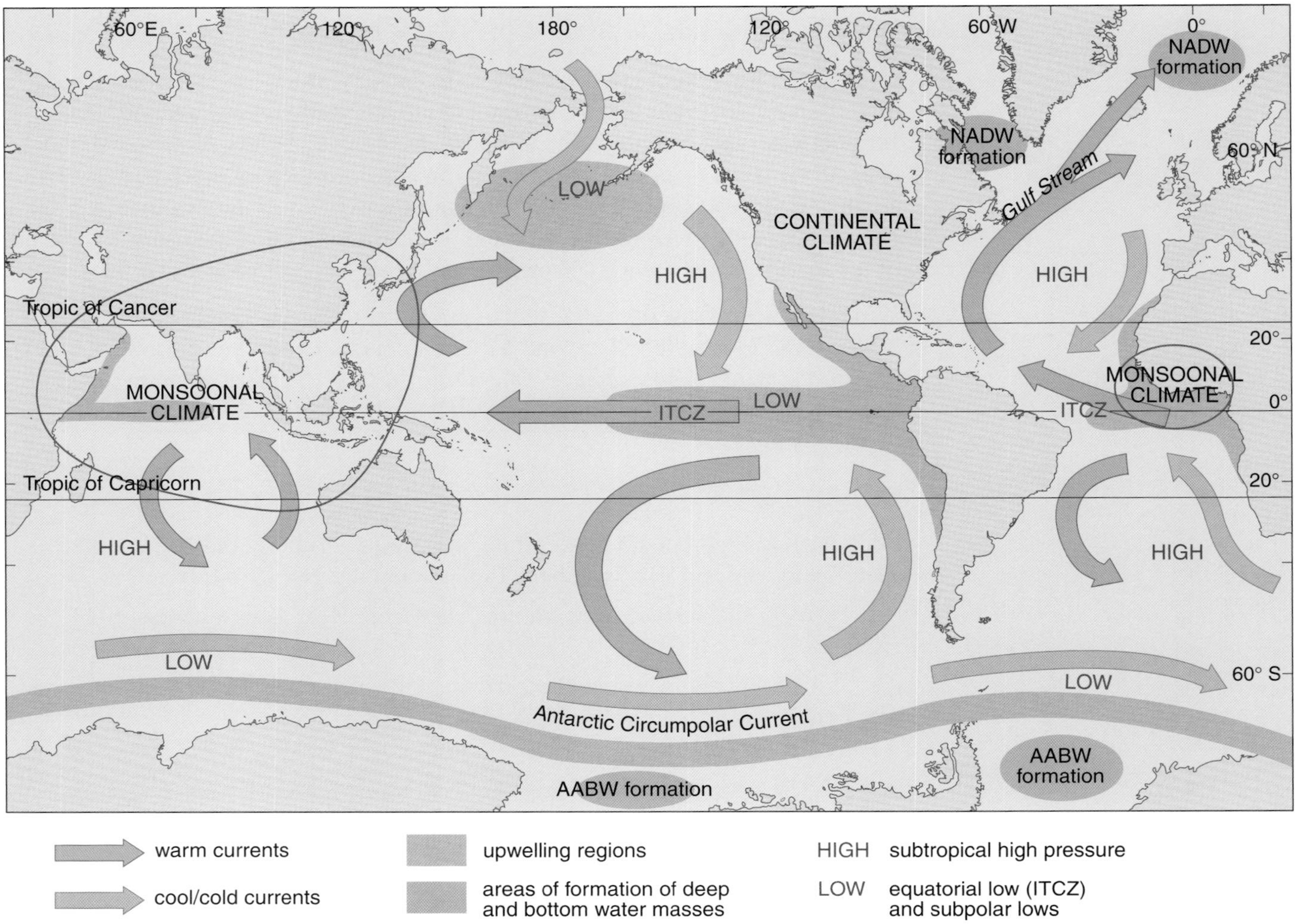

Figure 4.9 Highly simplified representation of the major surface currents (arrows) across the world. Regions of upwelling (green) and deep-water formation (blue) are also shown: see Sections 4.3.2 and 4.3.3. Note: NADW = North Atlantic Deep Water; AABW = Antarctic Bottom Water.

That, in turn, has a benign influence on the climate of Britain and northwest Europe. Lying downwind of these ocean waters, the region is much warmer than it would otherwise be, especially in winter: more on this later.

4.3.2 Wind-driven upwelling and downwelling

In certain ocean regions, wind action also causes *vertical* movements of water, through the downwelling of surface water and upwelling of subsurface water.

In the open ocean, **upwelling** is induced by a wind pattern that causes surface waters to move apart, or diverge, drawing up cooler water from below the thermocline to take its place (Figure 4.10). Typically, the wind pattern that induces upwelling is that associated with the semi-permanent low-pressure systems across the globe (Figure 4.3). So upwelling is most pronounced along the Equator and in the sub-polar regions of the ocean, as shown by the green tone in Figure 4.9.

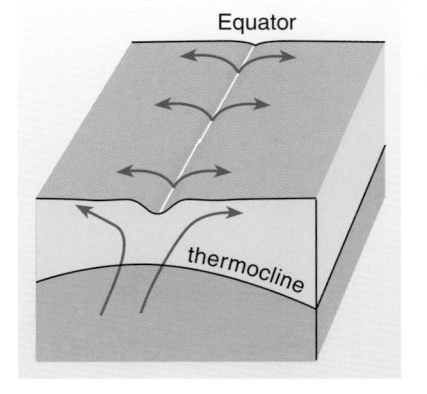

Figure 4.10 How the divergence of surface waters near the Equator brings cooler water from below the thermocline up to the surface ocean.

Also included in the diagram are important areas of *coastal* upwelling, off the west coasts of North and South America and Africa. The trade winds blow towards the Equator along these coasts. Because of the Coriolis effect (which turns flows to the right in the north and to the left in the south, remember), the surface-water movement is directed *away from* the coast. As it moves offshore, it is again replaced by cooler water that 'upwells' from below. Deep ocean waters are generally rich in dissolved nutrients, and areas of coastal upwelling (e.g. off Peru and Ecuador) favour development of the microscopic organisms at the base of the marine 'food chain' (Chapter 5), and hence support productive fisheries.

Wind-driven **downwelling** (not shown in Figure 4.9) occurs mainly in the centre of the ocean gyres. Here, the wind pattern associated with the subtropical high-pressure systems drives surface waters together, i.e. it causes them to converge and sink. However, the main mechanism that moves surface waters into the deep ocean is quite different.

Question 4.4

Look back at Figure 4.4a; concentrate on the equatorial South Pacific Ocean, specifically, the region between the Equator and the Tropic of Capricorn.

(a) How do sea-surface temperatures vary from west to east across this region?

(b) What two factors probably contribute to the pattern you identified in part (a)?

4.3.3 The deep circulation

The ocean's deep circulation system – the movement of water throughout the deep ocean – is known as the **thermohaline circulation (THC)**. It is so called because the driving force behind it depends on the density of seawater and that, in turn, is determined not only by the temperature of the water (whence 'thermo-'; see Box 4.2), but also by its salt content, or **salinity** (whence '-haline' from the Greek *hals* for 'salt'). By piecing together what is known about the paths of water through the ocean a picture has emerged of the main features of this global circulation system; often dubbed the ocean 'conveyor belt', it is illustrated in 'cartoon' fashion in Figure 4.11.

The whole system is driven by cold surface water sinking at high latitudes in winter – specifically, in the regions around Antarctica and in the northern North Atlantic indicated by a blue tone in Figure 4.9. This **deep-water formation** (*not* the same thing as wind-driven downwelling) is triggered by cooling at the surface. In winter, strong polar winds cool the surface water to such an extent that it becomes denser than the water beneath it and sinks. Convection cells are set up, and the ensuing deep mixing leads to the formation of what are known as 'deep water masses'. The sinking process is further enhanced in regions where cooling is sufficient to cause seawater to freeze (recall the map in Figure 4.5). When sea ice forms, the ice itself is frozen freshwater. The accompanying 'salt rejection' leaves behind cold, more-saline water that is very dense – dense enough to sink right down to the sea-bed. This highlights another important role that sea ice plays in the overall climate system, quite apart from its effect on surface albedo.

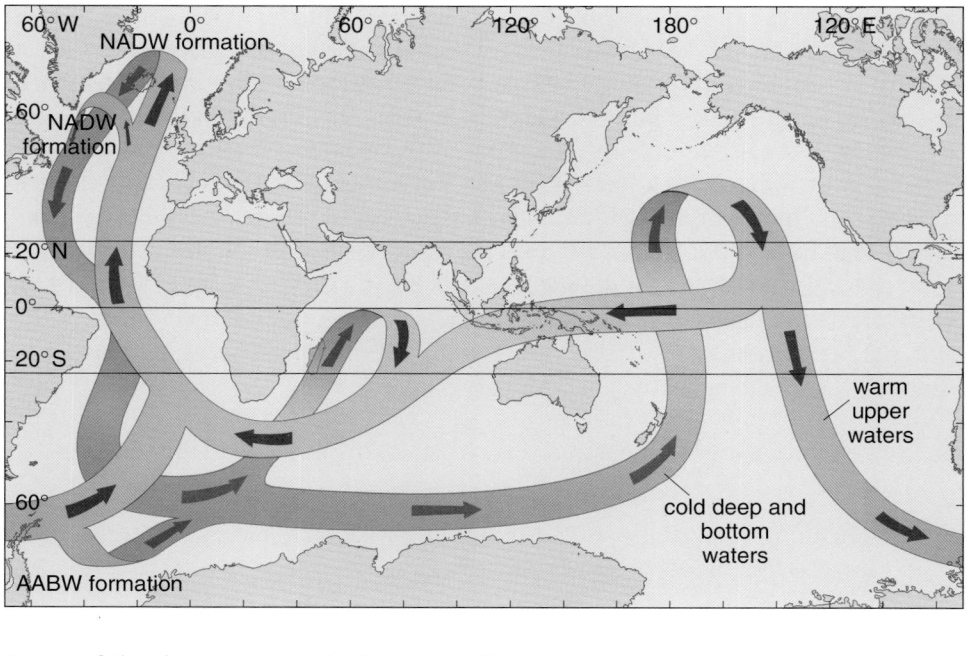

Figure 4.11 Schematic diagram of the global ocean conveyor, driven by the sinking of cold surface water at high latitudes. After sinking, cold water generally follows a path towards the northern Indian Ocean and northern Pacific; warm water in the upper ocean generally follows a return pathway towards the northern North Atlantic. You may see slightly different versions of this elsewhere, as the current flows in the Pacific and Indian Oceans (and the seas between) are not as well known as those in the Atlantic. NADW = North Atlantic Deep Water; AABW = Antarctic Bottom Water.

Some of the densest water in the ocean (known as Antarctic Bottom Water, AABW) is formed in this way around Antarctica. The other major sites of deep-water formation are two quite localised regions in the North Atlantic (see Figure 4.9) – one in the Nordic seas to the east of Greenland and the other in the south Labrador Sea, between Greenland and Newfoundland. Having sunk to the depths, water flows southwards through the Atlantic at 2–3 km below the surface as the so-called **North Atlantic Deep Water (NADW)**. As shown in Figure 4.11, the deep waters then follow a general path from the Atlantic and the Antarctic regions towards the Indian and northern Pacific Oceans, where they eventually rise to the surface to become part of the surface current system. Estimates vary, but it is reckoned that, once it has sunk from the surface of the North Atlantic, *deep water takes of the order of 1000 years to move around this conveyor and come to the surface again.*

The key point to register about the ocean conveyor is its overall effect. There is a net transfer of heat from the Pacific and Indian Oceans into the South Atlantic, and warm surface waters are effectively 'drawn' northwards *throughout* the Atlantic by the deep-water 'pumps' off Greenland – 'just as bathwater is sucked down into the plughole', as one author has put it. In particular, it is thought that this pumping mechanism increases the flow of warm water in the Gulf Stream and 'drags' it far enough north to warm the climate of Europe. The effect is staggering. It has been estimated that in winter about 1300 km^3 of water sinks from the surface of the North Atlantic each day, having been cooled by winds from 12–15 °C down to 1–4 °C. The quantity of heat given up to the air as the water cools is enormous. It amounts to a transfer of heat to the cold northern atmosphere at the prodigious rate of 10^{15} W – equivalent to one-third of the solar input in winter to the *entire* North Atlantic, and sufficient to warm the air over Europe by about 5 °C. Clearly, a weakening – or worse still, complete shutdown – of NADW formation would have serious implications for Europe's climate. As we noted in Chapter 1, this is one of the more scary scenarios in a global-warming future.

What could trigger a scenario like this? A clue lies in the fact that there is no comparable region of deep-water formation in the northern Pacific. Here, the salinity of surface water is simply too low: no amount of cooling can increase its density sufficiently for sinking to occur. In general, the salinity of seawater is affected by the balance between the input of freshwater – from rain, rivers and (in some locations, melting icebergs) – and its removal, mainly via evaporation. In subtropical regions, high evaporation typically wins the contest, and these ocean waters tend to be more saline. Because the large-scale circulation functions as it does, the North Atlantic (but not the northern Pacific) is kept supplied with warm, relatively saline seawater from regions to the south. This enrichment in salt is, in turn, the key reason why surface waters in the two pump sites, cooled by cold winds in winter, *do* become dense enough to sink.

■ So, to return to our original question, what could put a stop to this sinking process?

▨ A reduction in the salinity of North Atlantic waters caused, for example, by an increased input of freshwater into the region.

Has this ever happened before? With a growing body of proxy data (Box 3.1) to go on, researchers have begun to piece together a fairly detailed picture of climatic conditions in the North Atlantic region during the latter part of the last glacial period – and the subsequent widespread deglaciation, beginning around 17 000 years ago, that marked the transition to the Holocene. The salient features of this period are evident in the record from a Greenland ice core in Figure 4.12. Note first how the older, fully glaciated part of the record (to the left) is characterised by episodes of abrupt warming and rapid cooling, causing the climate to swing repeatedly between a colder and a warmer regime, sometimes in a matter of decades. Intriguingly, these temperature fluctuations (also evident in more muted form in the Vostok record; Figure 3.2) appear to be linked with significant changes in ocean circulation in the North Atlantic (recorded in marine sediments); specifically, with shifts in the location of NADW formation. In brief:

• The warmer periods coincide with times when NADW formation occurred in the Nordic seas, much as it does today.

• During the colder periods, however, NADW formation had shifted to lower latitudes, into the open North Atlantic south of Iceland, thus cutting off the supply of warm ocean waters to regions further north.

Figure 4.12 Temperature reconstruction from a Greenland ice core, covering the latter part of the last glacial period and the transition to the Holocene. YD represents the Younger Dryas, the cold period discussed in the text.

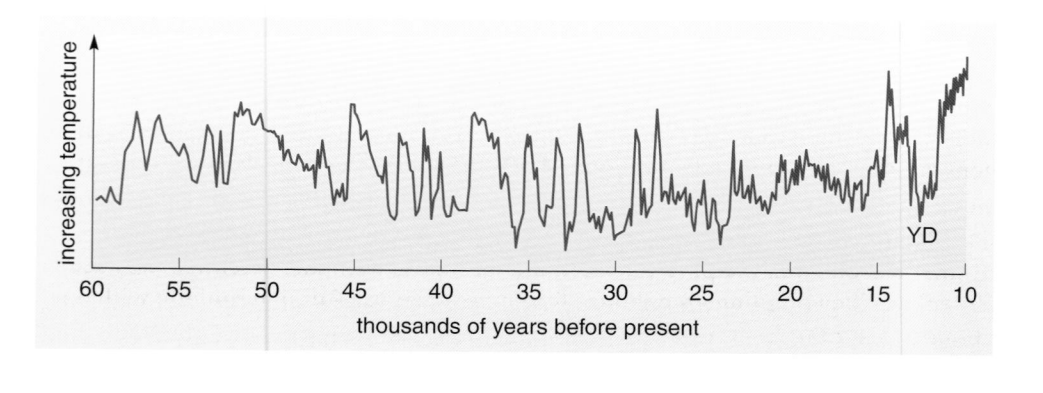

As yet, there is no agreement that the link between changes in ocean circulation and climate swings in the glacial world is a matter of 'cause and effect'. Even if it were (as many scientists suspect), some 'trigger' would be needed to initiate the shift from one mode of ocean circulation to the other, and the nature of this trigger remains unclear.

However that turns out, and more pertinent for our purposes, there *is* evidence that NADW formation shut down altogether at different times in the past – most recently, during a cold period known as the **Younger Dryas** (Figure 4.13), that set in about 12 000 years ago (see the right-hand end of Figure 4.12). This period of renewed cold interrupted the transition to the Holocene that began (in Greenland at least) with a rapid burst of warming about 14 600 years ago (also evident in Figure 4.12). The reversion to near-glacial conditions is documented in proxy data records throughout the North Atlantic region and elsewhere. The cold persisted for several hundred years and ended very abruptly (around 11 500 years ago) with another rapid burst of warming. Temperatures in Greenland jumped by over 5 °C in just 30 years.

Figure 4.13 The Younger Dryas is named after a beautiful alpine shrub, *Dryas octapetala*, which colonised Europe during this cold period.

Again, there is no agreed explanation for the onset and abrupt end of the Younger Dryas. Several factors probably contributed, but there is little doubt that the shutdown of NADW formation played a part in cooling the North Atlantic region. And here there is a plausible cause: a massive surge in meltwater from the northern ice sheets (perhaps triggered by the earlier warming) could well have pushed the salinity of surface waters *below* the threshold needed for deep water formation, effectively shutting down this part of the ocean conveyor.

But in a world without the vast North American and Eurasian ice sheets of glacial times, could continued global warming do the trick?

■ Look back at the information on 20th century changes in the Earth's climate system in Table 3.1, and the accompanying discussion in Section 3.4. Which of the trends identified there might, if continued for some time to come, have an adverse effect on NADW formation?

▨ Basically, you are looking for anything that would increase the input of freshwater into the North Atlantic region. So examples could include increased precipitation and glacier meltwater (either directly or brought into the region by increased river flow, say). A surge in ice discharge from the Greenland ice sheet would be particularly effective, given its proximity to one of the sink sites. Less obviously, a reduction in sea-ice formation in some critical areas could also have an effect, by reducing the enhancement in salinity due to the process of 'salt rejection'.

Current thinking on the prospects for the ocean conveyor in a warmer world is an issue we shall come back to in Chapter 7. For now, there is also another, more general, message to take from Figure 4.12. Whatever the underlying causes, it would seem that the Earth's climate system is highly sensitive to 'nudges', and prone to jump *rapidly* from one climate regime to another. Growing awareness of this 'lesson from the past' has seen one prominent climate scientist, Wallace Broecker, liken ongoing greenhouse forcing to 'playing Russian roulette with our climate' – another potent metaphor!

4.4 Ocean–atmosphere interactions

Throughout this chapter we have sought to stress the interactions between the atmosphere, and its behaviour, and the underlying surface. Since the latter is mainly ocean, it's no surprise that ocean–atmosphere interactions are particularly important to the functioning of the overall climate system. Indeed, the whole wind-driven surface current system is a manifestation of such interactions. In addition, we have the ocean as the main source of atmospheric water vapour (whence latent heat), together with the importance of its thermal inertia (Section 4.2) and global circulation pattern (Section 4.3.3) to regional climates. On a smaller scale, **tropical cyclones** (Chapter 1) are another manifestation of ocean–atmosphere interactions. These storms are fuelled by the latent heat liberated when huge quantities of water vapour condense. To get one started, a large amount of warm, moist air is required, and a continuous supply is needed to keep it going – conditions that are fulfilled over the warm ocean areas where tropical cyclones regularly form and track towards the coastal regions where they can wreak such havoc (recall Figure 1.11).

■   Sea-surface temperatures of 27 °C or higher appear to be critical to the formation of these storms. Look back at Figure 4.4. Can you now suggest why tropical cyclones rarely form over the South Atlantic or eastern South Pacific?

□   These ocean waters are relatively cool for tropical latitudes, due to the influence of cold ocean currents from further south (the eastern 'limbs' of the ocean gyres in Figure 4.9) and coastal upwelling (recall your thoughts on Question 4.4).

Given the conditions that are necessary for the birth and development of tropical cyclones, we might well expect to see an increase in the intensity and/or frequency of these damaging storms as the world warms up (a point we revisit in Chapter 7). As yet, there is no clear evidence that changes of this kind are underway – though once again, the 'noise' of natural variability makes it difficult to discern any underlying trend that could be due to recent climate warming.

With natural variability in mind, there is a further and very important consequence of interactions between the Earth's two dynamic fluid systems: this can sometimes lead to more than one relatively stable pattern of behaviour, resulting in an oscillation between one preferred state and another.

Several of these ocean–atmosphere oscillations have now been identified. The best known is the **El Niño–Southern Oscillation (ENSO)**, an interaction mostly in the tropical Pacific that alternates irregularly between its warm ocean state in the eastern equatorial Pacific (*El Niño*; see Box 4.3) and its cold state (*La Niña*). In either of these two extreme states, ENSO affects the intensity and positions of many weather systems around the world. The impacts are greatest in the tropical Pacific itself: regions that are usually dry experience torrential rain, which may cause floods and mudslides and encourage disease epidemics; other areas, usually with plentiful rain, may be stricken with drought. The result can be severe disruption to agriculture, fisheries, the environment, health, etc. in the affected areas, or an increased risk of forest fire. But it is now understood that

ENSO events have a significant influence on the state of the weather almost everywhere. On the time-scale of four to seven years at which it operates, ENSO is a major source of natural climate variability – on a local, regional and truly global scale. For example, it is generally agreed that the record-breaking El Niño event of 1997–98 (Box 4.3) contributed to the exceptionally high global temperature in 1998 (Chapter 3).

Box 4.3 El Niño

During an **El Niño** event, the 'normal' distribution of sea-surface temperatures across the equatorial Pacific (warmer to the west, cooler to the east; Question 4.4) is disrupted. The 'pool' of warm ocean water usually in the western Pacific migrates eastwards along the Equator, and then polewards along the coasts of North and South America (Figure 4.14). Coastal upwelling is suppressed and the associated fisheries crash.

This change in ocean state occurs in conjunction with a shift in the pattern of atmospheric circulation (called the Southern Oscillation) that sees a weakening of the low pressure normally centred over Indonesia, a reduction in the strength of the trade winds and a shift in weather patterns across the region. Indeed, it is not even possible to say whether an El Niño event is initiated in the ocean or in the atmosphere: so closely are the two dynamic systems *coupled* together in the tropical Pacific that they effectively act as one.

Is there a link between ENSO events and global warming? As yet, there is no consensus on this matter. However, there is evidence that the characteristics of ENSO changed during the 20th century. Since 1970, there were five El Niño events: two of these (1982–83 and 1997–98) were the strongest on record, and a third (1991–95) was the most prolonged. According to the WMO, there were just five events in the whole of the preceding seven decades.

April 25, 1997	June 25, 1997	November 10, 1997

Figure 4.14   Images derived from data collected by NASA's TOPEX/ Poseidon satellite showing sea-surface temperatures in the Pacific relative to average conditions (green). The images track the progress of the 1997–98 El Niño event up to its peak in November 1997. Note the build up of warmer-than-average water (white and red) in the eastern tropical Pacific, and the growing region of cooler-than-average water (purple) to the west.

This event also demonstrated that El Niño conditions can have another kind of environmental impact – one that helps to explain why coral reefs are on the IPCC's list of the natural systems most 'at risk' from significant global warming (Chapter 1, Table 1.1). It was responsible for unusually high sea-surface temperatures in many tropical regions, and led to the most widespread 'bleaching' of corals (Figure 4.15) ever recorded; reefs offshore from 32 countries were affected. Healthy corals usually recover from a short-term bleaching episode. Unfortunately, in many parts of the tropics, reefs are already under stress from a range of human activities – coastal pollution, tourism, fishing, etc. Such corals are more vulnerable to the effects of a bleaching event, and may be irreversibly damaged or killed. While a strong El Niño is not the same as global warming, its impact on coral reefs across the tropics is a foretaste of what might happen more frequently in a warmer world.

Figure 4.15 Coral reefs (a) healthy and (b) bleached. Corals are small colonial animals that live in close association with tiny algae; the corals provide shelter in their tissues for the algae, while the algae both colour and nourish (through their photosynthesis; Chapter 5) their hosts. Corals are very sensitive to sea temperatures; water that is warmer than normal by only 1–2 °C stresses the animals, causing them to expel their algae and take on a white or 'bleached' appearance.

(a)   (b)

Other ocean–atmosphere oscillations with a period of a decade or more have been identified in both northern Pacific and Atlantic regions. For example, the 'North Atlantic Oscillation' (NAO) results in a north–south shift (or vice versa) in the track of winter storms and depressions across the North Atlantic and into Europe. A so-called 'high NAO' winter is associated with mild temperatures, heavy rain and increased storminess across northern and western Europe, but drier weather in the Mediterranean. In recent decades, this pattern appears to have become more common than the opposite conditions (a 'low NAO' winter).

These interactions are more than scientific curiosities: they have a profound influence on regional climates, are a major source of natural variability in the climate system and may themselves be changing in response to global warming.

4.5 Linking the climate system together

The central message to take from this chapter can be stated succinctly. The exchange of energy, moisture and momentum across the surface–air boundary links the atmosphere, and *its* behaviour, to the rest of the climate system: to the ocean, with its own circulation patterns and shifting sea-ice cover; to the ice sheets and glaciers on land; to the land surface, with its varying topography, soils and albedo – and to the vegetation that grows there (Figure 4.16). Driven by the uneven and ever-changing distribution of solar energy at the Earth's surface, the flow of energy and moisture through this complex, interconnected system produces the pattern of climate zones and vegetation types across the globe.

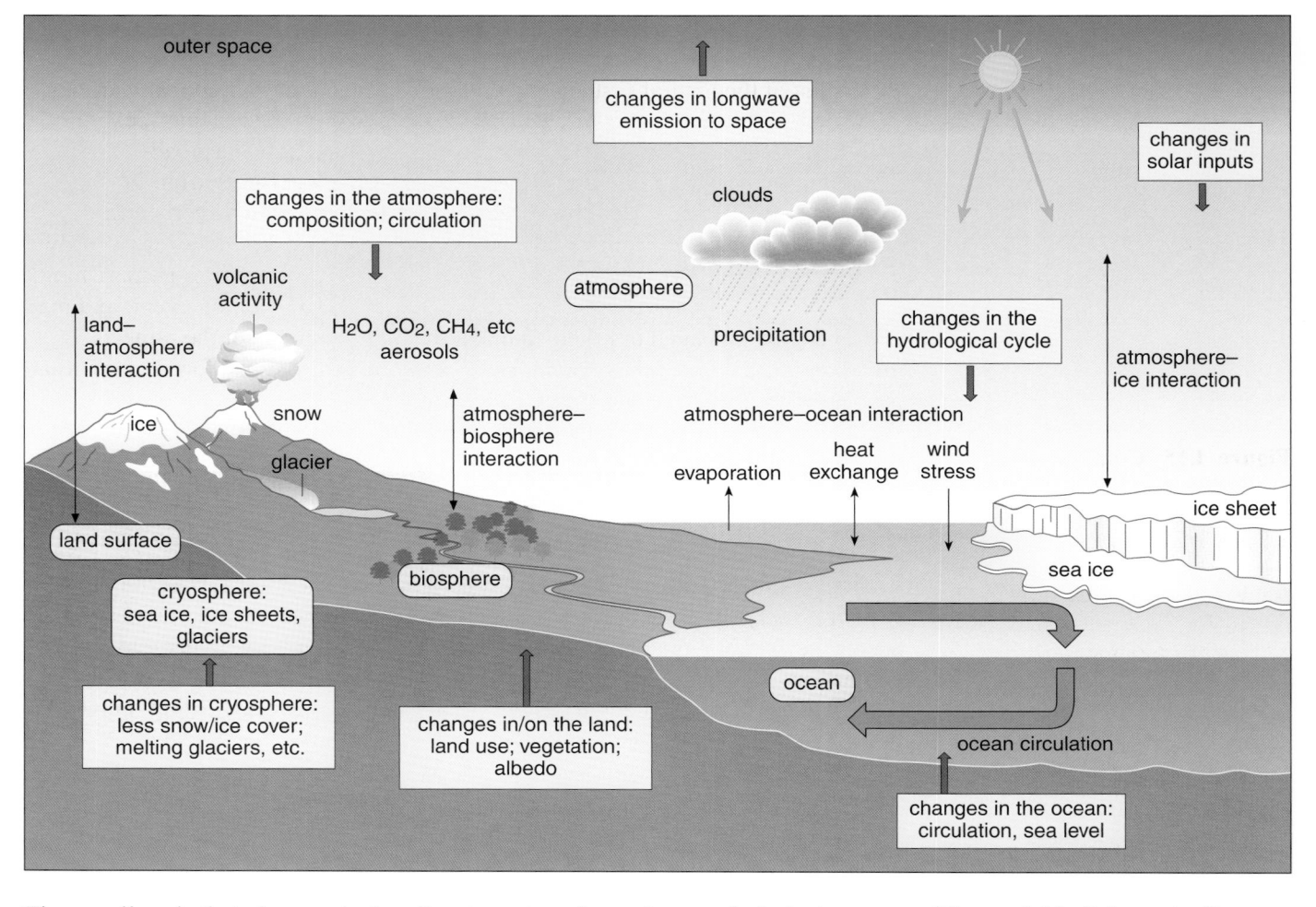

Figure 4.16 Schematic diagram of the global climate system, and some of the interactions between its component parts (yellow boxes). The rectangular boxes (pale brown) indicate processes likely to cause and/or contribute to changes in climate.

The corollary is that changes in the climate system do not happen in isolation: when one part of it changes, the other parts react as well. This relationship was implicit in our brief review of the evidence characterised in the IPCC TAR as 'a collective picture of a warming world' (Chapter 3). It is the fundamental reason why it is so difficult to predict how the 'greenhouse forcing' of the Earth's climate will turn out. In this context, you need to be aware of two characteristic features of the climate system.

4.5.1 Time-scales

The atmosphere is the most rapidly changing part of the climate system: weather conditions can change from minute to minute, hour to hour. Recall, though, how the thermal inertia of the ocean modulates the atmosphere's response to the annual cycle of solar heating. In a similar way, the capacity of the ocean to store huge quantities of heat has a 'buffering' effect on climate at the global level, and has long been expected to slow the pace of atmospheric warming in response to the enhanced greenhouse effect. There is now more evidence that this is happening. Water temperatures are rising in all ocean basins, and at much greater depths than previously thought. In a study published in 2005, researchers analysed some seven million temperature readings taken over 40 years to depths of 700 m. They concluded that about 90% of the warming during that period had gone directly into the ocean – enough energy to 'run the state of California for over 200 000 years', according to Tim Barnett, one of the researchers involved.

However, heat uptake by the ocean merely postpones the eventual atmospheric warming and ensures that any changes in GMST will continue for a very long time (a point we revisit in Chapter 6). In addition, current sea-level rise is mostly driven by thermal expansion (Section 3.4.1) from the warming of the upper levels of the ocean. Even if surface temperatures stabilise some time in the future, sea-level rise would continue *for hundreds of years* as the warming slowly spreads to all depths of the ocean, expanding an increasing volume of water. On top of this, there would be contributions from the melting of ice on land that would continue for *millennia*, due to the very slow response times of the major ice sheets (Section 3.4.1).

We shall come back to the important implications of these and other sources of '**inertia**' in the climate system in Chapter 7.

4.5.2 Feedbacks

Another characteristic of a complex, interconnected system like the climate system is that it often exhibits '**feedback**' when disturbed in some way, and that makes the eventual outcome even more difficult to determine. In general, interactions within the system can act either to *amplify* the original perturbation (**positive feedbacks**) or to *moderate* it (**negative feedbacks**): see Figure 4.17.

Figure 4.17 Schematic diagram illustrating the general effect of both positive and negative feedback.

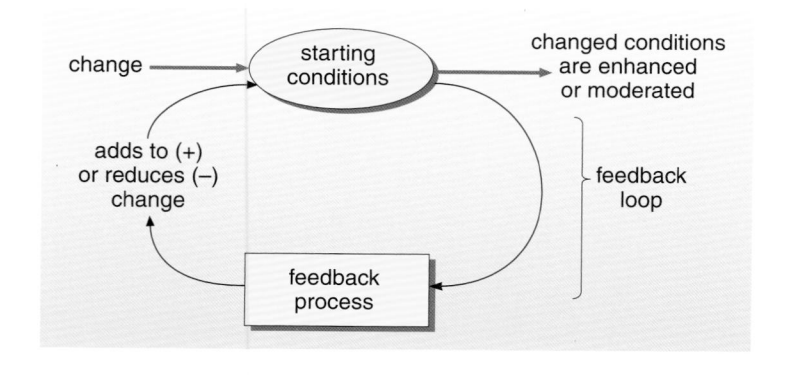

For our purposes, the pertinent examples are changes triggered by global warming that can, in turn, act to amplify or moderate a warming trend. For instance, as noted in Chapter 3, in recent decades the high latitudes of the northern landmasses have been warming at several times the global rate.

■ Which of the changes identified in Table 3.1 (Section 3.4) would help to explain this geographical pattern of warming?

▨ The general reduction in snow and ice cover at high northern latitudes. This exposes less-reflective (lower albedo) surfaces (be they land or sea) that absorb more solar radiation, leading in turn to an additional warming effect, which then helps to melt more snow or ice … and so on, in a sort of 'vicious circle'.

The operation of this positive feedback mechanism, known as **snow–ice albedo feedback**, is illustrated in Figure 4.18. The feedback associated with any reduction in sea-ice cover is expected to be stronger than that on land, since the ocean typically has a much lower albedo than most land surfaces (Section 2.1.1). In view of this feedback loop, climate scientists have long argued that high latitudes will act as the 'canary' in the climate system, with changes there providing an early warning that sustained global warming is underway. It would seem that they were right.

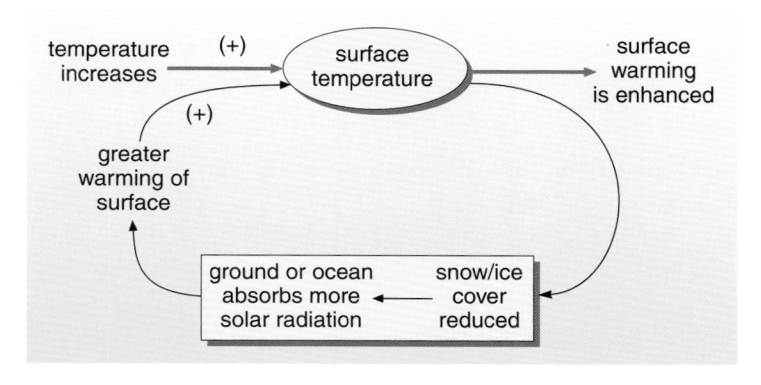

Figure 4.18   Schematic diagram of snow–ice albedo feedback – an example of positive feedback.

Question 4.5

According to the TAR (IPCC, 2001a): 'It is likely that total atmospheric water vapour has increased by several per cent per decade over many regions of the Northern Hemisphere'. Explain why an increase in water vapour content is consistent with global warming and how this increase can, in turn, act to amplify a warming trend. Draw a simple annotated diagram like the one in Figure 4.18 to illustrate this feedback loop.

The positive feedback mechanism in Question 4.5 is known as **water vapour feedback**. Operation of this feedback loop shows how the total amount of water vapour in the atmosphere can indeed be affected *indirectly* by human actions (Section 2.5), and in a way that acts to amplify the warming induced by the build up of other greenhouse gases.

■ Another possible consequence of global warming would be an accompanying increase in cloud cover due to the higher moisture content of the air. Why would a change in cloud cover be expected to act as a feedback mechanism?

▨ Because clouds play a crucial, albeit contradictory, role in the Earth's radiation balance (Section 2.2.3); recall that they both cool the planet (by reflecting incoming solar radiation) and warm it (by absorbing and re-emitting outgoing longwave radiation).

As noted earlier, the *net* effect of clouds in the current climate is a slight cooling of the surface. **Cloud feedback** is a measure of how global warming might *change* this situation; any *diminution* in the net cooling effect of clouds would constitute a *positive* feedback, and vice versa. So which is it likely to be? The short answer: in principle, it could go either way. The slightly longer answer is that the net effect will depend on how the complex interplay of many different factors (recall Figure 2.9) responds to climate warming – possible shifts in the patterns of cloudiness around the world, and in the radiative effects (often delicately poised between warming and cooling) of different types of clouds, etc. The only tool capable of capturing these effects is a climate model, so more on the issue of cloud feedback in Chapter 6.

Note that the feedbacks outlined above are all linked to changes in the hydrological cycle in a warmer world – one of the likely contributions to change in the climate system indicated in Figure 4.16. Another of the possibilities included there – change to the large-scale circulation of the ocean – was discussed in Section 4.3.3. Note that here too there is a link with the hydrological cycle. By altering the salinity of surface ocean waters, changes in rainfall, sea-ice formation and/or the input of freshwater from melting land ice can interact with the ocean conveyor, and hence affect climate (especially in the North Atlantic region).

However, there is yet another 'dimension' to the complexity of the climate system that we have not addressed so far: the role of the biosphere. True, we noted (Figure 4.8, Section 4.2) how terrestrial vegetation influences regional climate, through its role in the hydrological cycle and surface energy balance. But the wider biosphere (i.e. not just plants and not just on land) is also woven into the controls over the Earth's climate in a far more fundamental way – through its influence over the level of CO_2 (and indeed, other natural greenhouse gases; Box 2.6) in the atmosphere. As you will see in the next chapter, that provides scope for further interactions and feedbacks.

Summary of Chapter 4

1   The Earth's climate system (summarised in Figure 4.16) comprises the atmosphere, ocean, cryosphere (glaciers and ice sheets, snow cover, permafrost and sea ice), land surface and terrestrial vegetation – and all the processes that go on within and between these components. Driven by the uneven and seasonally varying distribution of solar radiation at the Earth's surface, the flow of energy and moisture through this complex, interconnected system produces the pattern of climate zones and vegetation types across the globe (Figure 4.6).

2   The worldwide distribution of temperatures and their seasonal variation depends mainly on latitude. Other factors include: the differential heating of land and sea; the influence of ocean currents; altitude; cloud cover; and surface albedo (especially snow- or ice-cover and vegetation type).

3   Driven largely by warming 'from below' in equatorial regions, the general circulation of the atmosphere determines the pattern of prevailing winds around the world, and acts to redistribute heat to higher latitudes.

4   The hydrological cycle (Box 4.1) is an integral part of the heat-redistribution system, through the evaporation of water and ensuing transport of the latent heat 'locked up' in water vapour by winds and vertical air movements. Cloud formation and high precipitation are associated with rising, humid air (as at the Intertropical Convergence Zone, ITCZ); sinking air (as

over the subtropical highs) is usually dry. Other factors that influence precipitation patterns and water availability on local or regional scales include: topography (e.g. the presence of mountain ranges); seasonally-reversing winds (monsoons) in tropical regions where the ITCZ migrates with the seasons; and the recycling of water by vegetation (via evapotranspiration), especially in areas of tropical rainforest.

5   The ocean plays several major roles in the overall climate system. It is the main source of atmospheric water vapour (the most important natural greenhouse gas), and hence latent heat. It stores and redistributes large amounts of heat, through the wind-driven surface current system and global thermohaline circulation (THC). Heat supplied by warm ocean currents (e.g. the Gulf Stream) has a significant influence on regional climates. Other manifestations of ocean–atmosphere interactions include:

- wind-driven downwelling of surface waters and upwelling of cooler, nutrient-rich subsurface waters
- tropical cyclones, and
- larger-scale phenomena such as the El Niño–Southern Oscillation (ENSO) and North Atlantic Oscillation (NAO) that are a major source of internally generated natural variability in the climate system.

6   The THC is driven by cold, saline water sinking at high latitudes due to cooling (and/or sea-ice formation) at the surface. There is concern that changes triggered by global warming could reduce the salinity of North Atlantic waters (e.g. an increased input of freshwater into the region and/or less sea-ice formation), thus weakening or shutting down the deep-water pumps that 'draw' the Gulf Stream far enough north to warm the climate of Britain and northwest Europe (see also Chapter 7).

7   Global warming will trigger feedbacks that can act to amplify (positive feedbacks) or moderate (negative feedbacks) a warming trend. Important examples linked to changes in the hydrological cycle include snow–ice albedo feedback and water vapour feedback (both positive) and cloud feedback (which could be either positive or negative).

8   There are many sources of inertia in the climate system, such as heat uptake by the ocean and its slow penetration to deeper waters, and the very long response times of the major ice sheets. These time lags mean that any changes in response to greenhouse forcing (rising global temperatures and sea levels) will continue long after atmospheric greenhouse gas concentrations are stabilised.

Questions for Chapter 4

Question 4.6

(a)   Suggest one way (other than through differences in surface albedo) in which regions covered in tropical rainforest play a different role in the climate system from arid desert regions or semi-arid grassland.

(b)   In view of your answer to (a), how might converting large areas of tropical forest to pasture (e.g. for cattle) have a direct effect on the climate of the region concerned?

Question 4.7

Look back at the information on 20th century changes to the Earth's climate system in Table 3.1 (Section 3.4). Identify changes that are consistent with an increase in the *rate* of the hydrological cycle in a warmer world. Explain your answer.

Carbon dioxide in the atmosphere: past, present and future

Evidence for the human impact on the atmospheric burden of greenhouse gases was reviewed in Chapter 2. Here we bring the spotlight to bear on CO_2 – the gas at the centre of current concerns. We know how the CO_2 level has changed since pre-industrial times: it has increased by over 30%. But to understand the contemporary trend, and assess how it may evolve over the coming decades and beyond, researchers need to pin down *all* of the factors that affect the CO_2 concentration in the atmosphere. That means going deeper than the most obvious anthropogenic source of the gas, the burning of fossil fuels. We also need to take on board the fact that atmospheric CO_2 is part of a *natural* cycle, the global carbon cycle.

Largely because of its involvement in living processes, carbon continually cycles through the different parts of the Earth – the biosphere itself, the atmosphere, the ocean and the outer parts of the solid planet (its soils, rocks and sediments). This *biogeochemical* cycle, and in particular the natural processes that act as sources and sinks for atmospheric CO_2, has been the subject of intensive study over recent decades. Much of this work has focused on the operation of the carbon cycle in the contemporary world, in an effort to quantify the impact of human activities. However, important insights have also come from studies of how carbon cycling responded to disturbance in the past, and that is where we start.

5.1 Entering uncharted territory

Figure 5.1 sets the CO_2 level today (378 ppm in 2004) in an even longer-term context than the past millennium (Section 2.5). The time-scales are those we considered in Chapter 3: approximately the past 10 000 years (marked by the relatively stable climate of the Holocene); and the glacial–interglacial cycles of the past 400 000 years or so.

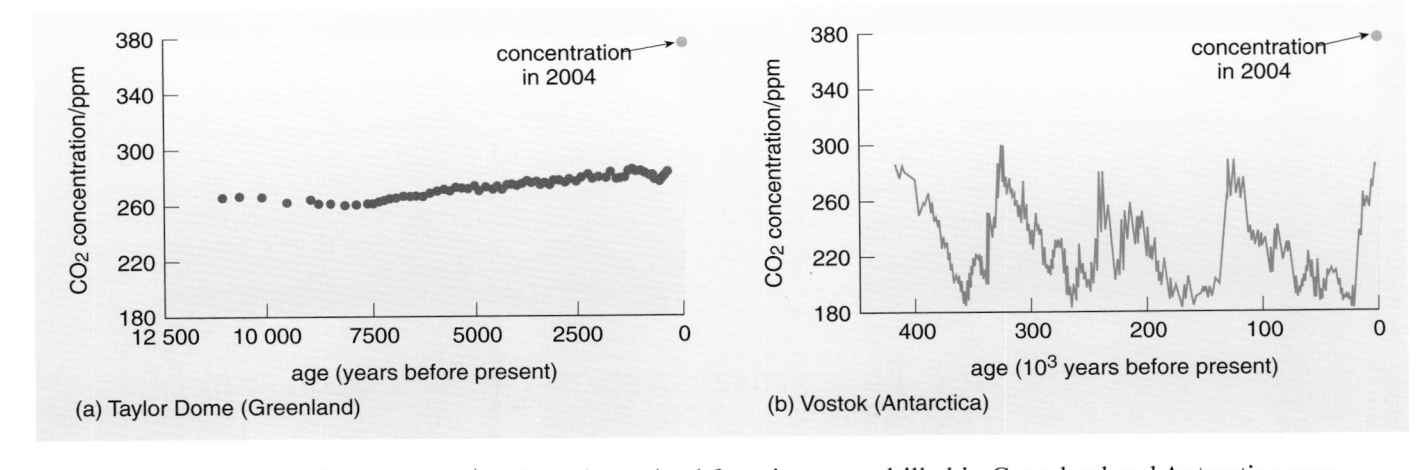

Figure 5.1 Atmospheric CO_2 concentrations determined from ice cores drilled in Greenland and Antarctica over approximately (a) the past 10 000 years and (b) the past 400 000 years (from the Vostok ice core; Section 3.1.1). The contemporary CO_2 level (378 ppm) has been added (in green).

■ From the geological perspective provided by Figure 5.1, is the recent rise in CO_2 concentration to 378 ppm unusual?

■ It certainly is! Indeed, the CO_2 level today is clearly *unprecedented* in the Earth's recent geological history. It is about 35% above the fairly stable baseline (280 ppm) that prevailed *throughout* the pre-industrial Holocene world (i.e. for about 9800 years), and is now higher than it was during any of the earlier interglacial periods of the past 400 000 years.

Other kinds of proxy data (Box 3.1) allow estimates to be made of CO_2 levels even further back in time. On this basis, the IPCC TAR concluded that it is 'likely' (66–90% probability; Box 3.2) that current concentrations have not been exceeded during the past 20 *million* years.

It is clear from Figure 5.1b that atmospheric CO_2 concentrations have varied in the past, in the absence of human intervention. Indeed, reference back to the temperature record deduced from the Vostok ice (Figure 3.2) shows that the CO_2 level moves approximately in concert with the rise and fall in temperature during glacial–interglacial cycles, oscillating between about 180 and 280 ppm. This raises an interesting question. Which comes first: the temperature change or the change in atmospheric composition?

To simplify what is still a challenging puzzle for palaeoclimatologists, it seems that the onset (and end) of glacial conditions is probably triggered by changes *external* to the Earth's climate system – specifically, by slow cyclical variations in the Earth's orbit and axial tilt (over periods of tens to hundreds of thousands of years) that alter the seasonal and latitudinal distribution of solar energy across the globe. The interactions and feedbacks *within* the climate system, whereby relatively small modifications to the energy budget in different parts of the world are translated into glacial–interglacial cycles, are by no means fully understood. Whatever the precise mechanisms, however, the data in Figure 5.1b imply that operation of the global carbon cycle is affected: the balance between the natural sources and sinks of CO_2 is perturbed, resulting in changes to its atmospheric concentration. Moreover, it seems that (in the past at least) these changes acted to amplify temperature trends that were already underway. For example, the cooling that marks the onset of glaciation would be enhanced by a drop in atmospheric CO_2, and vice versa with the rise in concentration during the transition to a warmer interglacial period.

Evidence that carbon cycling is influenced by changes elsewhere in the climate system has important implications. How will the natural processes that regulate atmospheric CO_2 respond as we move away from the domain characterised by the glacial–interglacial dynamics of the pre-industrial world? To begin to unpick this question, we turn now to the workings of the natural carbon cycle.

5.2 The global carbon cycle: a question of time-scales

A crude breakdown of the global inventory of carbon into its major 'reservoirs' is shown in Figure 5.2, along with estimates of their sizes and the annual transfers of carbon between some of them: refer to Box 5.1 (p. 124) for guidance on the

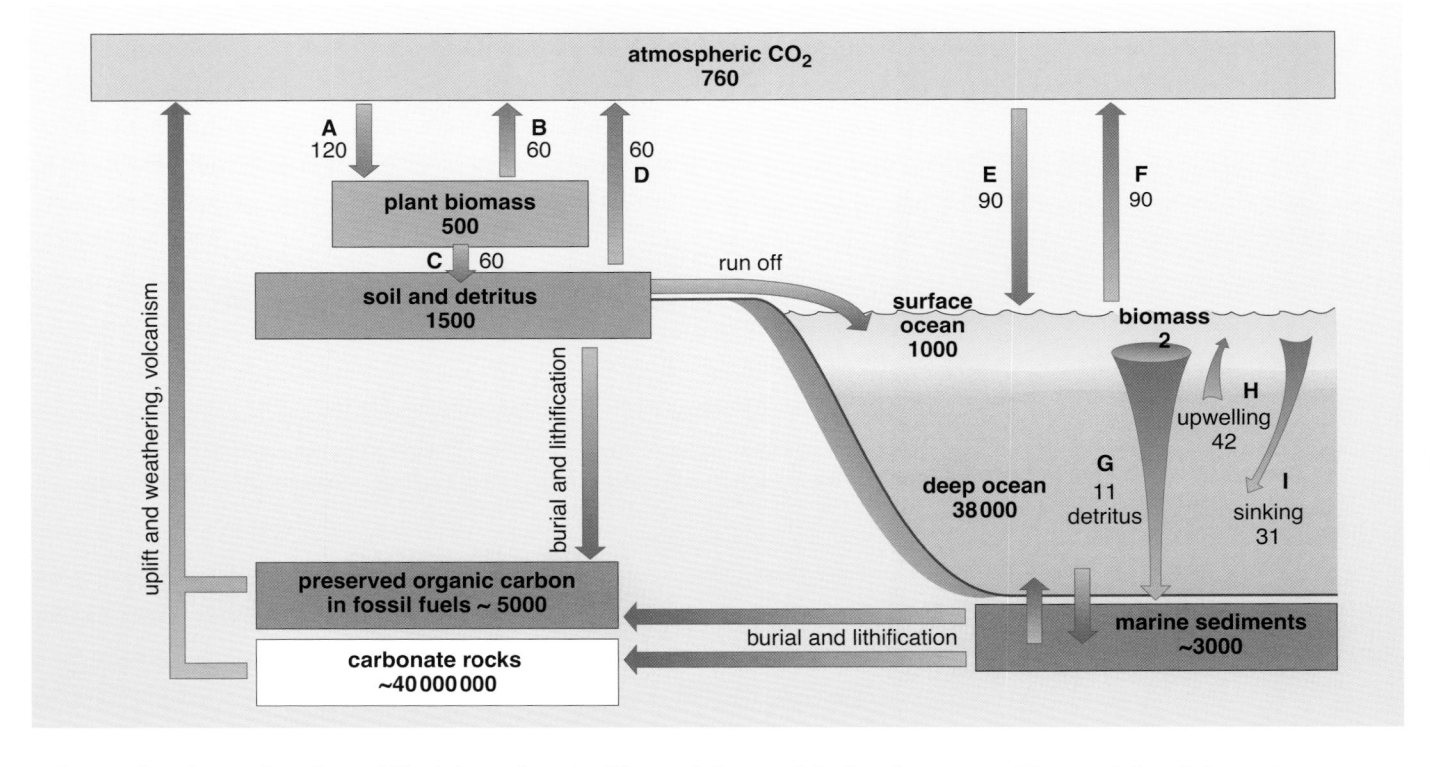

units used to 'count' carbon. All of the values in Figure 5.2 are *global* estimates. The atmospheric reservoir is now well characterised by routine monitoring, but difficult and still imprecise analyses underlie all of the other estimates. The values shown represent scientists' current 'best estimate' in each case, taken (for the most part) from the IPCC TAR.

Before we go any further, there are two general points to note about Figure 5.2. First, it represents the *natural* **carbon cycle** operating in a balanced or steady-state fashion. In particular, it shows a rough balance in the annual exchange of CO_2 between the atmosphere and, on the one hand, the land (a total of 120 GtC), and on the other, the surface ocean (a total of about 90 GtC). We have *not* included current estimates of any imbalance due to human activities: that issue is taken up in Section 5.3.

Secondly, the overall carbon cycle actually involves a hierarchy of subcycles that operate on very different time-scales, stretching from months/years to hundreds of millions of years. To probe the natural controls over atmospheric CO_2 on a time-scale relevant to the issue of anthropogenic climate change (years to a few centuries), we shall restrict attention to two of these subcycles.

- The short time-scale (months/years to decades) biological carbon cycle on land, or the **terrestrial carbon cycle**. This involves the atmosphere, living things (mainly plants) and dead organic matter in soil and detritus, and is linked together by biological processes (green arrows A to D in Figure 5.2).

- The intermediate time-scale (up to 1000 years) **ocean carbon cycle**, involving the atmosphere, surface ocean and deep ocean. This is linked together by a combination of chemical, biological and physical processes (blue arrows E to I in Figure 5.2).

Figure 5.2 Schematic representation of the natural carbon cycle, with the major global reservoirs and estimates of the mass of carbon (in GtC) stored in each (**bold** values). Arrows refer to processes that transfer carbon between reservoirs, with estimates of the rates of transfer in GtC y^{-1}. Green, blue and brown arrows relate to operation of the terrestrial cycle, oceanic cycle and long-term geological cycle, respectively: see text for further details on the processes represented by the letters A to I.

Box 5.1 Counting carbon

The global carbon budget is expressed in terms of the mass of carbon (indicated by attaching a 'C' to the unit) stored in each reservoir – in all the CO_2 in the atmosphere, for example. The masses involved are enormous, so the units of measurement in common usage may well be unfamiliar. There are two key things you need to know in order to navigate through the plethora of options.

- Masses may be expressed as multiples of grams (g) or **tonnes** (metric tons): 1 tonne (t) = 10^3 kg = 10^6 g.

- The SI prefixes for large powers of ten: **mega** (M) = 10^6; **giga** (G) = 10^9; **tera** (T) = 10^{12}; **peta** (P) = 10^{15}.

■ Express 1 PgC in terms of (i) kilograms; (ii) tonnes; (iii) megatonnes; and (iv) gigatonnes of carbon.

▨ 1 Pg = 10^{15} g = 10^{12} kg = $10^9 \times 10^3$ kg = 10^9 t = $10^3 \times 10^6$ t = 10^3 Mt or 1 Gt; so 1 PgC is equivalent to (i) 10^{12} kgC; (ii) 10^9 tC; (iii) 10^3 MtC; and (iv) 1 GtC.

Of course, in everyday language 10^6 is a million and 10^9 is a billion, so media reports often use these terms instead of the SI prefixes (mega and giga, respectively) – rightly so, since their job is to communicate with the public!

In reading about climate change, you will also come across information on emissions that uses masses of CO_2, instead of C, as the measure. To convert between these two measures, we need the relative atomic masses of carbon (12.0) and oxygen (16.0), and hence the relative molecular mass of CO_2 (44.0).

■ How much carbon is there in 10 g CO_2?

▨ 2.7 gC (to 2 significant figures). 44.0 g CO_2 contains 12.0 gC, so 10 g CO_2 contains 10 g × (12.0/44.0) = 2.73 gC.

More generally, to convert a mass of CO_2 (whatever the unit) into an equivalent mass of C, we multiply by the factor 12.0/44.0 (= 0.273). Conversely, to convert from a mass of C to a mass of CO_2, we multiply by the factor 44.0/12.0 (= 3.67).

These subcycles are 'geared' into the long-term geological cycle (involving rocks and sediments) by a series of very slow 'leaks', some of which are identified (but not quantified) alongside the brown arrows in Figure 5.2. We shall not consider these leaks, or the other slow processes that characterise the geological cycle, further. But it's worth noting one thing. Over the course of geological time, it was the preservation of organic matter on land or at the bottom of the sea that led, eventually, to the store of carbon in fossil fuels. By extracting and burning this fossil carbon, humans are effectively short-circuiting the long-term cycle, and bringing buried carbon back into circulation about 100 times faster than natural processes (e.g. volcanic eruptions) do.

5.2.1 The terrestrial carbon cycle

On land, most of the carbon stored in living things (or **biomass**) is in vegetation: all animals (including humans) account for only about 0.1% of the total. Thus, the 'living' terrestrial reservoir in Figure 5.2 is an estimate of the carbon in plant biomass in all terrestrial ecosystems, everywhere – about 500 GtC. Plants also drive the land-based carbon cycle, which is dominated by the biological processes of photosynthesis and respiration: consult Box 5.2 if you need to refresh your memory about these terms.

Box 5.2 Photosynthesis and respiration

Plants are *autotrophs* (literally 'self-feeders'): they take in CO_2 from the air through the pores or stomata in their leaves (Box 4.1). By harnessing the energy of sunlight, water (taken up by plant roots) is split, and the hydrogen is combined with CO_2 to manufacture simple sugars (such as glucose, $C_6H_{12}O_6$). Chemically, the overall process of **photosynthesis** can be represented as:

$$\text{solar energy} + 6CO_2 + 6H_2O \longrightarrow C_6H_{12}O_6 + 6O_2 \tag{5.1}$$

The simple organic compounds plants make by photosynthesis are, in effect, their food. The energy 'stored' in these compounds is released by cellular respiration, and is used to fuel the production of other, more complex, organic compounds and other processes. Chemically, *aerobic* (oxygen-using) **respiration** is identical with combustion, and essentially the *reverse* of photosynthesis; it returns some of the CO_2 plants take up to the atmosphere:

$$C_6H_{12}O_6 + 6O_2 \longrightarrow 6CO_2 + 6H_2O + \text{energy} \tag{5.2}$$

Only plants (and certain bacteria) are capable of photosynthesis, often referred to as 'fixing' carbon. All other organisms, collectively known as *heterotrophs* ('other feeders'), depend on plants for their fixed carbon and energy (i.e. food) – either directly (animals eating plants) or indirectly (animals consuming other animals). This category includes the **detritivores** (such as woodlice) that feed on plant debris (detritus) and **decomposers** (including fungi and bacteria) that cause the breakdown of dead organic matter in soils.

All organisms respire, and most of them do so aerobically (i.e. via Equation 5.2). Like autotrophic respiration, heterotrophic respiration returns CO_2 to the atmosphere.

Photosynthesis by green plants removes CO_2 from the atmosphere (Figure 5.2, arrow A). This is the key to an ecosystem's ability to 'fix' carbon, and is referred to as the **gross primary production (GPP)**. Globally, about half of the CO_2 that plants take up is returned to the air through their own (autotrophic) respiration (Figure 5.2, arrow B). The fixed carbon that remains is called the **net primary production (NPP)**; that is:

$$\text{NPP} = \text{GPP} - (\text{carbon respired by plants}) \tag{5.3}$$

- According to Figure 5.2, what is the global annual NPP of terrestrial ecosystems?

- Global GPP = 120 GtC y^{-1}, and half of this (60 GtC y^{-1}) is returned to the atmosphere by plant respiration (arrow B). So the *net* fixation of carbon per year is: NPP = (120 – 60) GtC y^{-1} = 60 GtC y^{-1}.

What happens to the carbon in NPP? It supports plant growth; i.e. it is incorporated into new plant tissues and stored for a time – in leaves, stems, wood or roots, for example. However, the ultimate fate of the carbon fixed in NPP is transfer to the store of dead organic matter in soil and detritus (Figure 5.2, arrow C), when plants (and the animals that eat them) die, trees shed their leaves or branches, etc. In the 'unperturbed' steady-state world of Figure 5.2, the rate at which carbon is transferred from the 'plant' to the 'soil' carbon pool (60 GtC y^{-1}) matches the global NPP: there is no *net* accumulation of plant biomass, and no net loss.

In Figure 5.2, the same goes for the stock of carbon in the world's soils. The input of carbon in dead matter (arrow C), which is equivalent to the global NPP, is matched by its loss by **decomposition** (arrow D). This returns carbon (as CO_2) to the atmosphere. Decomposition is just another name for the (heterotrophic) respiration of the countless organisms (decomposers and detritivores; Box 5.2) that derive their energy from the breakdown of dead organic matter in the soil. Thus on a global scale, virtually all of the carbon fixed in NPP is eventually returned to the atmospheric CO_2 pool through the respiration of decomposers and detritivores. (Natural wildfires account for a little.)

How long does it take for a carbon atom that enters as NPP to leave as respired CO_2? That depends. The length of time carbon atoms spend, on average, in one compartment of the overall cycle is called the **residence time** (or sometimes, the 'turnover time'). It can be estimated from the expression:

$$\text{residence time} = \frac{\text{stock in reservoir}}{\text{rate of input (or output)}} \qquad (5.4)$$

Question 5.1

Using information from Figure 5.2, estimate the average residence time of carbon in (a) plant biomass; and (b) soil organic matter.

The figures you calculated in Question 5.1 are *global* averages. Actual residence times vary greatly, depending on the longevity of the plant and tissue (e.g. leaf or flower as opposed to root or woody tissue) of which the carbon is a part, and upon the activity of the decomposers and detritivores in the soil. With around 75% of the carbon in terrestrial ecosystems in the soil, however, it is the rate of decomposition, especially by bacteria, that largely determines the overall time-scale for the return of CO_2 to the atmosphere. The main controls over bacterial activity are temperature and the availability of moisture and oxygen in the soil. Regions with cold or dry climates or with waterlogged soils, where oxygen is in short supply, have much longer residence times for carbon than warmer environments where soils are moist and well-oxygenated.

As any gardener will know, environmental conditions also affect plant growth, which reflects *net* carbon fixation (i.e. NPP). Above a minimum threshold (typically around 0 °C) photosynthesis and plant respiration both rise with increasing temperature, but in such a way that *net* photosynthesis (the difference between them) peaks in a particular temperature range for each plant species. It is less efficient if temperatures are below (or indeed, above) the optimum range. Photosynthesis can also be compromised by a lack of sunlight or a shortage of soil moisture (Box 4.1). Plants both gain CO_2 and lose water through the same pores (stomata) in their leaves. When stomata are open (to allow uptake of CO_2), loss of water from the plant by transpiration (Box 4.1) increases sharply and has to be replaced by uptake from the soil via the roots. If the water content of the soil is reduced, plants suffer from 'water stress' and the rate of photosynthesis declines. Temperature, water availability and access to solar radiation interact to impose complex and varying constraints on the NPP of vegetation in different parts of the world.

■ What else can limit plant growth? (*Hint*: why do farmers and gardeners apply fertilisers?)

▢ The supply of other key nutrients from the soil, especially nitrogen, phosphorus and potassium (the NPK of fertilisers; among other things, plants need nitrogen to manufacture the main enzyme involved in photosynthesis).

At the ecosystem level, carbon storage depends on the combined influence of these environmental factors on the rate of carbon input (NPP) and the rate of carbon output (mainly by decomposition, but also by wildfires). To take just one example, the world's forest ecosystems contain about 60% of the carbon stored on land. But the total carbon 'stock', and its distribution between the plant and soil pools, varies markedly among the forest ecosystem types characteristic of different climate zones (Figure 4.6, Section 4.2). Figure 5.3 illustrates the point. Study the figure and then answer the following question.

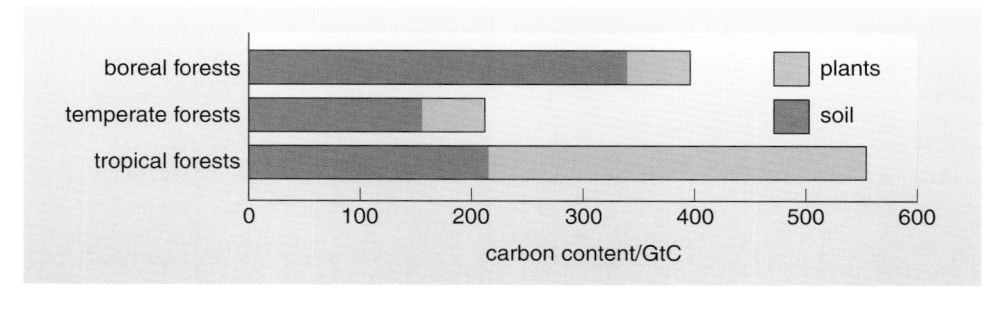

Figure 5.3   Terrestrial carbon stocks in soil and plants in different forest ecosystems.

Question 5.2

Among tropical, temperate and boreal (far northern) forests, compare (a) the total carbon stocks; and (b) the plant to soil carbon ratios. What geographical patterns do the two comparisons show?

Tropical forests contain the greatest total stock of carbon because they are more extensive than the other types of forest, and because the plant component has a higher *carbon density*; i.e. there is more plant biomass per unit area: about

Figure 5.4   The far northern forest is also called the *taiga*. Although sparse, it covers broad, uninterrupted expanses in North America (western Alaska to Newfoundland) and in Eurasia (Norway to the Pacific coast of Russia).

19 kgC m^{-2} for tropical forests, as against 13 kgC m^{-2} and 4 kgC m^{-2} for temperate and boreal forests, respectively. These differences in carbon density reflect differences in NPP. Year-round warmth and abundant rainfall make tropical forests the most productive ecosystems on Earth. Area for area, they are over six times more productive than boreal forests, where cold winters and a cool, very short growing season (when temperatures are sufficient for growth; Chapter 1) limit NPP. Boreal forests (Figure 5.4) still come next in terms of *total* carbon, however, because they cover a greater area than temperate forests and the *soil* carbon density is much higher than either of the other forest types.

■ Suggest an explanation for the geographical pattern of variation in the plant to soil carbon ratio.

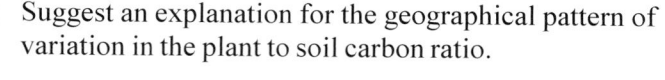

The ratio changes with latitude and climate, with a greater proportion of total C in the soil on moving from the tropics to the temperate zone to the boreal zone. The likeliest explanation is that the decomposition rate of organic matter in the soil is much lower in the cooler climates of the north than it is closer to the Equator.

The cold climate at high northern latitudes inhibits decomposition in other ways as well. Across a region that takes in large tracts of Alaska, Canada and Siberia, the seasonally thawed soil layer is underlain by permafrost (Chapter 3). This blocks downward movement of water and results in poorly drained, boggy soils. Evaporation is also limited, and the region is home to peat-rich bogs and mires that comprise about half of the world's natural wetlands. Overall, the wetlands and other ecosystems of the far north (boreal forest and the treeless tundra of the Arctic fringe; Figure 4.1) contain about 25% of the global pool of soil carbon. All wetlands, which include tropical swamps (Figure 5.5), are characterised by waterlogged soils where *anaerobic* (oxygen-free) conditions prevail. They are important players in the global carbon budget, and not only because they store large amounts of carbon below ground. As noted earlier (Box 2.6, Section 2.5), they are also the main natural source of methane (CH_4).

Like the global situation depicted in Figure 5.2, a 'mature' ecosystem (an area of forest, say) will be in a steady state if the rate of decomposition (a source of atmospheric CO_2) just balances the NPP (a CO_2 sink). In reality, this is rarely the case. On a local or regional scale, terrestrial ecosystems commonly act as a *net* sink for CO_2, or a net source – albeit on a temporary basis.

■ Given the discussion above, what *natural* factors are likely to affect the balance between carbon storage and release in a mature ecosystem?

Natural climate variability is an obvious candidate, since NPP and bacterial activity in the soil are both sensitive to climatic conditions. (Indeed, there is evidence to this effect in the *seasonal* oscillations of CO_2 levels about the long-term trend in the Mauna Loa data; Figure 1.5.) You may also have thought of natural fires, which release pulses of CO_2 into the atmosphere.

Figure 5.5   Tropical swamp forest in Kalimantan, Indonesia. Seepage from natural wetlands currently accounts for some 22% of global methane emissions (Box 2.6).

But what about the disturbance to natural ecosystems wrought by human activities? Today, the media often carry compelling images of tropical forest being hacked down and/or burnt (Figure 5.6). The scale of destruction *is* staggering: one recent estimate put the *annual* loss across the tropics at close to 9 million hectares (9×10^6 ha = 9×10^4 km^2). However, deforestation in the tropics only really got underway after the Second World War. Elsewhere, the practice of clearing forests, burning their wood and turning vast areas of virgin land over to agricultural use was already widespread before the 19th century. It reached a peak at temperature latitudes (e.g. in North America and parts of Europe) in the late 19th and early 20th centuries. Overall, there has been a 20% decrease in global forest area since 1850.

Figure 5.6   The aftermath of major forest fires in Indonesia in 1999. It is suggested that many fires were started deliberately to clear the forest for other uses, but then went out of control.

What impact has this wholesale 'deforestation and land-use change' (Section 2.5) had on the global carbon budget? The following question invites you to think about this, as a prelude to the discussion later in the chapter.

Question 5.3

On average, agricultural land supports a plant carbon density of about 0.5 kgC m^{-2}, and ploughing aerates the soil. With this in mind, explain how converting large areas of forest to agricultural use (first in temperate regions, and latterly in the tropics) has probably contributed to the build up of CO_2 in the atmosphere over the past 200 years or so.

5.2.2   The ocean carbon cycle

Atmospheric CO_2 is the primary link between the carbon cycle on land and that in the ocean.

■   Look back at Figure 5.2. How does the total amount of carbon in the ocean compare with that in the atmosphere and in terrestrial ecosystems?

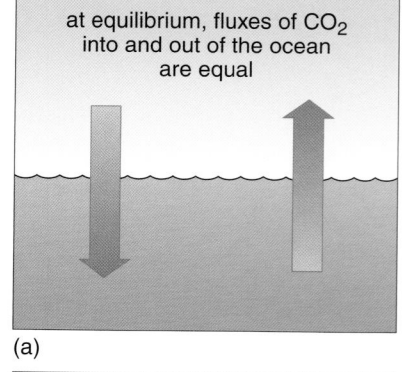

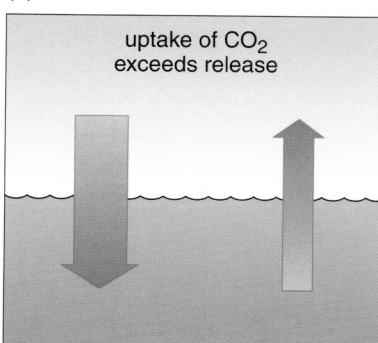

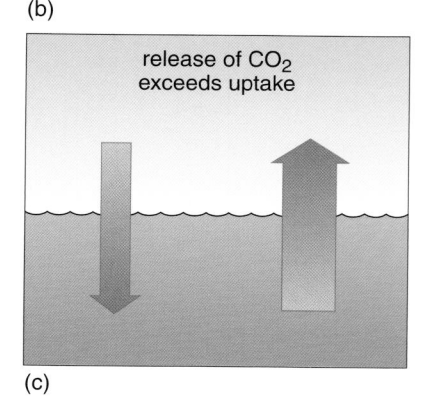

Figure 5.7   (a) At equilibrium, the exchange of CO_2 across the air–sea interface is balanced. Changing conditions (temperature or biological activity, as described in the text) can upset the balance, leading to a net uptake (b) or net release (c) of CO_2.

■ There is about 760 GtC in the atmosphere, and a total of around 2000 (500 + 1500) GtC on land and some 39 000 (1000 + 38 000) GtC in the ocean. So the ocean stores about 50 times as much carbon as the atmosphere, and about 20 times as much as the land.

Unlike the situation on land, nearly all of the carbon in the ocean is contained in what is known as **dissolved inorganic carbon (DIC)**. The ultimate source of most of this DIC is CO_2 that has dissolved in seawater. But once dissolved, CO_2 reacts with water and the carbon ends up apportioned among three *inorganic* chemical 'species': (1) dissolved CO_2 (molecules of CO_2, about 1% of the total); (2) bicarbonate ions (strictly, hydrogen carbonate ions HCO_3^-, about 91%); and (3) carbonate ions (CO_3^{2-}, about 8%). The relative proportions of these three components of DIC are determined in complicated ways by the chemistry of seawater, and we shall bypass the intricacies of that. However, we need to take note of some important consequences of this chemistry for the *natural* carbon cycle; i.e. for the natural controls over the movement of carbon through the ocean–atmosphere system depicted in Figure 5.2.

For a given level of CO_2 in the atmosphere, surface ocean waters can 'hold' only a certain concentration of dissolved (i.e. molecular) CO_2. At 'saturation', a dynamic steady state (or equilibrium) is established (Figure 5.7a): CO_2 both dissolves in and 'outgasses' from the surface ocean, but there is no *net* transfer in either direction. This gas exchange across the air–sea interface is fairly rapid, and *overall* the surface waters of the world's oceans are approximately in equilibrium with the overlying atmosphere as far as its CO_2 content is concerned. This is the situation depicted in Figure 5.2.

■ In terms of the arrows in Figure 5.2, what does this steady state mean?

■ The rate at which CO_2 dissolves in surface waters (arrow E) approximately balances the rate at which CO_2 outgasses from the ocean (arrow F) – at about 90 GtC in each direction per year.

Within this gross annual balance, however, there are regions of the world's oceans where *net* transfers of CO_2, both into (Figure 5.7b) and out of (Figure 5.7c) the surface ocean, do occur. The geographical distribution of these *natural* sinks and sources of atmospheric CO_2 is controlled by two main factors: (1) the warming and cooling of surface waters; and (2) biological activity within the ocean.

Like all gases (but unlike most soluble solids), the solubility of CO_2 increases with *decreasing* temperature (a very important fact to remember). In practice, this means that the cooling of surface waters tends to drive the net uptake of CO_2 (Figure 5.7b), whereas warming tends to have the opposite effect, with a net release of the gas to the air (Figure 5.7c).

■ Bearing in mind how the large-scale (thermohaline) circulation of the ocean operates (Section 4.3.3), which regions are likely to act as the main 'temperature-driven' natural sinks for CO_2?

■ High latitudes, where surface waters are subject to strong cooling in winter.

Where cooled surface waters become dense enough to sink, this feeds seawater that is relatively rich in dissolved CO_2 (and hence DIC) into the cold deep ocean.

This process, often dubbed the '**solubility pump**', is one reason why deep ocean waters have a *higher* concentration of DIC (about 35% higher, as a global average) than surface waters. But this is not the whole story. A further contribution to the enrichment in DIC (and indeed, other nutrients) at depth comes from the shifting pattern of biological activity within the ocean.

Like the situation on land, marine life depends (ultimately) on the carbon fixed by photosynthetic organisms – mainly free-floating, microscopic algae known as **phytoplankton**. They inhabit the uppermost sunlit 100 m or so of the ocean, known as the 'photic zone', and take their CO_2 from that dissolved in the water around them, *not* directly from the atmosphere. However, the nearly invisible 'forests' of phytoplankton in the world's oceans fix almost as much carbon as *all* land plants, and that has a profound *indirect* effect on atmospheric CO_2.

- ■ From Figure 5.2, the stock of carbon in marine plant biomass (mainly phytoplankton) is about 2 GtC. Given that global annual NPP in the ocean is estimated to be around 45 GtC y^{-1}, what is the average residence time of carbon in marine plants?

- ▨ On average, about (2/45) years, or roughly two weeks.

This short time-scale reflects the rapid recycling of carbon (and, incidentally, other nutrients) within the surface ocean. Phytoplankton are consumed by zooplankton (their microscopic animal counterparts) and other animals, or die in a matter of days and are colonised by bacteria, which decompose them. All these marine organisms respire, and the net effect is to return to the surface ocean most, *but not all*, of the dissolved CO_2 fixed by phytoplanktonic photosynthesis. About 25% of the fixed carbon escapes the recycling system, and is exported directly into the deep ocean: this is known as **export production** (Figure 5.2, arrow G). The underlying mechanism is the clumping together of planktonic debris, faecal pellets of animals and other organic detritus into particles (often referred to as 'marine snow') that are large enough to overcome the buoyancy of seawater, and so sink down through the water column.

Current estimates put global export production at about 11 GtC y^{-1} (as noted in Figure 5.2). Again, this global total is the result of *local* contributions, which are greatest in areas of rapid phytoplankton growth, known as 'blooms'. To cite just one example, such blooms sweep across the North Atlantic in late spring and early summer. At these latitudes, ocean waters mix to greater depths during the stormy winter months, enriching the surface layer in dissolved nutrients. As light levels increase in spring and surface waters begin to warm up, a seasonal burst of phytoplankton growth sends a pulse of fixed carbon into deeper waters (Figure 5.8), and draws atmospheric CO_2 into solution to compensate for the dissolved CO_2 removed by the high local NPP. In this way, areas of high phytoplankton productivity – which vary with the seasons and from place to place in the great ocean basins – act as further natural sinks for atmospheric CO_2 (Figure 5.7b).

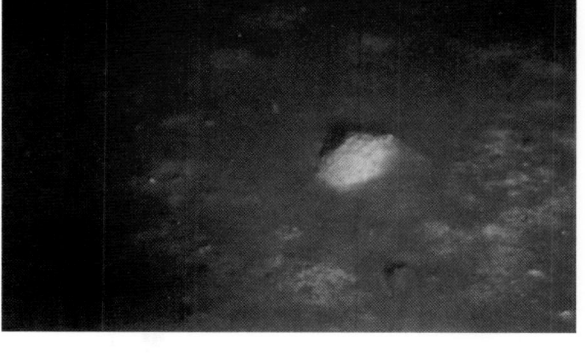

Figure 5.8   Marine snow carpeting the sea-bed and partially burying a mound made by an animal. Some creatures of the deep ocean time their reproductive cycle such that their young are able to take advantage of organic debris from the spring bloom in surface waters. (The field of view is about 50 cm across.)

The overall effect of the drawdown of CO_2 from the atmosphere, the fixation of dissolved CO_2 in surface waters, and the subsequent export of fixed carbon to deeper waters is called the **biological pump**. It has been estimated that this pump keeps atmospheric CO_2 concentrations about 150 to 200 ppm *lower* than would be the case in its absence.

■ If the biological pump were to work away year after year *in isolation*, what would be the eventual consequence?

▪ There would be a steady drain on the supply of DIC in the surface ocean, and, in turn, a continual drawdown of CO_2 that would gradually deplete the atmospheric reservoir.

Since this didn't happen during the 10 000 or so years that preceded the industrial age, there must be some other mechanism that keeps the DIC content of the upper ocean 'topped up'. This is where the dissolved carbon moved around by the ocean circulation comes in. As we noted earlier, deep ocean waters originate in high latitudes and tend to be relatively rich in DIC to start with. As these waters move through the depths, their DIC content is further enhanced by the debris raining down from above. On average, little of the organic matter in these particles survives the journey to the sea-bed. The rest provides food for a bizarre and diverse community of organisms in the deep sea, and the ubiquitous decomposers. Ultimately, the carbon is released as CO_2 by heterotrophic respiration and, in the cold depths of the ocean, this goes into solution.

Because of the general movement of deep water towards the northern Indian and Pacific Oceans in the 'global thermohaline conveyor' (Figure 4.11), a relatively large proportion of DIC-rich water eventually comes to the surface in these regions. Most of the rest returns through localised upwelling (e.g. along the Equator and in certain coastal locations; Figure 4.9). As cold DIC-rich waters warm up at the surface and re-equilibrate with the atmosphere, there is a net outgassing of CO_2 (Figure 5.7c). So these regions tend to act as natural sources of atmospheric CO_2.

The overall picture that emerges is, then, of a spatial separation across the world's oceans between the natural sources and sinks of CO_2: areas of deep-water formation and areas of high primary productivity (where there are flourishing phytoplankton populations) act as sinks; areas where deep DIC-rich waters resurface act as sources. Carbon is transferred *within* the ocean from natural sink regions to natural source regions via ocean circulation and the sinking of carbon-rich particles (Figure 5.9).

In terms of the global totals in Figure 5.2, the upward movement of deep DIC-rich water brings about 42 GtC in solution up to the surface ocean each year (Figure 5.2, arrow H). And every year, the sinking of surface waters (with a lower DIC-content) transfers about 31 GtC in the other direction (Figure 5.2, arrow I). In other words, there is a *net* transfer of some 11 GtC y^{-1} of dissolved carbon from the deep to the surface ocean, balancing the particulate carbon exported to the deep ocean via the biological pump.

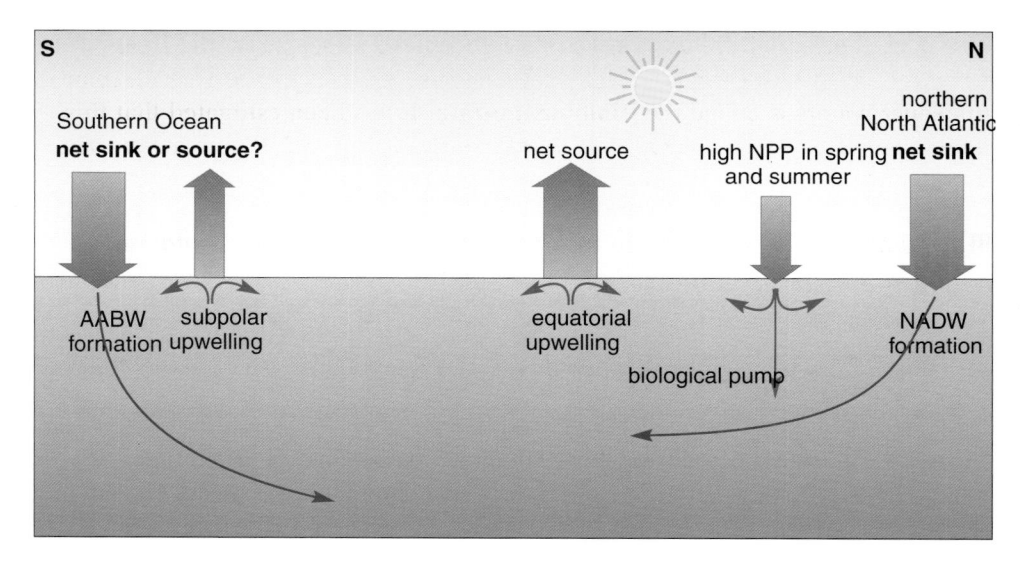

Figure 5.9 Sketch cross-section of the Atlantic Ocean to illustrate the spatial separation of the natural oceanic sources and sinks for atmospheric CO_2, and the connection between them. The diagram is drawn for the northern summer and so high primary productivity, contributing to the drawdown of CO_2, is shown for the North Atlantic. (NADW = North Atlantic Deep Water; AABW = Antarctic Bottom Water.)

Question 5.4

Given the information in Figure 5.2, estimate the average residence time of carbon in (i) the atmosphere; (ii) the surface ocean; and (iii) the deep ocean. Does your answer to (iii) have the order of magnitude you would expect? (*Hint*: look back at the discussion of the thermohaline circulation in Section 4.3.3.)

That completes our survey of the workings of the natural carbon cycle. But one final point is brought out by the answers to Questions 5.1 and 5.4. Among the 'active' carbon reservoirs we have focused on throughout this section, the atmosphere, land plants, soils and upper ocean are strongly linked: with relatively small stocks and large annual transfers, carbon moves around this set of reservoirs on a time-scale of years to a decade or so. Exchange of carbon between this fast-responding system and the deep ocean takes much longer (several hundred years). As you will see, this has important implications for the fate of *anthropogenic* CO_2.

5.3 Anthropogenic CO_2: balancing the books

How much CO_2 has been pumped into the atmosphere by human activities during the past 200 or so years? Table 5.1 (overleaf) gives recent IPCC estimates for the cumulative input over the period 1850 to 1998 from the two main anthropogenic sources: (1) burning fossil fuels; and (2) changing land use, where nearly 90% is attributed to the loss of carbon from forest ecosystems (as foreshadowed in Question 5.3). As you might expect, these historical assessments are difficult and uncertain, especially when it comes to tracking the changing pattern of carbon storage on land back through time.

■   How is this reflected in the entries in Table 5.1?

▨   The uncertainty associated with the 'land-use change' estimate is much larger. The 'central' or best estimate is 136 GtC, but there is a 5% probability (i.e. 1 in 20) that the actual input of carbon from this source was less than 81 GtC, or more than 191 GtC.

Table 5.1 Estimated anthropogenic emissions of CO_2 for the period 1850 to 1998, and the observed increase in atmospheric CO_2 (figures in brackets are 95% confidence limits). (Source: IPCC, 2000.)

Source	Mass of carbon/GtC
emissions from fossil-fuel burning	270 ($\pm$ 30)
emissions from land-use change	136 ($\pm$ 55)
increase in atmospheric CO_2	176 ($\pm$ 10)

■   Table 5.1 includes the observed increase in the carbon (as CO_2) content of the atmosphere between 1850 and 1998. What proportion of the estimated cumulative input from fossil-fuel burning and changing land use does this represent, expressed as a percentage?

▨   Taking the central estimates, the cumulative input was 406 GtC, so the atmospheric increase represents (176/406) × 100 = 43%.

So over half of the historical input of anthropogenic CO_2 has been locked away, or 'sequestered', again. But where exactly? Assessments of the situation over recent decades point to uptake by the ocean and by terrestrial ecosystems, in roughly equal proportions. For example, central estimates of the annual emissions of CO_2 during the 1980s, and the fate of the 'extra' carbon, are collected in Figure 5.10.

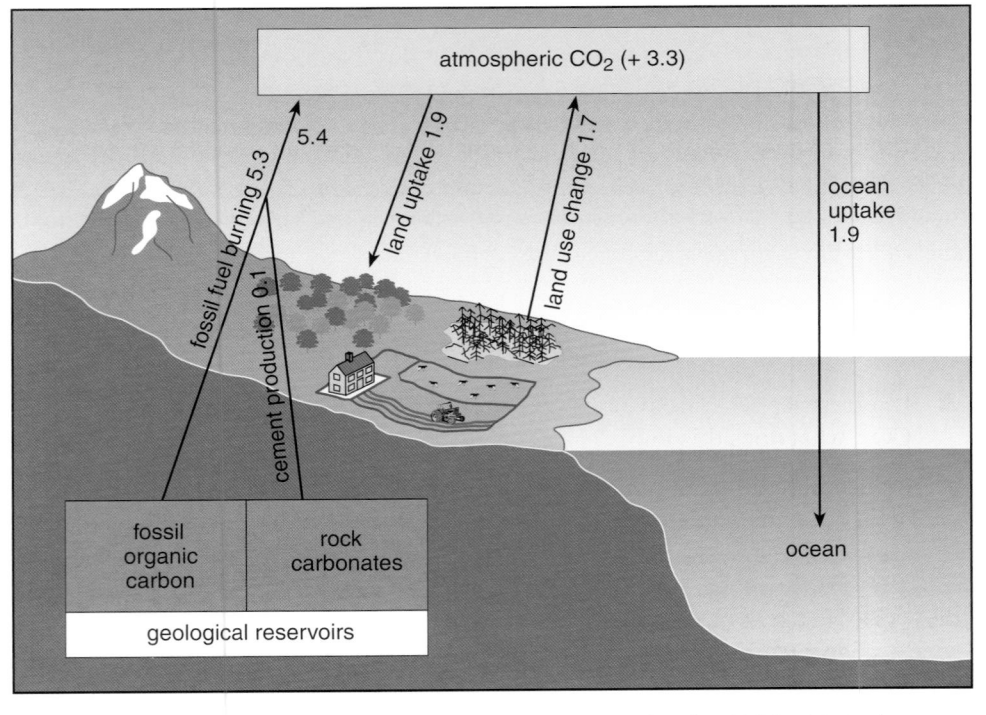

Figure 5.10 The global budget of *anthropogenic* CO_2 for the 1980s. Emission rates, uptake rates and the rate of increase in atmospheric CO_2 (+3.3) are estimated average annual values in GtC y^{-1}. Note that cement production involves roasting natural sources of $CaCO_3$ (calcium carbonate, or limestone) to give CaO (calcium oxide, or quicklime): this is a (small) non-combustion source of CO_2. (Source: IPCC, 2001a)

■ From the data in Figure 5.10, what proportion of anthropogenic CO_2 emissions is due to the burning of fossil fuels?

▨ Total annual emissions amount to $(5.3 + 0.1 + 1.7)$ GtC = 7.1 GtC, so fossil fuel CO_2 accounts for $(5.3/7.1) \times 100 = 75\%$.

At present, most of the rest is due to the CO_2 released by tropical deforestation, estimated as 1.7 GtC y^{-1} (in the range 0.6 to 2.5 GtC y^{-1}). However, this regional input is currently being offset by the 'extra' CO_2 taken up by terrestrial ecosystems across the world (estimated as about 1.9 ± 1.9 GtC y^{-1}) – sometimes referred to as the 'residual' terrestrial sink. Roughly the same amount $(1.9 \pm 0.6$ GtC $y^{-1})$ is removed each year by the ocean. Note again the very large uncertainties associated with these estimates.

■ The land-based and ocean sinks for anthropogenic CO_2 represent the response of the *natural* carbon cycle to ongoing disturbance – to the increase in atmospheric CO_2, and to the global warming and shifts in other climate variables around the world reviewed in Chapter 3. In the language of 'feedbacks' introduced in Section 4.5.2, how would you characterise this response?

▨ By absorbing part of the CO_2 released by human activity each year, natural processes (on land and in the ocean) are slowing down the build up of CO_2 in the atmosphere, and so acting as *negative* feedbacks in the overall climate system.

But what are the mechanisms behind these important negative feedbacks? And will they persist in future? Or to put it another way, can we rely on the terrestrial and oceanic sinks to go on soaking up such a large fraction of fossil fuel CO_2 (now the dominant anthropogenic source)? This perspective has driven a major research effort in recent years. In the next two sections, we look briefly at the insights emerging from such studies, and identify some of the more thorny issues that remain.

5.4 Sinks for anthropogenic CO_2 on land

■ If terrestrial ecosystems are currently acting as a net sink for anthropogenic CO_2, what does this imply?

▨ Somewhere on land, the rate of carbon fixation (NPP) exceeds the rate of carbon loss by decomposition (and wildfires), resulting in net carbon storage.

Since the early 1980s, satellite-borne sensors have been monitoring the state of the world's vegetation. Analysis of the data indicates that recent decades have seen a widespread 'greening' of the planet, with an increase in plant growth across many regions; some estimates suggest that global NPP may have increased by around 6% between 1982 and 1999, for example. This and other lines of evidence (e.g. 'inventories' of carbon stocks) point to the world's forests as the main terrestrial sinks for anthropogenic CO_2 – with significant uptake at mid- to high northern latitudes (temperate and boreal forests), and in the tropics as well, *despite* ongoing deforestation (i.e. carbon storage has increased in some areas of undisturbed forest). Several likely mechanisms have been identified. The four main ones are outlined below.

1   The beneficial effects of extra CO_2 in the atmosphere

A CO_2-enriched environment could be stimulating plant growth – a phenomenon known as the **carbon dioxide fertilisation effect**. Experimental studies have shown that most plant species do indeed respond to raised CO_2 levels with increased photosynthesis, enabling them to fix carbon at a higher rate. It can be a large effect under ideal 'glasshouse' conditions (where extra CO_2 may be introduced artificially to increase productivity) – up to 20–40% more growth for a doubling of atmospheric CO_2 in some cases. However, the strength of the response varies markedly from species to species, and eventually 'saturates'; at high CO_2 concentrations (typically above about 800 ppm), there is no further effect on NPP. In the 'real' world, the response to elevated CO_2 levels is also affected by complicated interactions with other environmental factors, especially at the ecosystem level (a point we return to shortly).

2   The effects of recent climate change

When it comes to the impact of changing climatic conditions on the productivity of the world's ecosystems, there are few definitive answers. Rather, assessments have identified a mix of possible beneficial and adverse effects. Take rising temperatures, for example.

■   As we noted earlier (Section 3.4.2), this has extended the growing season in mid- to high latitudes. How has this probably contributed to the uptake of anthropogenic CO_2?

▪   By increasing the productivity (i.e. NPP) of temperate and boreal forests (as noted above).

In the tropics, by contrast, most plants already operate close to their optimum temperatures for net photosynthesis (Section 5.2.1). Here, higher temperatures may have little effect, or be positively detrimental – especially if they also result in increased evapotranspiration in water-deficient ecosystems. Changes in rainfall patterns affect water availability and the length of the growing season. In the arid and semi-arid regions of the tropics and subtropics (Figure 4.6), for instance, wetter regimes would likely increase NPP, but drought would have the opposite effect. Cloud cover can be beneficial to NPP in dry areas with high solar radiation, but detrimental in areas of low solar radiation (e.g. the far north). And so on.

■   Given this brief summary, what is likely to determine the global balance between the positive and negative effects of climate change on plant NPP?

▪   How the *regional* aspects of climate change affect the existing constraints on plant growth in different parts of the world.

Studies suggest that recent climate changes around the globe (of the kind reviewed in Chapter 3) have indeed acted to ease these constraints in many regions, promoting increases in NPP over the past 20-odd years. Equally, though, some vegetated areas saw a fall in NPP during this period; this has been attributed to more adverse climatic conditions (e.g. reduced rainfall).

3   The effects of increased 'nitrogen deposition'

Plant growth may be enhanced through the increased availability of soil nutrients, especially nitrogen – and not only through the widespread use of artificial fertilisers. As we noted earlier (Box 2.6), the high-temperature combustion of fossil fuels generates various nitrogen oxides, including nitric oxide (NO). In the atmosphere, NO is rapidly converted to other, more soluble nitrogen compounds (e.g. nitric acid, HNO_3) and 'washed' out by rainfall. The deposition of this extra 'fixed' nitrogen (mainly as nitrate, NO_3^-) can stimulate growth in ecosystems where this is a key limiting factor.

4   The effects of land-use management

Managed forests go through a cycle of logging and regrowth. Several studies have suggested that, on average, such forests in northern mid-latitudes (in North America and northern Eurasia) are currently in a period of rapid regrowth. During such periods, there is a year-on-year increase in NPP and in the carbon stored in trees and other woody vegetation. In turn, this increases the input of organic matter to the soil. But this pool of carbon responds more slowly, and there is a time lag before the rate of decomposition 'catches up'. In the meantime, carbon storage exceeds carbon release, and the forest acts as a net sink for atmospheric CO_2. In a similar way, the encroachment of woody vegetation onto abandoned farmlands or grasslands can act as a carbon sink.

To sum up: In the TAR, the IPCC concluded that all four of these mechanisms have probably contributed to the observed increase in plant growth around the world, though their relative contributions in different regions remain uncertain. However, they also stressed that (IPCC, 2001d):

> The recent global net uptake of CO_2 by terrestrial ecosystems is partly the result of time lags between enhanced plant growth and plant death and decay.

But what of the future? If recent climate changes, combined with the fertilisation effects of increased atmospheric CO_2 and nitrogen (N) deposition, have been largely beneficial to plant growth, should we not look forward to a 'greenhouse world' with equanimity, or even enthusiasm? Could a planet Earth with longer growing seasons, more rainfall and a CO_2-rich atmosphere prove to be a 'plant heaven', as some sceptics have claimed, with burgeoning growth in the world's forests acting as an ever more efficient sink for fossil fuel CO_2? One problem with this somewhat Utopian vision is brought out by the article from *New Scientist* reproduced in Extract 5.1. Read through the article, and then do the question that follows.

Extract 5.1 Don't count on plants to save the world from global warming. From *New Scientist*, 14 December 2002, p.18.

Anil Ananthaswamy

It is a convenient argument against trimming carbon dioxide emissions: as CO_2 levels in the atmosphere rise, plants will grow faster and bigger, locking up more of the gas and keeping levels in check. But a study on the likely environmental impact of CO_2 emissions has revealed a fatal flaw – plant growth can actually drop if temperature and moisture levels creep up as well.

Atmospheric CO_2 levels have risen more than 30% in the past century and further increases are almost certain. Previous studies have shown that more CO_2 means faster photosynthesis, and hence faster plant growth, which ought to strip more CO_2 out of the atmosphere. But most of these studies looked at the effect of CO_2 alone. When researchers factored in other influences on plant growth such as water or nitrogen, the results were ambiguous.

To get a definitive answer, Christopher Field and his team of ecologists at Stanford University in California set up a three-year study. They investigated how changes in CO_2 levels affected the growth of natural grassland when accompanied by other anticipated environmental changes such as higher rainfall, temperature and nitrogen levels in the soil.

The study was carried out in a protected reserve called the Jasper Ridge in Stanford. Field's team marked out plots of land and sealed them in enclosures so that they could control the environmental conditions in each plot. First they raised just the CO_2 levels, from the ambient levels of about 380 parts per million to 680 parts per million.

As expected, plant growth rates jumped, with an increase of 32% in the third year of the experiment. But in plots where they changed temperature as well as water and nitrogen levels, raising the CO_2 levels actually had the reverse effect. In these plots, net plant growth fell by an average of more than 9% when CO_2 levels were raised, compared with plots where CO_2 was kept at the ambient level (*Science*, Vol. 298, p. 1987).

So why does increasing CO_2 levels make the plants grow less? "We honestly don't know what the mechanism is," says Field. But the researchers' hunch is that bacteria and fungi in the soil somehow fare better under the elevated CO_2 levels and outcompete plants for nutrients such as potassium or phosphorus.

"It's a really excellent study", says Peter Reich, a global climate change expert at the University of Minnesota in St Paul. He says it is surprising that increasing CO_2 can have such a strong damping effect when combined with other environmental factors. But Reich is worried that scientific funding policies are hampering such long-term studies in real ecosystems. "We can't be comfortable that we really know what the combination of things we are doing to the globe will lead to", he says.

■   What is the main message to take from the study referred to in this article?

▨   Predictions based on ecosystem responses to elevated CO_2 *alone* can be misleading in a world where other key environmental factors (temperature, rainfall and N-availability) are all changing at the same time.

To date, this study is one of very few that have attempted to assess how the NPP of a real ecosystem (a grassland in this case) responds to *simultaneous* changes in two or more of these factors. The finding of CO_2-induced reductions in plant productivity is rare, but it does highlight the potential complexity of ecosystem responses to a suite of interacting environmental changes – a point we alluded to earlier.

■   If further increases in atmospheric CO_2 in future are virtually certain (Section 5.6), what is fundamental to the issue of whether recent increases in the NPP of vegetation will continue?

▨   How the climate system responds to continued 'greenhouse forcing' (Chapter 2); i.e. *future* climate change, especially at the regional level.

Without pre-empting the discussion of climate modelling studies in Chapter 6, we can say that all such studies agree on one thing: continued global warming will intensify the hydrological cycle, with consequent increases in average global precipitation *and* evaporation (recall Question 4.7). However, there is much less agreement about how the geographical and seasonal patterns of rainfall around the world are likely to change in future. The influence of changes in rainfall *and* temperature on soil moisture – the water 'available' to support plant growth – is even less clear cut. Bear in mind, though, that a warmer world could see both heavier rainfall *and* an increased risk of drought in some regions – a picture that already seems to be emerging (recall Table 3.1; Section 3.4.1). In short, there is no guarantee that shifts in climatic conditions, which have helped to promote plant growth over the past 20-odd years, will support a continuing increase in global NPP in future.

■   What else is central to the role of the world's terrestrial ecosystems as a *continuing* sink for fossil fuel CO_2?

▨   How future climate change affects bacterial activity in the soil, and hence the rate at which CO_2 is released to the air by decomposition.

In practice, the respiration of soil bacteria is very sensitive to temperature, and decomposition rates are expected to accelerate in a warmer world. For this reason, there is particular concern about the *enhanced* warming at high latitudes (due to the snow–ice albedo feedback loop; Section 4.5.2), since these regions currently hold about 25% of the global stock of soil carbon (Section 5.2.1) – some 375 GtC.

Finally, we should bear in mind that continued global warming will affect ecosystems in other ways as well, with potential implications for carbon storage on land. Already there are signs that recent changes in climate around the world have resulted in a 'spatial shift' in plant and animal ranges (Section 3.4.2), and we can expect this trend to continue. In many cases, established species will suffer as climatic conditions in their existing environments become hostile to their well-being. For example, it is thought that (with enhanced warming at high latitudes) the southernmost flanks of the boreal forest could revert to scrubby grassland, while forest trees invade the tundra regions to the north. In the long term, forest areas could 'migrate' and re-establish. But in the short term, the loss of trees during the transition could release significant amounts of carbon into the atmosphere. Changing climate can also affect the incidence of other disturbances – such as attacks by insect pests and other plant pathogens (e.g. various fungal diseases), or the damage wrought by severe storms or wildfires.

All the issues touched on above are, of course, pertinent to one of the main causes for concern about ongoing global warming – its impact on the natural environment. If we keep the focus on the more narrow issue of carbon sinks, however, what can usefully be said about the combined effects of elevated CO_2, higher temperatures, and changes in soil moisture, nutrient availability and various disturbance regimes in the coming decades, and beyond? The short answer is that there must be considerable uncertainty about how the strength of the terrestrial sink might change in a world where fossil fuel CO_2 emissions continue to rise. Global emissions amounted to some 5.3 GtC y^{-1} during the 1980s (Figure 5.10), but had increased to 6.3 GtC y^{-1} by the 1990s, and are still rising (see Section 5.6). The slightly fuller answer is that, with so much scope for complex interactions, this issue can only really be addressed through modelling studies of the kind referred to earlier. From the assessment of such studies for the TAR, the IPCC concluded that (IPCC, 2001d):

> The uptake [of anthropogenic CO_2] will decline as forests reach maturity, fertilisation effects saturate, and decomposition catches up with growth. Climate change is likely to further reduce net terrestrial carbon uptake globally.

The provisions of the Kyoto Protocol have given the issues discussed above an added *political* dimension. Under the terms of the treaty, industrialised nations can also claim 'carbon credits' (Box 1.3) by investing in **'carbon sequestration'** schemes. Planting *new* forests, at home or abroad, is top of the list. Forestry companies are already planning to join the anticipated global market in certified 'forest sinks'. Such *afforestation* schemes can have potential benefits – for flood or soil erosion control, for example, or the restoration of degraded environments. But are they an effective strategy for 'managing' future CO_2 levels in the atmosphere, or an inherently risky one?

Activity 5.1

Allow about 30 minutes

(a) Explain, *in a couple of sentences*, why new forests do have potential as sinks for fossil fuel CO_2.

(b) At present, a rapidly growing forest in the temperate zone can accumulate about 5 tC per hectare per year (5 tC ha^{-1} y^{-1}).

(i) What area would a newly established forest need to occupy in order to match the current annual CO_2 emissions from the USA alone (around 1.5 GtC y^{-1})?

(ii)   What proportion of the continental USA (with a total land area of some 9.8×10^8 ha) does this represent? Does this sound like a realistic proposition?

(iii)   Would the forest go on acting as a net carbon sink indefinitely? (*One sentence*)

(c)   Given your answers to (b) (and the discussion in this section), note down (as a list of bullet points) any concerns you have about planting forests to 'soak up' CO_2 as a substitute for reducing energy-related emissions.

5.5 Sinks for anthropogenic CO_2 in the ocean

In sharp contrast with the situation on land, current thinking maintains that the marine *biosphere* plays no part in the uptake of anthropogenic CO_2, despite the importance of the biological pump for the ocean's natural carbon cycle. We come back to this point later on, but first we focus on the non-biological mechanism that *is* thought to be responsible for sequestering 'extra' CO_2 in the deep ocean – essentially, the solubility pump and the large-scale circulation of the ocean. In the words of the TAR (IPCC, 2001a):

> The increase of atmospheric pCO_2* over pre-industrial levels has tended to increase uptake into natural CO_2 sink regions and *decrease* release from natural outgassing regions […] Uptake of anthropogenic CO_2 is strongest in regions where 'old' waters, which have spent many years in the ocean interior since their last contact with the atmosphere, are re-exposed at the sea surface to a contemporary atmosphere which now contains anthropogenic CO_2 […] In an upwelling region, for example, the natural component of the air–sea flux may be to outgas CO_2 to the atmosphere. The higher atmospheric pCO_2 of the contemporary atmosphere *acts to reduce this outgassing relative to the natural state*, implying that more carbon remains in the ocean […] This represents uptake of anthropogenic CO_2 by a region which is a [natural] source of CO_2 to the atmosphere. The additional carbon in the ocean resulting from such uptake is then transported by the surface ocean circulation and eventually stored as surface waters sink […] into the deep ocean interior.

> [Our italics. *pCO_2 stands for the 'partial pressure' of CO_2 in the atmosphere, an alternative measure of its concentration.]

■   What is the significance of the phrase 'eventually stored' in this quote from the IPCC?

▪   Once in the deep ocean, 'fossil' carbon is effectively 'buried', since it will be centuries (on average) before it returns to the surface ocean (recall the long residence time of water, and hence dissolved carbon, in the deep ocean; Question 5.4(iii)).

■ What factor limits the uptake of anthropogenic CO_2 by the mechanism identified by the IPCC?

▪ The rate at which older, deeper waters are exposed at the sea surface to the 'extra' CO_2 in the atmosphere.

As the IPCC goes on to say:

> In principle, there is sufficient uptake capacity [...] in the ocean to incorporate 70 to 80% of anthropogenic emissions to the atmosphere, even when [cumulative] emissions of up to 4500 PgC [GtC; Box 5.1] are considered [...] *The finite rate of ocean mixing, however, means that it takes several hundred years to access this capacity.* [Our italics]

Indeed, it was a dawning recognition that ocean uptake could not keep pace with the rate of CO_2 emissions that led Roger Revelle to sound his warning 50 years ago (Chapter 1). The constraint imposed by the slow exchange of water between the surface and deep ocean has important implications for the effectiveness of the oceanic sink for anthropogenic CO_2 in future.

■ How will the *proportion* of annual CO_2 emissions that can be taken up by the ocean change as the rate of emission increases?

▪ It will decline, due to the finite rate of exposure of older, deeper waters to the anthropogenic CO_2 in the atmosphere.

On top of this, several climate modelling studies suggest that changes in ocean circulation in a global-warming future could *reduce* the rate of exchange between surface and deep waters. In short, it seems that the negative feedback afforded by the oceanic uptake of anthropogenic CO_2 is also likely to weaken in future. Note too that continued warming of surface waters would tend to drive CO_2 out of solution, further increasing its atmospheric concentration.

But what about the assumption implicit in the discussion above – effectively that the biological pump plays no role in sequestering 'extra' CO_2? This view is grounded in the finding that the growth of phytoplankton, the driving force behind the export of fixed carbon to the deep ocean, does not respond directly to elevated CO_2. Rather, it is controlled by other factors: light, temperature and, most importantly, by the availability of dissolved nutrients such as nitrogen (N) and phosphorus (P). The supply of these key limiting nutrients is, in turn, shaped by the ocean circulation, which both moves them around in surface waters and brings up nutrient-rich waters from below. In the TAR, the IPCC cautions that: 'Our incomplete understanding of present day nutrient controls on productivity limits our ability to predict future changes in ocean biology and their effect on CO_2 levels'.

Yet plans are already underway to 'fertilise' the oceans on a commercial scale with another nutrient, iron – plans promoted as a means to increase the efficiency of the biological pump, and thereby lock up large amounts of fossil fuel CO_2 in the deep ocean. Such schemes, exemplified by the Planktos 'Green Tag' programme (Figure 5.11), draw on the work of the late John Martin, who once quipped: 'Give me half a tanker of iron, and I will give you the next ice age'. The following Activity gives you some of the background, and a chance to think through some of the implications.

Planktos Green Tags will become a new form of Eco-Security which equate to sequestered biomass CO2, also known as a carbon offset credit. The Planktos ocean mission is to generate a greater valuation of assets in the ocean environment and our Green Tags are a first step.

By joining in research with major academic organizations from around the world we will focus research efforts on the hypothesis of the late Professor John Martin who first suggested that *forests at sea*, plankton blooms, might be stimulated to grow by the addition of tiny amounts of natural iron micronutrients. Planktos multi-disciplinary efforts will integrate engineering and economics research along side biological and ocean science programs.

With the introduction of Planktos Green Tags later this summer we will provide a means for corporations and individuals to participate. Each tag unit represents the sequestered biomass (sunken) equivalent of one ton of atmospheric CO2. An average US household contributes 15 tons of CO2 to the global greenhouse blanket each year might offset that burden through the purchase of just $60 (15) Planktos Green Tags. Planktos Green Tags can even be provided as a flexible tax deductible contribution that supports ocean research. Details on the Planktos Green Tag page at www.planktos.com/greentags.htm.

Figure 5.11 Extract from a press release posted on the website of the Planktos Foundation, May 21 2002.

Activity 5.2

Allow about 1 hour

This activity is based around 'The Oresmen', a news feature published in *Nature* (Vol. 421, 9 January 2003, pp. 109–110). You can find this article by going to the Topic 5 page of the S250 website and selecting the link labelled 'Topic 5 Activity 5.2'. Read through the article and then work through the following questions.

(a) Concentrate on the fifth paragraph in the article, which begins: 'George's idea is workable'. Basically, this gives a simplified description of how the biological pump works. Comment briefly on *one* way in which the final sentence is misleading or unclear. (*2–3 sentences*)

(b) Outline the scientific basis for believing that fertilising the ocean with iron could provide a long-term sink for fossil fuel CO_2, noting any issues that would be central to the effectiveness of such a sink. (*1–2 short paragraphs*)

(c) What appear to be the driving forces behind the fertilisation experiments being undertaken by organisations such as Planktos (see also Figure 5.11) and GreenSea Venture? (*1–2 sentences*)

(d) Note down, as a list of bullet points, the main concerns about fertilising the oceans identified in this article.

(e) Summarise, *in a couple of sentences*, your *own* overall view of commercial ocean-fertilisation projects as a strategy for 'managing' future CO_2 levels in the atmosphere.

5.6 Projections and scenarios: tools for thinking about an uncertain future

In the previous couple of sections, we have focused on the issue of 'retrieving' anthropogenic CO_2 from the atmosphere – whether that be through the natural responses of terrestrial and ocean carbon cycling to ongoing global change, or through purposeful attempts to enhance carbon sequestration on land (e.g. by planting 'forest sinks') or in the ocean (e.g. by 'manipulating' the biological pump). In exploring the uncertainties about how effective these retrieval mechanisms are likely to be in future, our implicit assumption has been that global CO_2 emissions will continue to rise for a good while yet. This would seem reasonable in view of the past and current trends evident in Figure 5.12.

Clearly, the developed world was indeed responsible for the bulk of CO_2 emissions throughout much of the last century – the point we emphasised in discussing the ethical aspects of climate change in Chapter 1. Note, though, that recent decades have seen a rapid growth in emissions from some developing countries, notably China and other parts of Asia. This trend is due to a combination of factors including population growth, economic development and social and technological change. There is nothing new in this story. Historically, these are the underlying forces that have driven growing energy requirements and fossil-fuel consumption since the dawn of the industrial age. Indeed, the IPCC TAR concluded that: 'Emissions of CO_2 due to fossil-fuel burning are virtually certain [>99% probability] to be the dominant influence on trends in atmospheric CO_2 concentration during the 21st century'.

Figure 5.12 Contributions to global CO_2 emissions (due to fossil-fuel burning and land-use change) from various countries and regions during the 20th century. Annual emissions from 'developed' countries (Annex I in the jargon of the UNFCCC; Box 1.3) are shown in the bands of colour from light red at the bottom up to dark red around the middle. Emissions from the 'developing world' (Non-Annex I countries) are shown in the remainder of the colours except for the uppermost dark blue band. This represents the additional (and growing) contribution from aircraft and shipping worldwide. (Source: Matthews, 2004.)

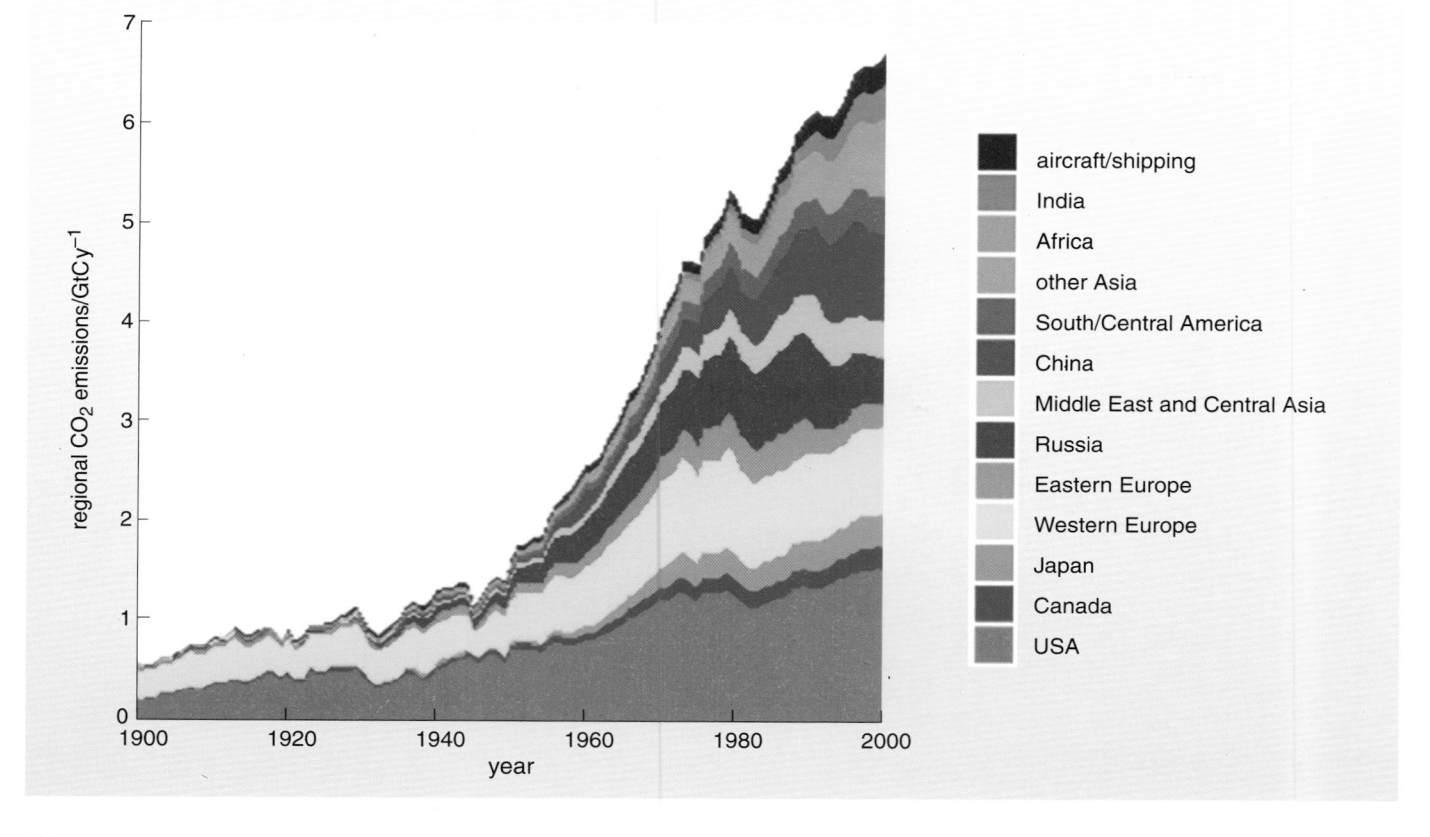

But imagine being faced with the task of predicting how energy-related CO_2 emissions for the whole globe will *actually* evolve over the course of the 21st century. To get a feel for the uncertainties and complexities involved, we need to think through the driving forces behind CO_2 emissions in a bit more detail. We shall do that in the context of an assumption that lies at the heart of the IPCC's analysis in the TAR. This is the notion of a **'business as usual' (BaU)** emissions future. Think of this as an attempt to address the question: 'How might CO_2 emissions evolve *in the absence* of direct intervention by governments to try to limit emissions?'

At first sight, the emphasis on 'no (climate policy) intervention' seems a curious one. Climate change is a real and growing concern. Moreover, the Kyoto Protocol is an example of an existing 'policy intervention' on the part of governments; if achieved, it will affect trends in emissions from industrialised countries. Yet in the TAR, the influence of such climate policies is effectively 'factored out'. The rationale behind this strategy is to explore the potential consequences of choosing to ignore the 'early warning signs' reviewed in Chapter 3, and simply carry on with business as usual. Keep this in mind as you read on.

5.6.1 Thinking about future CO_2 emissions

It helps to frame the discussion in terms of the following simple expression:

$$CO_2 \text{ emissions} = \boxed{\text{population} \times \text{energy use per head} \times \\ CO_2 \text{ emissions per unit of energy used}} \qquad (5.5)$$

Here, the first two terms on the right-hand side are the main determinants of global energy demand, while the final one relates to the supply side.

In general, economic well-being and the overall level of economic activity (commonly measured as the gross domestic product, or GDP) is one of the most important determinants of a country's per capita energy use (the second term in Equation 5.5). But the link is a complex one, dependent on the mix of more or less energy-intensive sectors – different industries; transport and residential needs; business, commercial and service activities; and so on. Climate (e.g. demands for heating and/or air conditioning) and geography (e.g. transport distances) also come into the equation. And so, of course, do the income levels, lifestyles and consumption patterns of the population (Figure 5.13).

Figure 5.13 Many aspects of our lives in the developed world that are treasured and/or envied help to drive up per capita energy use and CO_2 emissions.

- Global power consumption (i.e. the average rate of energy use by human societies worldwide) is currently around 12 TW (12×10^{12} W). Assuming a global human population of six billion, what is the average per capita power consumption?

- Average per capita power consumption = $(12 \times 10^{12}$ W$/6 \times 10^9) = 2 \times 10^3$ W or 2 kW.

However, this global average conceals major disparities between different countries: per capita power consumption is more like 12 kW in the USA, 4–5 kW (on average) in Europe and Japan, and well below 1 kW in many developing countries. Since at present energy demand worldwide is mostly met by burning fossil fuels, there are similar differences in per capita CO_2 emissions. Bear in mind, though, that alleviating poverty and achieving social and economic development are urgent priorities in the developing world (Chapter 1). Indeed, recent years have seen robust economic growth in both China and India, and per capita energy use and CO_2 emissions there are rising rapidly.

So what about forecasting future trends in global CO_2 emissions? In outline, that requires predictions of population trends (recall Figure 2.17, Section 2.5) and economic growth rates around the world, the relationship between economic development and energy consumption, and the proportion of those demands that will be met by burning fossil fuels. Thinking through linkages in the energy-economy system, in turn, brings in the influence of a host of social, cultural, technological and political factors. Here, it helps to think about a concrete example.

Activity 5.3

Allow no more than 15 minutes

Passenger vehicles (cars) are currently the fastest-growing source of CO_2 emissions in the UK. Drawing on your own experience of life in the UK (or elsewhere in Europe), jot down any factors you feel could influence the trend in emissions from this source over the next 20 years or so, noting possible sources of uncertainty.

Hopefully, this brief pause for thought has given you some insight into the problem of 'forecasting the future' when a major driving force is future human behaviour, and trends depend on a complex set of demographic, socioeconomic, political and/or technological interactions. We live in a world of such forecasts. Familiar examples include: interest and savings rates, house prices, traffic levels, manufacturing output, high street spending, internet access and so on. But how many times have you been aware of forecasts like these being wrong? Or, as one recent article put it (Hasselmann et al., 2004): 'Who could have foreseen only 20 years ago the development of the internet, the rapid economic growth in China or the political transformation of the former Soviet Union?'.

A key factor in how economic growth translates into changing energy demand is the pace of technological change. On the one hand, this helps to fuel the very consumption patterns that result in profligate per capita energy use (Figure 5.13). On the other, it holds out the promise of more 'energy-efficient' technologies in future. But how will energy prices, regional income levels, government polices, business and consumer attitudes and priorities (toward environmental protection in general, say), and so on affect the rate of 'take-up' of new, energy-efficient technologies and other energy-saving measures – not only in developed countries, but also elsewhere around the world? In short, what are the prospects for rapid improvements in energy efficiency in a BaU future?

Energy demand translates into CO_2 emissions through the combination of sources used to supply that demand (the final term in Equation 5.5). Of the fossil fuels, coal is the most 'carbon intensive'; i.e. burning coal releases more CO_2 per unit of energy generated than the other fuels (Figure 5.14). In the UK, for example, total CO_2 emissions fell by about 14% during the 1990s. This has been attributed, in part, to the 'dash for gas'; i.e. a major shift from coal- to gas-fired electricity generation. If repeated worldwide, such fuel switching could act to slow the growth in global CO_2 emissions.

Unfortunately, this is an unlikely scenario. At the global level, coal accounts for some 70% of known reserves of fossil fuels (in terms of their carbon content). This is even more true at the regional level; populous and rapidly industrialising nations such as China and India have huge reserves of coal, but are relatively poor in oil and gas. Indeed, the Middle East holds over 65% of the world's known oil reserves, and accounts for some 30% of natural gas as well.

How will growing demands for oil and gas, together with other factors (e.g. political instability in the Middle East; recall Figure 1.7), affect world energy markets and fossil-fuel usage in future? And what about the availability, cost effectiveness and rate of take-up of alternative energy sources? In short, what kinds of cars will we drive in future (Figure 5.15)? Will we even drive cars? And where will our electricity come from? In the absence of a policy incentive to look elsewhere, will the world remain wedded to energy systems that are largely based on burning fossil fuels, and possibly increasingly reliant on coal? Or will

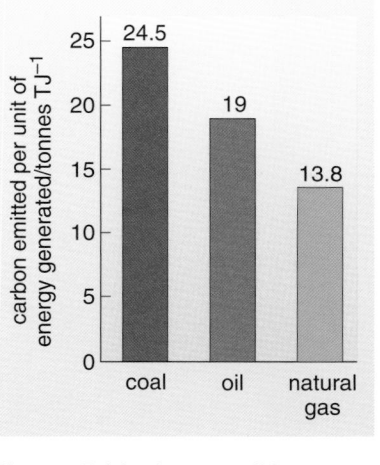

Figure 5.14 Average CO_2 emissions (expressed as the carbon equivalent) per unit of energy generated for coal, oil and natural gas (1 TJ (terajoule) = 10^{12} J; Box 5.1).

Figure 5.15 The shape of things to come? Part of a 'solar hydrogen' demonstration plant in Germany. To the left is an array of solar photovoltaic cells; electricity generated by these cells is used to split water into H_2 and O_2 (via electrolysis). The hydrogen is liquefied and stored in large tanks (to the right), providing a liquid H_2 filling station for a test car converted to run on this fuel. Alternatively, electric vehicles can be powered by hydrogen/oxygen fuel cells – devices that convert the energy released by recombining H_2 and O_2 directly into electricity. In both cases, the only 'exhaust' product is water.

some combination of technological, social and economic developments drive a natural shift to 'renewable' energy sources (solar, wind, wave, etc.) and other 'clean' (i.e. low- or zero-carbon) technologies? For example, how will concerns about climate change affect public attitudes to the nuclear option, which has its own baggage of health, environmental and security concerns – over issues such as reactor accidents, the safe disposal of radioactive waste, nuclear weapons proliferation, and so on?

For our purposes, the important general point is that there are very large uncertainties associated with any projection of global energy requirements and fossil-fuel consumption, even in the short term. Predicting trends in the rate of deforestation and other changes in land use is subject to similar constraints. And yet some idea of what CO_2 emission levels *might* be under different circumstances is an essential first step if we are to investigate the uncertainties surrounding our climate future. The way that the IPCC has tried to handle the complexities involved is to use 'scenario analysis'.

5.6.2 Alternative futures for atmospheric CO_2

An **emission scenario** is not a definitive prediction of how future CO_2 emissions will evolve. It is an image of what *could* happen given certain assumptions about how the drivers of emissions might change and/or interact during the century ahead. In the IPCC TAR, these assumptions are allied to a set of narratives or 'storylines' that describe plausible ways in which the world might develop – effectively, a set of 'what if' alternative futures. They are summarised in Box 5.3.

On the basis of these scenarios, the answer to what global CO_2 emissions might be over the course of the 21st century is shown in Figure 5.16a (ignore part b for now). *Note again that these emission scenarios are not the result of explicit climate-protection policies.* The descriptions in Box 5.3 do not tell us exactly how the key driving forces (population, income, technological change, etc.) result in each emissions pathway. But they clearly represent radically different views of how global society will evolve.

The implication that has for the shape of the world's future emissions trajectory is evident in Figure 5.16a: it is highly uncertain. Global emissions may increase dramatically (as in the A1F1 case, say). Alternatively, the drivers of emissions

Figure 5.16 Possible 'business as usual' futures: changes in (a) CO_2 emissions (from fossil fuels and changing land use), and (b) the atmospheric concentration of CO_2 during the 21st century, based on the scenarios in Box 5.3.

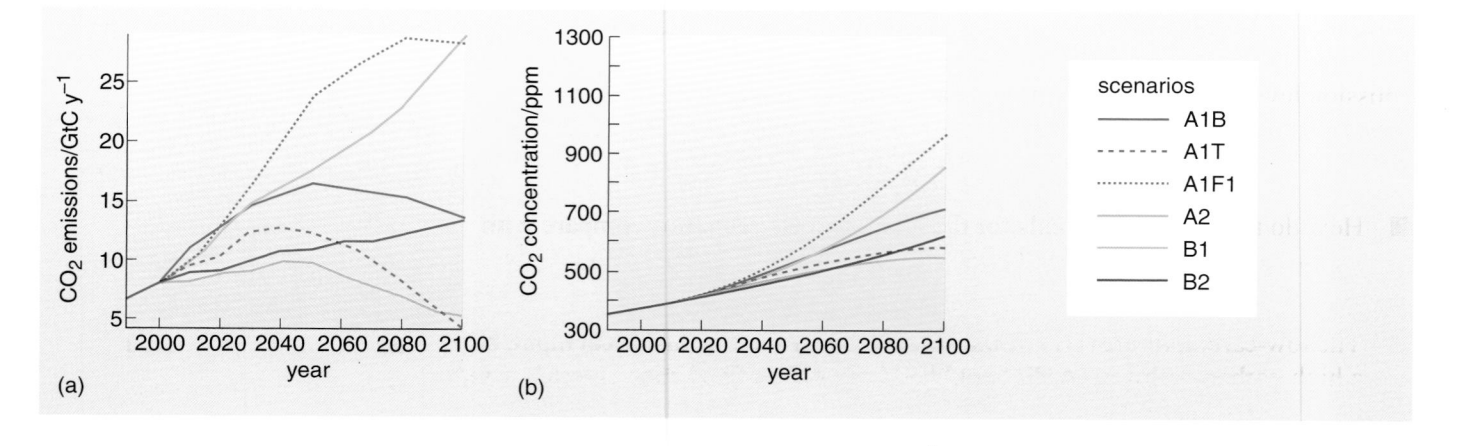

(a)

(b)

scenarios
—— A1B
------ A1T
········· A1F1
—— A2
—— B1
—— B2

Box 5.3 Ways in which the world might develop: the basis of the IPCC TAR emission scenarios (IPCC, 2001a)

Basically, there are four main storylines – two centred on economic development (coded A) and two on environmental improvements (coded B). In more detail:

The A1 storyline describes a 'convergent' world with rapid economic growth during the 21st century, increased cultural and social interactions, and a substantial reduction in the regional variations of income per head. Global population rises during the first half-century, peaks mid-century, then declines. New and efficient technology is rapidly introduced. This storyline develops into three strands that explore alternative directions of technological change in the energy system: A1F1 (fossil-fuel intensive); A1T (transition to non-fossil fuels); A1B (a balance across all energy sources).

The A2 storyline describes a world that remains heterogeneous, with regional identity being preserved and lower income growth per head. Global population rises continuously throughout the century. The introduction of new and efficient technology is more fragmented and slower than in the other scenarios.

The B1 storyline describes a world with the same population growth as A1. There are rapid changes in economic activity away from production towards a service and information economy. Clean and efficient technologies are introduced. Like A1, this storyline describes a convergent world, with the emphasis on global solutions to social and environmental problems.

The B2 storyline describes a world with population increasing throughout the 21st century, but at a lower rate than A2. Levels of economic growth and technological development are lower than those of A1 and B1. Like B1, environmental protection is an underlying theme, but with a focus on local and regional solutions.

may change *naturally* in a way that will fairly soon slow, and then reverse, the current upward trend (as in B1, say). Indeed, we can view these two scenarios, A1F1 and B1, as defining a sort of 'envelope of uncertainty' about future emission levels. Together, they provide an upper and lower bound to the *cumulative* input of anthropogenic CO_2 to the atmosphere over the next 100 years. This perspective is borne out by the figures collected in Table 5.2.

■ How do the cumulative totals for the A1F1 and B1 scenarios compare with the input of anthropogenic CO_2 to the atmosphere over the past 200 or so years (406 GtC)?

▪ The low-carbon future (B1) would still add over twice the historical input, but a high-carbon pathway (A1F1) could add more than five times as much – and on a shorter time-scale.

Table 5.2 How much carbon might we add to the atmosphere this century?

Scenario	Cumulative CO_2 emissions 1990–2100/GtC
A1F1	2190
A2	1860
A1B	1500
B2	1160
B1	980

Is there any way of assigning relative probabilities to the various scenarios in Figure 5.16a? This issue is the source of considerable debate among experts. For example, some analysts have argued that scenarios having more extreme values for their cumulative emissions should be regarded as less likely than those near the middle of the range. More generally, judgements about the relative likelihood of different futures inevitably reflect very human preconceptions, values and feelings. One expert's judgement of what constitutes a range of 'plausible futures' may be quite different from another's. Faced with the difficulty of combining disjoint expert opinions, the IPCC TAR treated *all emission scenarios as equally plausible* – largely on the grounds that any attempt to assign relative probabilities is tantamount to making predictions about factors that are best regarded as unpredictable (for all the reasons we rehearsed in Section 5.6.1).

So what might the alternative futures in Figure 5.16a mean for the level of atmospheric CO_2 in the century ahead? As you have seen, there are large uncertainties about how natural carbon cycling, on land and in the ocean, will respond to further disturbance in future. In other words, there is no guarantee that the proportion of anthropogenic emissions that accumulates in the atmosphere in the future will be the same as it was in the past (i.e. 43%). Indeed, there are good reasons to suppose that the strengths of the terrestrial and oceanic sinks for anthropogenic CO_2 are likely to weaken in future, leaving a higher proportion of cumulative emissions in the atmosphere. This is why researchers need complex computer models in order to explore the relationship between future CO_2 emissions and atmospheric concentrations.

Now concentrate on Figure 5.16b. For each scenario, this shows the results of 'feeding' the time-evolving change in annual emissions in Figure 5.16a into models that simulate the workings of the carbon cycle, and thereby calculate the proportion removed each year, and hence the year-by-year change in atmospheric CO_2.

- ■ From Figure 5.16b, the CO_2 levels in 2100 are projected to be about 550 ppm and 950 ppm for the B1 and A1F1 scenarios, respectively. How do these values compare with the pre-industrial level (280 ppm)?

- ■ According to these scenarios, the CO_2 level could be double to well over three times the pre-industrial value by the end of the century.

The projections in Figure 5.16b include model-based estimates of the way future climate change could affect the natural carbon cycle. However, the IPCC TAR goes on to stress that: 'Uncertainties, especially about the magnitude of climate feedbacks [on] the terrestrial biosphere, cause a variation of about −10% to +30% around each scenario'. The upshot is that the *full* range of projected CO_2 concentrations for the end the century is even wider – some 490 to 1260 ppm. Note that the top end of this range would represent more than a *quadrupling* of the pre-industrial level.

The results of these modelling studies also highlight a crucial distinction we did not make earlier. In Question 5.4 (Section 5.2.2), you estimated that CO_2 has a *residence time* in the atmosphere of about four years. This is a measure of how long, on average, a molecule of CO_2 stays in the atmosphere, and reflects the rapid cycling of carbon through the land–atmosphere–surface ocean system. It is quite different from the much longer time-scale over which the atmospheric concentration of CO_2 adjusts or responds to a sustained *imbalance* between the sources and sinks of the gas.

There is evidence to this effect in Figure 5.16b. In only two cases (B1 and A1T) is there a suggestion that the atmospheric CO_2 concentration is beginning to 'stabilise' (i.e. level off) by the end of the century – albeit at roughly double the pre-industrial level (560 ppm). Yet in both of these scenarios, emission rates peak within a few decades, and then decline steeply to levels well below current values (Figure 5.16a). In other words, *it takes a long time for the atmospheric concentration of CO_2 to respond to falling emission rates.* This slow response is a manifestation of the finite (and limited) rate at which natural processes can remove the quantities of 'extra' CO_2 that have already accumulated in the atmosphere, and lock up the carbon in long-term storage – in long-lived trees, say, or more permanently, in the deep ocean.

These constraints give *anthropogenic* CO_2 a long 'effective' atmospheric lifetime, usually put at around 100 years; this is the value that was included in Table 2.2 (Section 2.5). In the words of a recent review of what is known about the carbon cycle (Falkowski *et al.*, 2000):

> although natural sinks can potentially slow the rate of increase in atmospheric CO_2, there is no natural saviour waiting to assimilate all the anthropogenic CO_2 in the coming century.

This is another very important example of inertia in the climate system (Section 4.5.1) – as indeed, are many aspects of human behaviour! The policy implications of the mixture of inertia and uncertainty that characterises the climate change issue are taken up in Chapter 7. First, we look at how the uncertainties manifest in Figure 5.16 are compounded by the further layers of modelling studies that are used to 'translate' these scenarios into projections of future climate change. This is where climate models come centre stage.

Summary of Chapter 5

1   Contemporary CO_2 levels are unprecedented in the Earth's recent geological history (the past 400 000 years), and possibly higher than at any time in the past 20 million years.

2   The natural processes that regulate atmospheric CO_2 are part of the global carbon cycle (summarised in Figure 5.2). Two subcycles are relevant to the time-scales of interest in the context of anthropogenic climate change: the biological carbon cycle on land (arrows A to D in Figure 5.2) and the ocean carbon cycle (arrows E to I in Figure 5.2). Carbon moves fairly rapidly through the atmosphere, land plants, soils and surface ocean; exchange between this fast-responding system and the deep ocean takes much longer.

3   Terrestrial ecosystems store carbon in their plants and soils. Carbon fixation by plants (i.e. net primary production, NPP) supports their growth and removes CO_2 from the atmosphere; decomposition of organic matter in the soil releases

CO_2. At the ecosystem level, *net* carbon storage results if the rate of carbon input (NPP) exceeds the rate of carbon loss by decomposition (and wildfires); and vice versa. Plant growth and decomposition rates depend in complicated ways on various environmental factors (climatic conditions, nutrient and oxygen availability in the soil, etc.), and vary markedly among the ecosystem types characteristic of different climate zones. Widespread deforestation and land-use change by humans has led to a net loss of carbon from both the 'plant' and 'soil' pools since pre-industrial times, adding to the CO_2 content of the atmosphere.

4   The ocean stores carbon mainly as DIC (dissolved inorganic carbon), present at higher concentrations in the deep ocean. Overall, there is a roughly balanced exchange of CO_2 between the atmosphere and the surface ocean, but net transfers occur naturally in certain ocean areas: the cooling that drives deep-water formation leads to a net uptake of CO_2; the upwelling and warming of 'old' DIC-rich waters from the ocean interior leads to a net outgassing of CO_2. There is also a drawdown of atmospheric CO_2 in areas where high phytoplankton productivity sends a pulse of fixed carbon into the depths (the biological pump), where it adds to the DIC-content of deep ocean waters.

5   Burning fossil fuels currently accounts for some 75% of anthropogenic emissions of CO_2; most of the rest is due to tropical deforestation. Over half of the historical input of anthropogenic CO_2 has been removed from the atmosphere by land and ocean sinks.

6   The recent net uptake of anthropogenic CO_2 by terrestrial ecosystems (mainly forests) is partly the result of time lags between enhanced plant growth and plant death and decay. Several factors have contributed to the enhanced growth: the fertilisation effects of extra atmospheric CO_2 and increased nitrogen availability; the beneficial effects of recent climate changes (e.g. longer growing seasons); and forest regrowth on previously logged lands. The complexity of ecosystem responses to the combined effects of a continued increase in atmospheric CO_2, both directly (via CO_2 fertilisation) and indirectly (through the effects of the resulting climate changes on both plant growth and decomposition rates in different parts of the world) means that there is considerable uncertainty about how the strength of the terrestrial sink for anthropogenic CO_2 might change in future. Modelling studies suggest it is likely to weaken, adding to other concerns about planting 'forest sinks' as a substitute for reducing energy-related emissions (Activity 5.1).

7   The marine biosphere plays no part in the uptake of anthropogenic CO_2. Rather, ocean uptake is strongest in upwelling regions where older, deeper waters are re-exposed at the sea surface to a contemporary atmosphere that now contains more CO_2. This reduces the natural outgassing of CO_2, implying that more carbon remains in the ocean and is eventually stored in the deep ocean as surface waters sink. The finite rate of exchange between surface and deep waters means that the oceanic sink for anthropogenic CO_2 becomes progressively less effective as global emissions increase. There are reasons to question both the effectiveness and the potential knock-on effects of proposals to increase ocean uptake of fossil fuel CO_2 by deliberately 'manipulating' the biological pump (Activity 5.2).

8   The limited rate at which natural processes can lock up the carbon in anthropogenic CO_2 in long-term storage (e.g. in the deep ocean) puts CO_2 into the same 'long-lived' category as some other greenhouse gases (e.g. N_2O and the CFCs; Table 2.2, Section 2.5); its atmospheric concentration will respond only slowly to efforts to curtail emissions.

9   Projecting future global emissions of CO_2 is a highly complex task. There are inherent uncertainties over the way key factors (demographic, socioeconomic, political, technological, etc.) that drive fossil-fuel use (and deforestation) might change and/or interact during the century ahead. In the IPCC TAR, the problem was tackled by constructing a range of emission scenarios, allied to a set of storylines that describe alternative ways in which global society might evolve (Box 5.3). All scenarios were treated as equally plausible and all assume no explicit 'climate protection' policies, though some represent very low carbon futures. On the basis of these alternative 'business as usual' futures, atmospheric CO_2 could be twice to well over three times the pre-industrial level by 2100; it could be even higher if uncertainties about possible climate feedbacks on the terrestrial carbon cycle are included.

Questions for Chapter 5

Question 5.5

(a)   In carving up the global inventory of carbon (e.g. Figure 5.2), the size of the atmospheric pool is usually equated with the mass of carbon in CO_2. Yet the atmosphere also contains methane (Table 2.1, Section 2.1.2). Why is the emphasis on CO_2 justified?

(b)   As a result of anaerobic decomposition, large amounts of methane are trapped (in various forms) in the permafrost at high northern latitudes. Why is this a potential cause for concern in the event of continued global warming?

Question 5.6

Suppose you were interested in investing in a 'forest sink' project. One company promises that you could earn $40 per tonne of carbon sequestered, while another offers $11 per tonne of CO_2. Which is the better deal?

Question 5.7

At the global level, the transport sector is heavily dependent on products derived from oil. However, in some countries relatively poor in fossil fuels (e.g. Brazil), petrol is already 'diluted' with ethanol (C_2H_5OH, ordinary alcohol) derived from plant material (biomass) via a biological fermentation process. Burning such fuels still releases CO_2 to the atmosphere. So why would replacing petrol with carbon-based fuels produced from biomass be a potentially useful strategy for slowing the further accumulation of CO_2 in the atmosphere?

Chapter 6

Modelling climate and climate change

6.1 Introduction

By this stage, you probably have a fair idea of just how complex the Earth's climate system really is. How the climatic conditions around the world result from the combined influence of, and interactions between, the atmosphere, ocean, cryosphere, land surface and biosphere was the central thrust of Chapter 4. That message was crystallised in the schematic representation of the climate system in Figure 4.16 (Section 4.5). Since then, you have seen how the carbon cycle adds further strands to the web of processes (physical, chemical and biological) that binds the total 'Earth system' together (Chapter 5).

In this chapter, we focus on the modelling tools that are designed to integrate what is known about the many thousands of processes and interactions that make up the climate system, and hence simulate how it functions as an *interconnected* whole. These tools, referred to in general terms as **climate models**, are mathematical constructs. Put simply, they reduce the climate system to sets of mathematical relationships (i.e. equations) that describe the behaviour of its component parts, and the interactions between them. The most sophisticated versions are run on the world's largest and fastest supercomputers, and are the source of the (sometimes alarming) projections of how the 'greenhouse forcing experiment' going on in the real world might turn out. These days, these visions of the future are often conveyed through impressive, colourful and graphic outputs (e.g. see Figure 6.1).

As noted in Chapter 1, the results of modelling studies feature prominently in successive IPCC reports, and are the basis for a great deal of the work that is informing decision making on climate change. Yet climate models can only ever be approximate representations of the 'real world' system. As the *Concise Oxford Dictionary* (9th edition, 1995) puts it, a model is 'a simplified (often mathematical) description of a system etc. to assist calculations and predictions'. Computer models of highly complex systems are invariably constructed within particular constraints (not least the cost and availability of computing power) and involve a process of selection and simplification. The inevitable consequence is that the images conjured up by the climate modellers' 'crystal balls' are decidedly murky. Simple and obvious questions about our climate future still have only complex and uncertain answers.

This makes climate models a favoured target for those who remain sceptical about the seriousness of the greenhouse warming problem: the models are either notoriously wrong – a stance we might characterise as the 'garbage in, garbage out' school of thought – or they can be 'tweaked' to do almost anything. To get some perspective on claims of this kind, we need to take a closer look at the (necessarily imperfect) tools constructed by climate modellers. So, how are climate models put together? How do the constraints referred to above affect the assumptions and approximations built into the current generation of models? How are the models used? And how confident should we be about what they tell us?

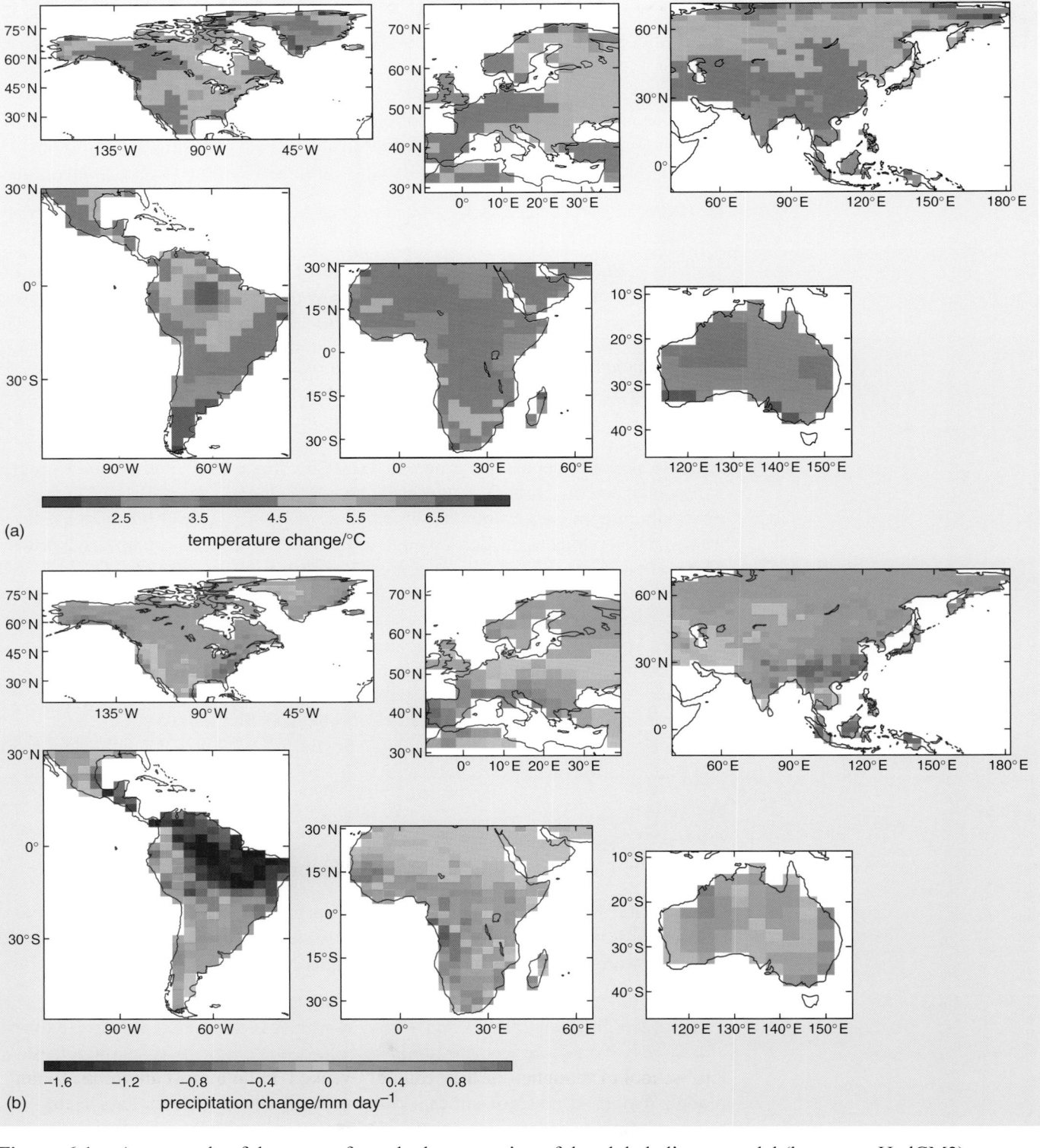

Figure 6.1 An example of the output from the latest version of the global climate model (known as HadCM3) developed by the Hadley Centre (for climate prediction and research), established within the UK Meteorological Office in 1990. The images show the projected changes in (a) annual mean surface temperature (in °C) and (b) average daily precipitation (in mm per day) between the present day and the 2080s, for the 'middle-of-the-range' A1B scenario (Figure 5.16). In this case, the model predicts a rise in GMST of 3 °C by the end of the 21st century.

6.2 How climate models are put together

To predict the climatic effects of possible future increases in atmospheric CO_2 (like those in Figure 5.16b, say), a model needs to simulate all the important processes governing the future evolution of the climate. To that end, the ultimate aim is to model as much as possible of the whole of the Earth's climate system, so that all the components can interact and predictions of climate change will continuously take into account the effect of feedbacks within and between these components.

■   What important feedbacks, linked to changes in the hydrological cycle, were identified in Section 4.5.2?

▪   The main ones were snow–ice albedo feedback and water vapour feedback (both positive), and cloud feedback (which could be either positive or negative). Recall too the scope for 'feedback' on the large-scale circulation of the ocean (the thermohaline circulation, or THC), should changes in the input of freshwater (e.g. increased rainfall or the melting of land ice) and/or sea-ice formation have a significant effect on ocean salinity, especially in the North Atlantic (Section 4.3.3).

Climate modelling began in earnest in the 1970s. Since then, models of the main components of the climate system have been developed separately and then gradually integrated, or 'coupled' together, as computing power has increased. Today, the versions at the cutting edge of the modellers' craft are usually known as **coupled atmosphere–ocean general circulation models (AOGCMs)**. All such models incorporate sub-models of the components that together make up what is often referred to as the 'physical' climate system (summarised earlier in Figure 4.16): the atmosphere; ocean and sea ice; land surface and land ice. As indicated in Figure 6.2, the coupling process then comes down to allowing the atmosphere model to interact with the other model components, essentially via mathematical descriptions of the *physical* processes that link (couple) them together in the real world – the exchange of energy, moisture (through evaporation and precipitation) and momentum (Section 4.5) across the surface–air boundary.

■   What aspect of the Earth's *overall* climate system is missing from Figure 6.2?

▪   The exchange of CO_2 across the surface–air boundary, and hence (by implication) any representation of the land and ocean carbon cycles.

A few AOGCMs do now incorporate some carbon cycle processes in an interactive way (see Chapter 7). But for now, we put that development to one side and stick with the more restricted view of what constitutes a 'climate model' in Figure 6.2.

To get a feel for the strengths and shortcomings of such models, it helps to take a closer look at one core element of all AOGCMs – the atmospheric component. Known as an atmosphere GCM (AGCM), this is similar in principle to the global models that are used for weather forecasting. In both cases, the atmosphere is represented as a three-dimensional array of 'boxes', as shown in Figure 6.3. The boxes are defined in the horizontal by a 2-D grid (latitude × longitude) spread over the surface of the globe (like the grid squares on a map). The third dimension is altitude, with the atmosphere being sliced up into a series of concentric shells; typically, there are 20 levels or so in the model.

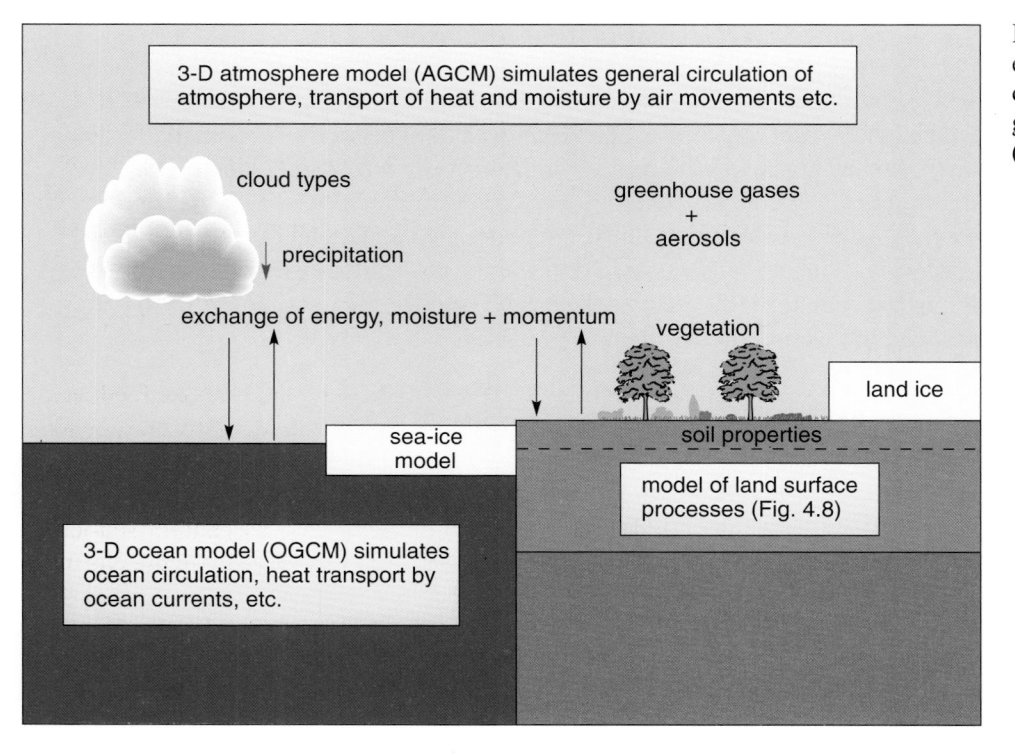

Figure 6.2 Component elements (sub-models) of a coupled atmosphere–ocean general circulation model (AOGCM).

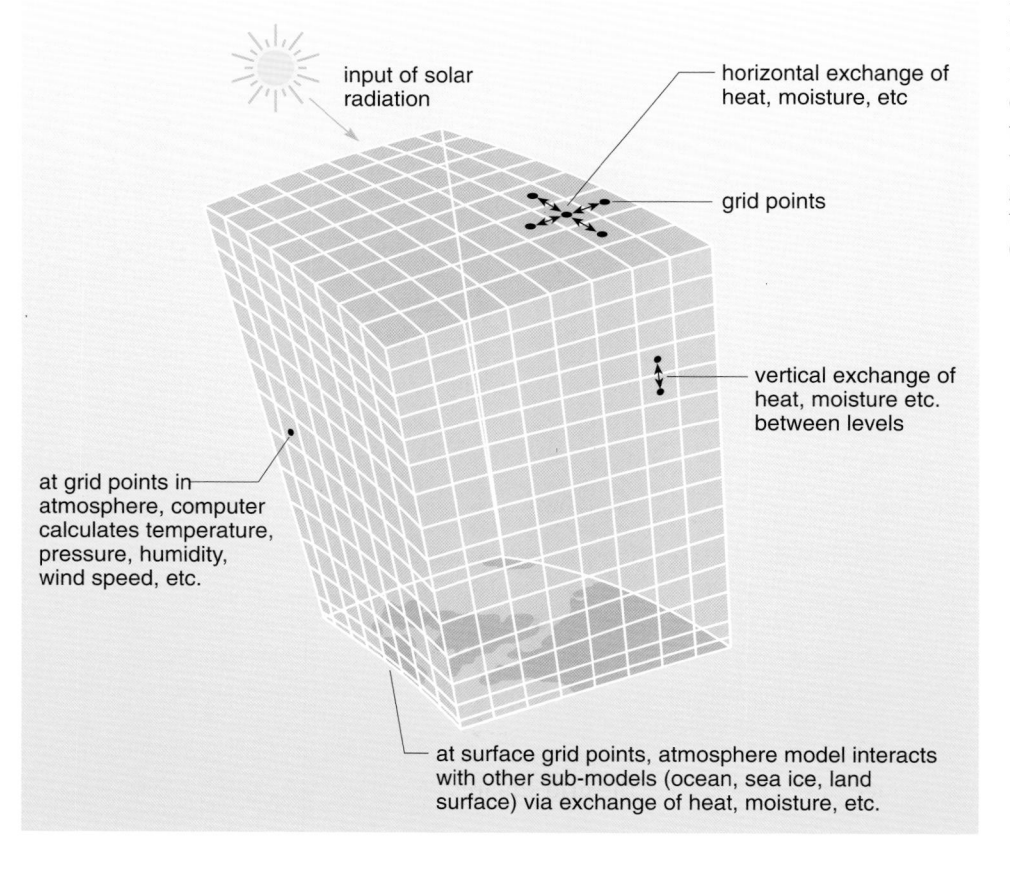

Figure 6.3 Illustration of the 3-D grid in an AGCM. The levels in the vertical dimension are not equally spaced; they are closer together near the surface, where we are more interested in what is going on. The top level is typically at about 30 km altitude (middle of the stratosphere).

157

The mathematical formulation of the model involves a set of equations that together describe the physics and dynamics of the atmosphere and the ensuing transport of heat and water vapour by winds and vertical air movements. It is worth emphasising that these equations are based on well-established physical laws, as they apply to a fluid (the atmosphere) on a rotating planet, under the influence of a differential heating (between low and high latitudes) caused by an external energy source (the Sun). There are also equations for the absorption/scattering of incoming solar radiation and the absorption/re-emission of outgoing longwave radiation (by greenhouse gases), and for the interactions (with other model components) at the planetary surface.

Most of the equations in the model describe the way in which atmospheric variables like wind speed, pressure, temperature and humidity (i.e. water vapour content) change with time and with location. Given some specified set of initial conditions (appropriate to a particular time of year, say), values of these quantities at each of the grid points (indicated in Figure 6.3) are computed by solving a pretty formidable set of equations. The computer then 'steps' forward in time, through a pre-set interval (commonly a half-hour), and repeats the whole set of calculations – thereby building up a picture of how each of these quantities, and the pattern of moving weather systems they represent, changes through the model year (equivalent to 17 520 time steps!).

In terms of model construction, practical constraints come down to the enormous amount of computation required in order to calculate *each* of the basic atmospheric variables at *each* grid point at *each* time step. The better the 'spatial resolution' of the model (i.e. the finer the grid and the smaller the boxes), the greater the requirement for high computer capacity and speed. In general, modellers have to strike a compromise between resolution and run time. Atmosphere models used for weather forecasting, where interest centres on what is going to happen over the next five days or so, can have a much finer grid (around 50 km in the horizontal plane) than the versions included in AOGCMs that are used to project the state of the climate decades into the future. Currently, this constraint is such that typical AGCMs have a horizontal resolution of about 250 km. So the model world actually looks like the patchwork of grid 'squares' evident in Figure 6.1. Notice that there are just five of these for the whole of Britain and Ireland.

This limited spatial resolution creates other problems, because it means that AGCMs cannot *directly* simulate several small-scale atmospheric processes of critical importance to climate in the real world. Examples include small-scale convection processes, and many key aspects of the hydrological cycle, such as the evolution and radiative effects of individual clouds, rainfall and so on. Modellers include the effects of such 'sub-grid scale' processes in an approximate way through a technique known as **parameterisation**. Basically, this involves devising a simple scheme (i.e. a set of step-by-step rules for the computer to follow, known as an 'algorithm' in computer-speak) whereby the phenomenon in question is related to the large-scale variables that are computed directly. Developing and testing parameterisation schemes that reliably incorporate sub-grid scale effects is one of the most challenging and controversial parts of the climate modellers' task. Some of these schemes are now well-constrained by observations and are believed to be quite reliable.

Others are more questionable due to an inadequate understanding of the controlling mechanisms, or a lack of observational data, or both.

To take one concrete example, *cloud parameterisation schemes* are clearly central to the issue of assessing the strength and direction (positive or negative) of cloud feedback revisited above. In principle, the scheme used should incorporate descriptions of the way clouds form and go on to produce rain or evaporate again, together with all the radiatively important cloud properties noted in Section 2.2.3 (type and coverage, height, liquid water or ice content, etc.). In practice, however, most climate models still employ fairly simple cloud schemes.

Typically, the presence or absence of cloud in a model grid box is determined by a threshold humidity value: if the computed humidity is above the threshold value, cloud is deemed to be present; if it is below that value, cloud is absent. The actual threshold value (a 'parameter' in the model) can be adjusted or 'tuned' by experiment to ensure that the fractional cloud cover (another parameter in the model) in a given grid box is approximately that observed in the real atmosphere. Thus, 'tuning' (or 'tweaking') to determine the optimal values for certain model parameters is, in fact, an essential part of constructing a 'good' model. Other tunable parameters are included in schemes describing the cloud-to-rain conversion process, and so on. Until recently a typical model would allow for three types of cloud (low, medium and high), each with *prescribed* radiative properties. More-sophisticated parameterisation schemes do now incorporate some representation of the water or ice content of clouds, and the effect that has on their radiative properties. But the detailed formulations differ markedly from one model to another, and there is no obvious way of checking the relative merits of these more complicated schemes.

Similar approximations and simplified formulations (parameterisations) are embedded in the other submodels that together make up an AOGCM. We consider these under two broad headings.

The ocean and sea ice

For climate prediction, as opposed to weather forecasting, the most important elaboration of a global atmospheric model is the inclusion of the influence of the ocean.

■ How does the ocean play a key role in issues that are central to the future evolution of climate in response to ongoing greenhouse forcing?

▨ Two main issues were identified in Chapter 4: (1) because of its thermal inertia, the ocean slows the pace of climate warming (Section 4.5.1); (2) the implications for regional climates of possible changes in the THC, and hence heat transport by ocean currents. To these we can add the implications for regional climate *variability* of possible shifts in the pattern (intensity and/or frequency) of El Niño events and other manifestations of ocean–atmosphere interactions (e.g. the North Atlantic Oscillation, NAO; Section 4.4).

To address these issues, it is necessary to model the ocean circulation (in a three-dimensional ocean GCM, or OGCM) and its interactive coupling to the atmospheric circulation (in an AGCM), as shown in Figure 6.2. Coupling models of these two dynamic systems is both technically difficult and highly demanding of computer resources. It was achieved in a satisfactory way only during the late 1990s – a major step forward for the credibility of climate modelling.

Again, computational constraints limit the spatial resolution of OGCMs, with attendant problems for the representation of sub-grid scale processes (e.g. various aspects of ocean convection and mixing) that are an integral part of the circulation system in the real world. Although there are still many gaps in the detailed understanding of ocean behaviour, recent research has helped to pin down the small-scale processes that are most relevant to climate, leading to significant improvements in the parameterisation schemes used to represent them. As a result, coupled AOGCMs do now produce broadly realistic simulations of natural large-scale circulation patterns, and the associated heat transport.

Recent years have also seen incremental improvements in modelling the influence of sea ice. Several AOGCMs now incorporate physically based treatments that allow the model to track the growth and decay of sea ice, and the effect that has on the albedo and on the salinity of surface waters, and hence deep-water formation.

Land-surface processes

Modelling the land-based component of the climate system comes down to formulating descriptions of the processes and properties (assembled in Figure 4.8; Section 4.2) that govern the exchange of energy, moisture and momentum with the atmosphere. In practice, these land–atmosphere interactions are represented (via parameterisation schemes) as functions of the surface characteristics we identified earlier: the topography, the presence of ice sheets, glaciers and snow cover, the type of vegetation and soil, and their albedos, together with some measure of the water-holding capacity of the soil. This information is drawn from global data sets that have been improved using satellite observations.

■ Look back at Figure 4.8. The land surface parameterisations embedded in most current AOGCMs incorporate some representation of all the factors collected there. Why is this important if model predictions are to take into account the effect of possible changes in the state of the land surface?

▨ One issue is the effect of albedo feedback due to changes in snow/ice cover. Beyond that, we know that plant growth around the world will be affected by climate changes (increased temperature, shifts in rainfall patterns, etc.) and their knock-on effects for soil moisture (Chapter 5). Changes in vegetation and soil moisture can, in turn, affect the surface albedo and transfer of water vapour to the atmosphere (through altered evaporation and transpiration rates) – potential feedbacks that are a further manifestation of the interconnectedness of the climate system.

Successful simulation of the land surface energy and water budgets is also central to model-based assessments of the potential impacts of future climate change – and not only for natural ecosystems (and their role as sinks for anthropogenic CO_2, our main focus in Chapter 5).

- What issues are of direct concern for different human societies around the world?

- Some of the most important issues were touched on in Chapters 1 and 3: the effects on agricultural production and food supplies; the implications for freshwater resources; the effect on sea levels of changes in the total *volume* of land ice; and the disruption associated with localised extreme events such as floods, droughts, storms and heat waves.

From this perspective, the limited spatial resolution of global models again creates problems. Chief among these is the difficulty of doing justice to the true 'heterogeneity' of the land surface, given the large areas defined by the model grid (some 250 km × 250 km). This has implications for the simulation of climate on local or regional scales, since conditions in the real world are influenced greatly by relatively small-scale features, such as mountains or the actual mosaic of vegetation types (e.g. forest as opposed to open grassland or cropland). Further problem areas include the treatment of soil moisture, surface runoff, snow and land-ice processes (relevant to the way ice sheets and glaciers respond to climate warming). Currently, the latter are represented in only a rudimentary way in most global models.

In summary

Comprehensive climate models (AOGCMs) put together as outlined above are the most complete and potentially powerful tools for simulating climate change. But the limitations and shortcomings we have highlighted sound a cautionary note. In reality, knowledge about many important climate processes is incomplete and often inaccurate. Furthermore, the climate prediction business involves a small tight-knit community. Today, there are just 20-odd major modelling groups around the world, including the Hadley Centre in the UK (see Figure 6.1). The climate models developed by these groups are all linked by the same data sets, and share many of the same basic equations, premises and techniques; errors in one may therefore occur in others. On the other hand, the detailed formulations differ; each model is a compromise as to how many processes are included, at what level of complexity and with what resolution, given limited computer and human resources. So how do the models compare, and how do we check their simulation skills?

6.3 How good are the models?

The first, and most obvious, test of a climate model is how well it can reproduce the present climate and its geographical and seasonal variations. Recall (from Chapter 1) that 'climate' always refers to 'climatological averages' – values of important parameters (such as the mean surface temperature or mean precipitation for each month, say) averaged over a period of years. In Figure 3.3, for example, the reference period was the 30 years from 1961 to 1990. Equally, the model should produce the kind of year-by-year and decadal-scale variability observed in the real world (and evident in Figure 3.3a).

Thus, the check referred to above involves running a so-called **control simulation**, with model inputs appropriate to a specified 'present day' period.

Apart from factors such as the distribution of incoming solar radiation through the model year, that comes down to specifying the atmospheric burden of CO_2 and other greenhouse gases. Here, the *fixed* concentrations input to the atmosphere model typically reflect the average values during the reference period. The model is run for several decades of simulated time in order to generate a 'present day' model climate (means of temperature, precipitation, etc. and how they vary across the globe and with the seasons). These outputs are then compared in detail with the observed data.

Based on a pretty exhaustive exercise of this kind, the IPCC TAR noted improvements in simulation skills since its previous report (in 1996) and concluded that coupled models (AOGCMs):

- Provide credible simulations of both the annual mean climate and the seasonal cycle over broad continental scales for most variables of interest for climate change; clouds and humidity remain a problem, though the match between models and observations has improved somewhat.

- Generate realistic patterns of interannual and decadal-scale variability.

- Give a reasonable account of phenomena such as monsoons and the NAO, and are beginning to exhibit variability in the tropical Pacific that resembles ENSO.

An equally strong message, however, is that there are still significant errors on the regional scale – an inevitable consequence of the models' fairly coarse spatial resolution and other shortcomings. For example, coupled models do an excellent job reproducing the timing and magnitude of seasonal temperature variations across the globe, but the absolute temperatures they predict can be off by up to 4 °C in some regions. In general, the models are less good at reproducing variations in other climate parameters, especially those involving aspects of the hydrological cycle such as precipitation. Here, errors are highly variable from region to region and among models; they range from −40% to +80% of the average seasonal rainfall, for example.

Alongside the detailed scrutiny of control simulations, there are two other tests that have helped to build confidence that current models are treating the essential climate processes with reasonable accuracy, at least on the large scale.

1   Experiments designed to simulate the climate at times in the distant past (e.g. 20 000 years ago) when important factors – such as the Earth's orbital characteristics (Section 5.1) and/or the level of atmospheric CO_2 – were different than they are today. When the parameters appropriate to a particular period are input into a model, a different climate results – in broad agreement with the conditions implied by palaeoclimate data. Such studies generate confidence that models can simulate important features of climatic regimes substantially different from our own.

2   Experiments designed to track the climatic response to the evolution of natural and anthropogenic forcings over the past century or so, as discussed in Chapter 3 (Figure 3.15, Section 3.5.2). As noted then, there are large uncertainties in the estimated contributions from certain factors, especially solar variations and aerosols. Nevertheless, the fact that coupled models can successfully reproduce the bumpy rise in GMST seen in the past 100 years is a testament to their simulation skills.

No one model validation experiment alone is enough to create confidence in that model's ability to simulate future climate change in response to ongoing greenhouse forcing. But considered together, results from the wide range of experiments probing the validity of various coupled models led the IPCC to conclude that such models are 'suitable tools to provide useful projections of future climates'. Because climate processes are so firmly interlocked with one another, it is difficult to diagnose just where the deficiencies lie in any given model. Nor is it possible to identify a 'best' model; one may be more reliable than another for a particular climate variable, but less so elsewhere. In the words of the IPCC, 'it is important to utilise results from a range of coupled models'. The force of this advice will become apparent shortly.

6.4 Modelling climate change: uncertainty in model predictions

The emission scenarios we looked at in Chapter 5 (Figure 5.16) suggest that atmospheric CO_2 is likely to reach double its pre-industrial level (i.e. some 560 ppm) sometime in the present century. Of course, it may continue to rise well beyond that. But a CO_2 concentration double that of pre-industrial times is probably the lowest level likely for stabilising atmospheric CO_2 in a BaU (business-as-usual) future (Section 5.6.2) – and even that presupposes a major breakthrough in low-cost, low-carbon energy technologies and/or a radical shift in attitudes favouring environmental protection over the traditional carbon-intensive path to economic development (recall Box 5.3). For this reason, the projected effect of a CO_2-doubling (which translates into a radiative forcing of 4 W m^{-2}; Section 2.4) has been widely used as a benchmark to compare the output from different climate models.

■ In the context of future climate change induced by greenhouse forcing, is it sufficient to focus solely on the level of atmospheric CO_2?

▪ No. There will be contributions from further changes in other greenhouse gas concentrations as well, just as there was in the past (recall Figure 2.18; Section 2.5).

In experiments designed to compare model-based estimates of the climate system's response to greenhouse forcing, the notion of a CO_2-doubling is, then, a surrogate for 'a given amount of greenhouse forcing'. With this in mind, two kinds of standardised experiments are commonly used.

1 Equilibrium climate change experiments

First, the model is run (for several decades of simulated time) with CO_2 fixed at the pre-industrial level (280 ppm); then it is run again with the CO_2 level fixed at double this value (560 ppm). The results are typically summarised as the calculated difference in GMST between the two runs. This is known as the model's **climate sensitivity** (implicitly to a CO_2-doubling), often denoted by the symbol $\Delta T_{2\times}$ (read as delta-t-two-times). What this climate sensitivity parameter actually represents is the projected global warming that would result *eventually* if CO_2 were doubled instantaneously and then held fixed forever, so that the climate system settles to a new 'CO$_2$-doubled' equilibrium state. This is clearly a long way from what is actually going on in the real world (see below). Nevertheless, the values of ΔT_{2x} generated by different models do provide a controlled way of comparing their estimates of just how 'sensitive' the climate system might be to a given amount of greenhouse forcing. Note too that the 'differencing' technique helps to remove the effects of systematic errors that are common to both runs.

2 Transient climate change experiments

Experiments of this kind come closer to the real-world situation, allowing model outputs to be compared in terms of their answers to the following question: how will global warming evolve in time in response to a particular and gradual increase in greenhouse forcing? Again, the standardised experiment starts with CO$_2$ at the pre-industrial level (280 ppm). The CO$_2$ concentration is then increased at 1% a year, compounded (like compound interest) so that it doubles after 70 years; thereafter, it is held at that level (i.e. 560 ppm) indefinitely. Because of the absorption characteristics of CO$_2$, this scenario translates into a linear increase in radiative forcing for the first 70 years (and at a rate roughly equivalent to that currently being induced by the entire suite of greenhouse gases), and a constant value (of 4 W m^{-2}) thereafter, as shown in Figure 6.4.

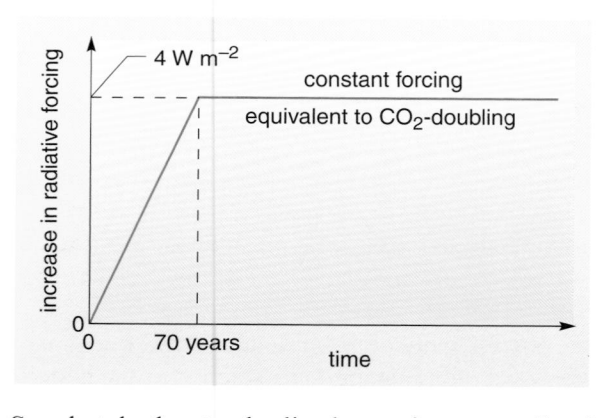

Figure 6.4   The radiative forcing due to a 1% per year CO$_2$ increase for 70 years, and a constant concentration (double the pre-industrial level) thereafter.

So what do the standardised experiments outlined above tell us about the uncertainties in climate model predictions?

6.4.1 Climate sensitivity: 'when doubt is a sure thing'

The seven state-of-the-art AOGCMs reviewed in the IPCC TAR have climate sensitivities that range from 1.7 to 4.2 °C. This large spread of values reflects the different approximations and simplified formulations built into the various models, and in particular, the effect that has on how important feedbacks act to amplify or moderate the warming. For example, all models agree that water vapour feedback makes a significant positive contribution; it approximately doubles the warming from what it would be for fixed water vapour. By contrast, the different cloud formulations noted earlier translate into a wide range of model-based estimates for the amount, *and even the sign*, of cloud feedback; it is negative in some cases (for models at the low end of the ΔT_{2x} range), and strongly positive in others (for models at the top end). Equally, models differ in the way they incorporate feedbacks due to reduced snow/ice cover or changes in vegetation cover, and so on.

Box 6.1 Do-it-yourself climate modelling

Launched in September 2003, climateprediction.net (Figure 6.5) is an innovative project that aims to explore the uncertainty in climate model predictions in a systematic way, by using 'distributed' computing. This strategy has been used before, notably in the SETI@home project; over one million volunteers are currently scanning radio-telescope data for signs of extraterrestrial intelligence, during downtime on their home PCs.

Likewise, participants in climateprediction.net download from the internet their own unique version of the Hadley Centre's global climate model, and run it on their own PCs. Each version includes a particular combination of different, but plausible, values for the 'tunable' parameters in various parameterisation schemes (for clouds, rain, etc.). Thanks to the enthusiasm of tens of thousands of people worldwide, the project's first report (Stainforth *et al.*, 2005) had already identified model versions with broadly realistic control climates, yet with simulated climate sensitivities that range from 2 °C to over 11 °C! Work still remains to investigate the uncertainty caused by changing more of the model's parameters (e.g. in the ocean component or land-surface schemes), or by making large changes in the structure of the model.

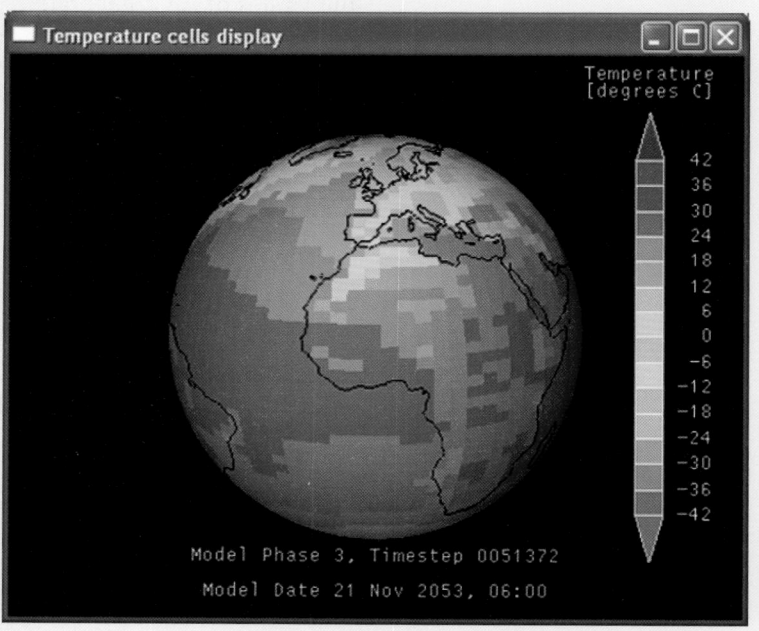

Figure 6.5 Example screen shot from the climateprediction.net project.

The possibility (however remote) of climate sensitivities well beyond the top end of the official range was not included in the TAR. No less important, direct experience of cutting-edge climate modelling is a novel, and potentially powerful, means of communicating the uncertainties of climate science to the people who matter most – the general public.

More telling is the fact that successive IPCC reports have found no compelling evidence to alter, or narrow, the range of 'accepted' climate sensitivities (1.5 to 4.5 °C) identified in one of the first major assessments of the greenhouse problem, a 1979 report from the US National Academy of Sciences. In other words, over 25 years of intensive research has made no dent in the factor-of-three uncertainty in this key parameter. Indeed, surveys of expert opinion suggest that many researchers suspect the full range of uncertainty about the 'true' climate sensitivity (i.e. that of the *real* climate system) could be even wider than that implied by existing full-scale climate models. Certainly, there is currently no consensus about the relative likelihood of different values within, or indeed outside, the accepted range. Efforts to resolve this situation are underway (e.g. see Box 6.1); in the meantime, we shall have to live with the large (and frustratingly recalcitrant) uncertainty in climate sensitivity.

6.4.2 How will global warming evolve in time?

An example of the output from a transient simulation of the kind described above is shown in Figure 6.6; in this case, the coupled AOGCM used has a climate sensitivity of 3.5 °C.

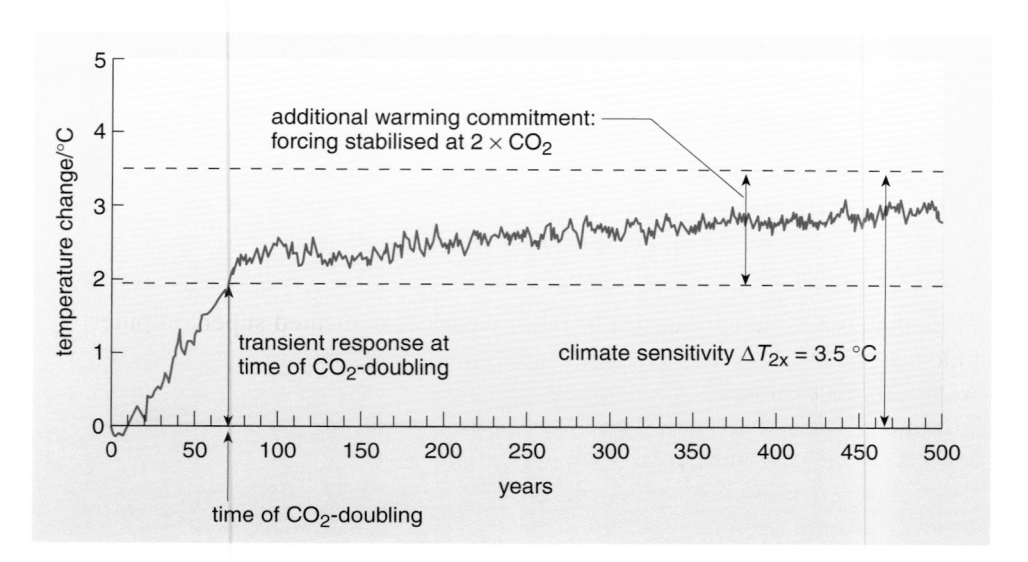

Figure 6.6 The time-evolving change in GMST in response to the forcing in Figure 6.4, as simulated by a particular AOGCM (developed by the Geophysical Fluid Dynamics Laboratory in the US, one of the pioneers of climate modelling), with a climate sensitivity of 3.5 °C. The short-term temperature fluctuations are a manifestation of the 'internal' variability generated by ocean–atmosphere interactions in this coupled model (as in the simulations of 20th century warming we looked at in Section 3.5.2; Figure 3.15).

■ According to Figure 6.6, what is the rise in GMST *at the time* of CO_2-doubling (i.e. after 70 years)?

▨ It looks to be around 2 °C in this case.

■ This is often referred to as the '*realised*' warming at this stage. Why is it less than the model's climate sensitivity (3.5 °C), and why does the GMST go on rising long after the CO_2 level (and hence radiative forcing) is stabilised? (*Hint*: look back at the discussion in Section 4.5.1.)

▨ The answers lie with the influence of the ocean's thermal inertia – that is, how heat uptake by the ocean (as simulated in the model) slows the pace of climate change in response to ongoing greenhouse forcing, but merely postpones the eventual equilibrium warming.

Note the time-scale implied by this simulation: the GMST goes on rising for *hundreds of years* – and would continue to do so until the 'additional warming commitment' for a CO_2-doubling (an extra 1.5 °C in this case, indicated in Figure 6.6) was ultimately realised, and the system settled to a new equilibrium state.

■   What is the important message (stated in more general terms in Section 4.5.1) to take from this example?

▨   There will always be some additional warming 'in the pipeline' long *after* the CO_2 level in the atmosphere (or more generally, the total atmospheric burden of greenhouse gases) is stabilised, *and there is absolutely nothing we can do to stop it.*

The point we want to emphasise here is that different coupled AOGCMs simulate a different time-evolving response to the same trajectory of radiative forcing (i.e. that shown in Figure 6.4). However, detailed analysis indicates that each model's transient response is effectively determined by two characteristics: the model's climate sensitivity; and the simulated rate of heat storage in the ocean.

This turns out to be very useful. It takes weeks of dedicated supercomputer time to run a single century-long transient simulation with a comprehensive AOGCM. To explore the climatic effects of a wide range of plausible future emission scenarios (allied to the storylines in Box 5.3, say), simpler climate models are also commonly used. Typically, such models include a much-simplified treatment of the dynamics of the climate system, but they can be calibrated to match the climate sensitivity and ocean heat uptake of a particular AOGCM, and hence yield an equivalent time-evolving response in various globally averaged quantities – notably the change in GMST, and the effect that has on global sea level (through thermal expansion and land-ice changes).

These simple models are computationally fast, so long transient simulations can be repeated many times over with changed inputs, thus allowing assessments to be made of the projected global warming:

•   for *different* values of the climate sensitivity and ocean heat uptake, set in turn to match the characteristics of different AOGCMs, and

•   for various scenarios of the *total* human-induced radiative forcing of climate over the century ahead.

■   Note the emphasis on the word 'total'. What other anthropogenic contributions need to be included in these radiative forcing scenarios – apart from those due to future changes in the atmospheric concentrations of CO_2 and other greenhouse gases?

▨   Contributions from the (largely negative) forcing associated with anthropogenic aerosols, i.e. sulfates (due to SO_2 emissions) and various carbonaceous particles (from fossil fuel and vegetation burning), and how these might evolve over time in future, as they have in the past (Sections 2.5 and 3.5).

It was modelling studies of this kind that produced the wide range of projected global warming and sea-level rise for the end of the 21st century reported in the IPCC TAR (and referred to in Chapter 1).

6.5 Stages in modelling future climates: from emissions to impacts

To explore the uncertainties that surround our climate future, the IPCC followed the strategy outlined in Figure 6.7 (effectively, a more elaborate version of your thoughts on Question 3.5); some of the intermediate results produced by the successive layers of modelling studies indicated there are collected in Figure 6.8 (again reproduced from the TAR). As far as CO_2 is concerned, we have already traced through the journey from Stage 1 to Stage 3 in Figure 6.7: the resulting emission scenarios and projections of future atmospheric concentrations we looked at then (Figure 5.16) are included in Figure 6.8.

Figure 6.7   The sequence of modelling studies used by the IPCC to transform plausible BaU futures (summarised in Box 5.3) into projections of future climate change, and its impacts.

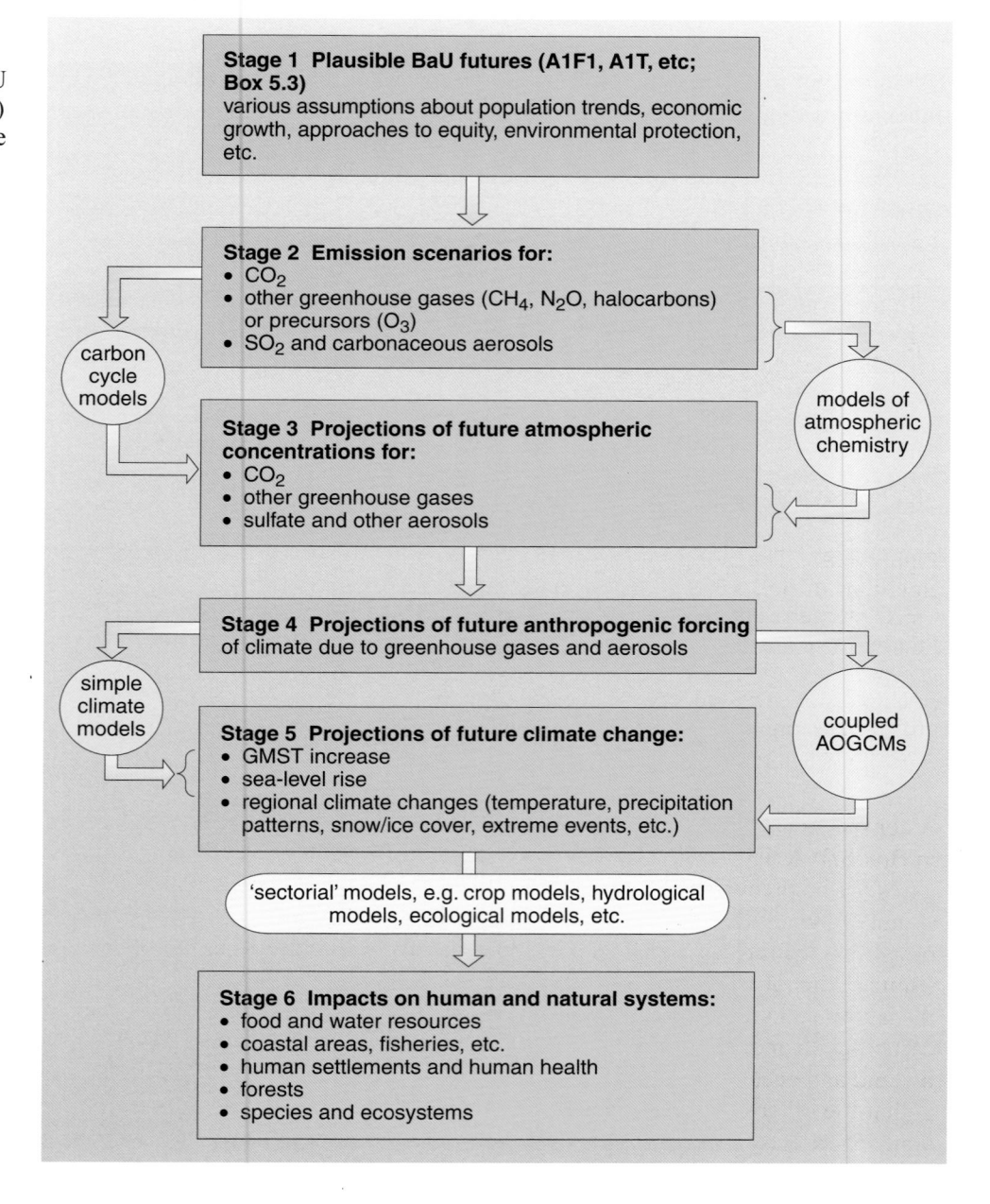

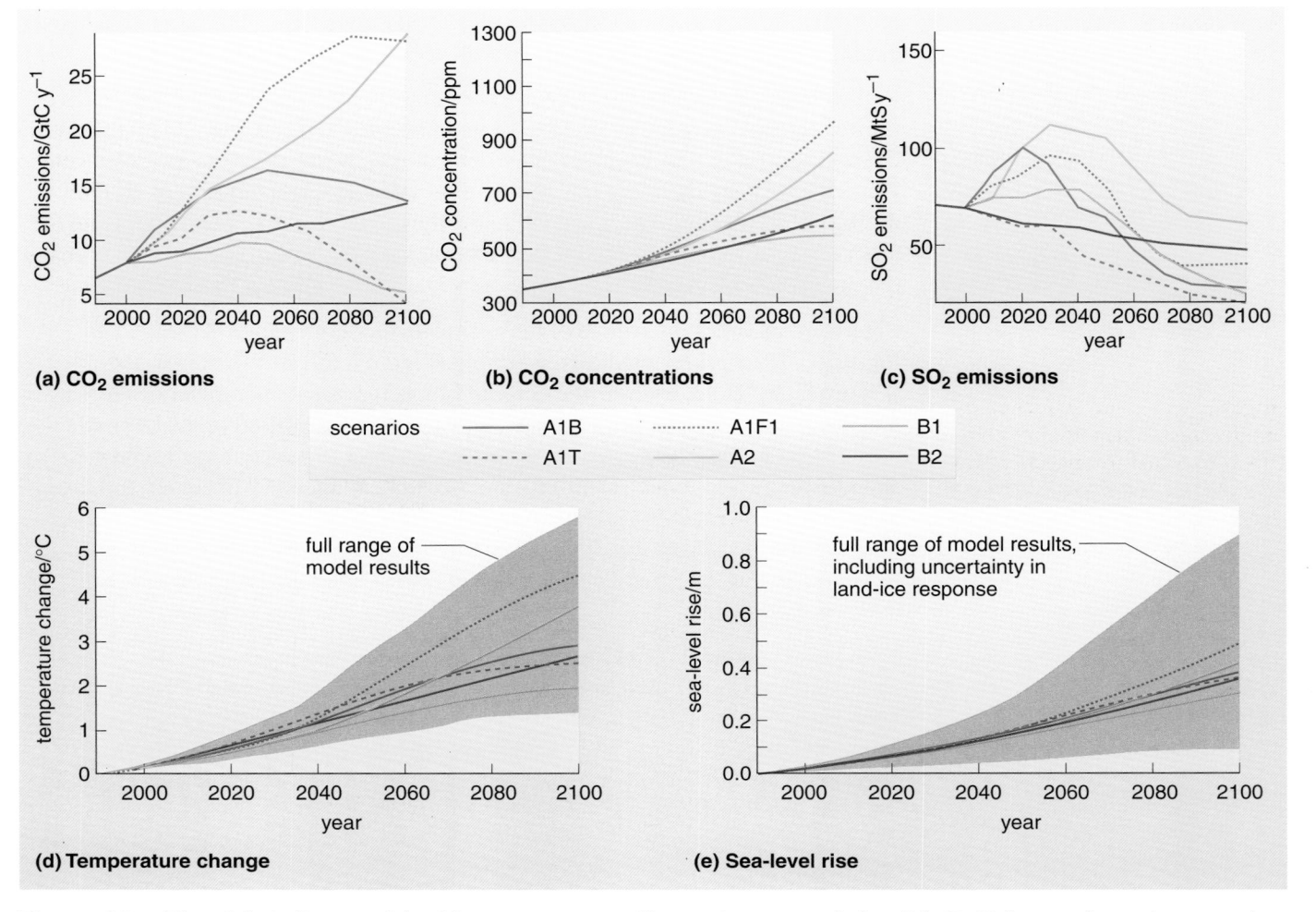

Figure 6.8   The global climate of the 21st century, according to the range of plausible BaU futures for anthropogenic emissions in Box 5.3. The figure shows projected (a) CO_2 emissions; (b) CO_2 concentrations; and (c) SO_2 emissions. Emission scenarios for other greenhouse gases and aerosols are not shown, but were included in the analysis (e.g. see Figure 6.9 in Question 6.2). Parts (d) and (e) show the projected changes in GMST and sea-level rise, respectively, produced by a simple climate model when tuned to match the response of a number of coupled AOGCMs with a range of climate sensitivities (1.7 to 4.2 °C; Section 6.4.1) and ocean-heat uptake; see text for further details. Note that the projected warming and sea-level rise does *not* allow for uncertainties in projecting greenhouse gas and non-sulfate aerosol concentrations for given emission scenarios. (Source: IPCC, 2001a.)

A consistent set of emission scenarios (i.e. again allied to the alternative futures in Box 5.3; A1F1, A1T, A2, etc.) was generated for each of the other greenhouse gases (or its precursors, in the case of tropospheric ozone; Box 2.6), and for SO_2 (Figure 6.8c) and other anthropogenic aerosols. These were converted into projections of future atmospheric concentrations, using models that effectively simulate the rate at which each component is removed from the atmosphere (i.e. its natural sinks). This step (Stage 3 in Figure 6.7) is analogous to the use of carbon-cycle models to calculate the year-by-year uptake of anthropogenic CO_2 by land and ocean sinks (Section 5.6.2). The difference (indicated in Figure 6.7) is that the other greenhouse gases are removed by chemical reactions *within* the atmosphere (noted in connection with the CFCs in Section 2.5), not uptake at the surface. We shall bypass the details, but note simply that the role played by atmospheric chemistry in the 'life cycles' of the other greenhouse gases adds yet another layer of complexity to the overall climate system.

Returning to Figure 6.7, the output from Stage 3 amounts to a set of alternative futures for the atmospheric burden of greenhouse gases and aerosols. Translating the time-evolving change in each component into an equivalent radiative forcing then yields a range of scenarios for the total anthropogenic forcing of climate during the 21st century (Stage 4). Finally, these are fed into a simple climate model – calibrated, in turn, to match the transient response of current state-of-the-art AOGCMs.

Figure 6.8 includes the results of these climate modelling studies (Stage 5 in Figure 6.7): the projected global warming (Figure 6.8d) and sea-level rise (Figure 6.8e). Here, each of the coloured lines represents the mean of the model-simulated response for a particular scenario (identified in the key); the grey region represents the full range of the model results, i.e. for all scenarios and all values of climate sensitivity and ocean heat uptake. The upper and lower bounds to these regions yield the range of projected climate change for the 21st century that made headline news when the TAR came out in 2001: *global warming of 1.4 to 5.8 °C between 1990 and 2100, and sea-level rise of 0.09 to 0.88 m.*

With these comments (and the discussion in earlier chapters) in mind, concentrate now on Figure 6.8 and its caption; then work through the following questions. They will help you to set the projections above in the context of 20th century climate warming, and then get you thinking about the many sources of uncertainty that eventually produce such a wide range of possible climate futures – a task we identified back in Chapter 1.

Question 6.1

(a)   How does the magnitude, and by implication the *rate*, of the projected warming for the century ahead compare with that experienced over the past 100 years (i.e. the best estimate of a rise in GMST by 0.6 °C; Section 3.1.2)?

(b)   Express the projected sea-level rise between 1990 and 2100 as an average annual rate of increase in mm per year. How does this compare with the observed rate of increase during the 20th century (Table 3.1, Section 3.4.1)?

In view of mounting evidence for the widespread effects of relatively modest 20th century warming (noted at various points in Chapters 3 to 5), it would seem prudent to be fairly alarmed by the comparisons in Question 6.1. Indeed, the IPCC go on to conclude that the projected rate of warming 'is very likely [90–99% probability; Box 3.2] to be without precedent during at least the last 10 000 years, based on palaeoclimate data'.

On the other hand, the consequences of continued climate warming will clearly be a good deal more serious if events unfold according to the top end of the projected range, rather than the lower end – the message crystallised in Figure 1.15 and the accompanying discussion of potential climate change impacts in Section 1.5. So what about the uncertainties referred to above?

■   What two major sources of uncertainty are included in the analysis behind the global warming projections in Figure 6.8d?

▨   Uncertainty about future human behaviour, embodied in the wide range of emission scenarios at the start of the analysis; and at the other end, uncertainty about the climate system's time-evolving response to the resulting change in radiative forcing, but only within the range implied by the climate sensitivities and ocean heat uptake simulated by existing AOGCMs.

Although unwilling to assess the relative likelihood of different outcomes within the ranges noted above (for all the reasons rehearsed in Sections 5.6.2 and 6.4), the IPCC TAR does conclude that these two sources of uncertainty contribute in roughly equal measure to the wide range of possible outcomes.

■   What additional source of uncertainty is included in the projections of sea-level rise in Figure 6.8e?

▨   Current estimates of uncertainty in the contribution from land-ice changes (i.e. in the response of glaciers and ice sheets to climate warming, referred to in Section 3.4.1).

■   According to the caption to Figure 6.8, what potential source of uncertainty is *not* included in these projections for the global climate of the 21st century?

▨   How future emissions translate into future atmospheric concentrations, for both greenhouse gases and non-sulfate aerosols. Note, for example, that the range of CO_2 concentrations in Figure 6.8b is the same as that in Figure 5.16b (i.e. 550 to 950 ppm) – and not the wider range (490 to 1260 ppm, noted in Section 5.6.2) that includes uncertainty about the effects of climate-change-related feedbacks on the natural carbon cycle, especially on land.

Similar uncertainties come into the picture for other greenhouse gases. For example, it is quite possible that future climate change could affect *natural* sources of methane (e.g. emissions from natural wetlands; Box 2.6, Section 2.5). Equally, atmospheric chemistry is a complicated business; modelling that chemistry inevitably introduces uncertainty into projections of the greenhouse gas concentrations resulting from a given emission scenario. Recall too the points raised at the end of Section 2.5 (and revisited in Section 3.5) over the complicated climatic effects of the different aerosols generated by human activities – another potential source of uncertainty about future anthropogenic forcing that was not included in the IPCC's analysis.

In short, uncertainty about the human impact on the global climate of the 21st century effectively 'cascades' up through the layers of modelling studies depicted in Figure 6.7 – and, given the points noted above, could well be even larger than the headline uncertainty ranges reported in the IPCC TAR (a point we revisit in Chapter 7).

■   Now think about the final stage in Figure 6.7, where projections of global climate change are 'translated' into assessments of the potential consequences for human societies and ecological systems around the world. What issue is central to assessments like this?

■   The *geographical* distribution of the response to continued greenhouse warming – i.e. how the resulting changes in climate variables (temperature, rainfall patterns, snow cover, extreme weather events, etc.) will vary from location to location.

Such questions can only be addressed through simulations with coupled AOGCMs – the source of images like those from the Hadley Centre model in Figure 6.1, for example. Further uncertainty inevitably intrudes at this stage, for all the reasons noted in our earlier critique of these models. Nevertheless, there are certain robust features of the projected climate changes that are not only common to the output from different models and for a range of scenarios, but also broadly consistent with recent trends observed in the real world (reviewed in Section 3.4). Based on an analysis of available simulations with state-of-the-art AOGCMs, the IPCC concluded as follows (IPCC, 2001a):

• It is very likely (90–99% probability) that nearly all land areas will warm more rapidly than the global average, particularly those at northern high latitudes. Typically, the warming in northern North America, and northern and central Asia, exceeds the global average by over 40% (a pattern evident in Figure 6.1a).

• Climate warming will intensify the hydrological cycle, with consequent increases in globally averaged water vapour concentration, evaporation and precipitation during the 21st century – a conclusion alluded to earlier (Section 5.4).

• It is likely (66–90% probability) that northern mid- to high latitudes will see increased precipitation during the 21st century.

• Northern Hemisphere snow cover and sea-ice extent will decrease further, and glaciers and ice caps are projected to continue their widespread retreat.

• The Antarctic ice sheet is likely to gain mass (because of greater precipitation), whereas the Greenland ice sheet is likely to lose mass (greater ablation will exceed gains from increased precipitation) – in line with the conclusions in Box 3.4, Section 3.4.1.

Given the effort and resource devoted to the development of comprehensive climate models, these rather limited conclusions might seem a somewhat meagre return on that investment. Again, we can trace this back to the emphasis on consensus in IPCC reports. To illustrate the point, all models do, in fact, project regional changes in precipitation in future, with increases in some parts of the world and reductions elsewhere – a picture evident in Figure 6.1b. Increased precipitation at mid- to high northern latitudes is a consistent theme (whence the third bullet point above). Elsewhere though, different models tend to produce inconsistent and sometimes contradictory results for a particular region, especially at low latitudes. For example, the Hadley Centre model projects a drier (and much hotter) climate in Amazonia by the late 21st century (Figure 6.1b), whereas some of the other models indicate increased regional rainfall, or little change. Inconsistencies like this clearly have knock-on effects for detailed impact assessments at the regional, much less local, level.

That brings us back to the messy reality signalled at the beginning of this topic: there is plenty of evidence that temperatures are rising and will continue to do so, but lots of uncertainty about the amount and details of future change. In this context, the IPCC was applauded for its efforts to inject some rigour into its treatment of uncertainty in the TAR, notably through the 'likelihood' language we have emphasised throughout this topic. But at the same time, it was criticised for not going far enough. In particular, it was argued that the Panel's failure to assess the relative likelihood of different global warming futures left its findings open to biased interpretation: people would (and indeed did) simply latch onto those projections that best suited their preconceptions. So has a deeper insight into the factors that feed into the uncertainties about our climate future, coupled with a better understanding of the underlying science, helped to arm you against this kind of 'chicanery'?

The following activity invites you to reflect on this question. It will also help to gather your thoughts before we return to the issue that is central to decision making on climate change: what do we mean by 'dangerous' interference with the climate system, and what should we do about it?

Activity 6.1

Allow about 45 minutes

Consider the following sceptical viewpoint: 'Don't believe claims by the usual 'eco doom-and-gloom' brigade that the world will be a scorching six degrees hotter by the end of the century if we don't act now to cut back on our energy-intensive lifestyles. According to the IPCC, it's just as likely to be a mere degree or so warmer, and we've already survived that kind of warming over the last century. We should just wait and see what happens, not risk taking unnecessary action that would damage economic growth.'

(a)   What implicit assumption is involved in a categorical statement that the world is 'likely to be a mere degree or so warmer' by the end of the century? (*A short paragraph*)

(b)   Suppose you want to convince someone (a friend or colleague, say) that climate change is a credible, and potentially serious, threat and that a 'wait-and-see' response (i.e. little or no action to curb the growth in global CO_2 emissions) is an inherently risky strategy, despite the uncertainties in the science. Select five or six key *scientific* points from this and earlier chapters that you would use to back up your arguments. Note these down as a set of bullet points. (*A few sentences for each*)

Summary of Chapter 6

1   Comprehensive climate models are powerful tools for simulating the behaviour of the climate system, and its response to radiative forcing. State-of-the-art models (coupled atmosphere–ocean general circulation models, AOGCMs) include sub-models of the main components of the climate system (atmosphere; ocean and sea ice; land surface and land ice), and allow these components to interact in a dynamic way so that projections of future climate change can take into account the effects of important feedback processes. Such models are improving steadily, but still have inevitable limitations and shortcomings. In particular, computational constraints impose a fairly coarse

spatial resolution. Vital small-scale processes (clouds, rainfall, ocean mixing, the influence of vegetation and other land-surface characteristics, etc.) are incorporated through simplified (and sometimes questionable) parameterisation schemes.

2   The coupled AOGCMs developed by different modelling groups (e.g. the Hadley Centre in the UK) share many features in common, but the detailed formulations differ. Validation studies generate confidence that current AOGCMs can simulate important features of the Earth's present (and past) climate, but reveal significant errors on the regional scale that differ from model to model.

3   In experiments designed to compare model outputs, different AOGCMs simulate a different time-evolving rise in GMST in response to the same gradual increase in atmospheric CO_2 (a surrogate for 'greenhouse forcing' in general). Each model's response is effectively determined by two characteristics of the model: its 'climate sensitivity', and the simulated heat uptake by the ocean:

- The climate sensitivity (given the symbol $\Delta T_{2\times}$) is defined as the *equilibrium* global warming (i.e. rise in GMST) that would occur eventually in response to a CO_2-doubling; it effectively integrates the effects of feedbacks within the climate system. Uncertainty about cloud feedback is a major factor in the wide range of model-based estimates of climate sensitivity. Currently, there is no consensus about the relative likelihood of different values within (or outside) the long-accepted range (1.5 to 4.5 °C).

- As expected, heat uptake by the ocean (as simulated by a particular AOGCM) slows the pace of climate warming, but merely postpones the eventual equilibrium warming.

4   Because long simulations with coupled models are so computer-intensive, the projections of future climate change in the IPCC TAR used a simpler type of climate model, calibrated in turn to match the characteristics (climate sensitivity and ocean heat uptake) of various AOCGMs.

5   In the analysis reported in IPCC TAR, uncertainties about human impact on climate during the 21st century cascade up through the successive layers of modelling studies (summarised in Figure 6.7) that were used to transform a wide range of plausible 'business as usual' emission scenarios (allied to the alternative storylines in Box 5.3) into projections of future climate change and its impacts. Two major sources of uncertainty – about future human behaviour (i.e. emissions) and about the climate system's response to radiative forcing (especially the climate sensitivity value) – contribute roughly equally to the wide range of possible outcomes: global warming of 1.4 to 5.8 °C by 2100, and sea-level rise of 0.09 to 0.88 m. Other factors not included in the IPCC's analysis (e.g. uncertainties about climate feedbacks on the carbon cycle) mean that the full range of uncertainty about our climate future could be even wider (see also Chapter 7).

6   The projected rate of warming is significantly higher than that experienced over the 20th century, and very likely (90–99% probability) to be without precedent during at least the past 10 000 years. The high end of the projected range (5.8 °C) approaches the size of the temperature increases seen only during the transition from glacial to interglacial conditions.

7   Full-scale simulations with coupled AOGCMs agree on certain features of the projected climate changes at the regional level, many of which are broadly

consistent with recent observed trends: enhanced warming at high latitudes; continued retreat of sea ice and glaciers; a more intense hydrological cycle; etc. All models also project significant shifts in precipitation patterns around the world. Increased precipitation at mid- to high northern latitudes is a consistent theme; elsewhere the projected changes differ from model to model.

Questions for Chapter 6

Question 6.2

Figure 6.9 shows the range of emission scenarios for methane adopted in the TAR, and the resulting projections of future methane concentrations.

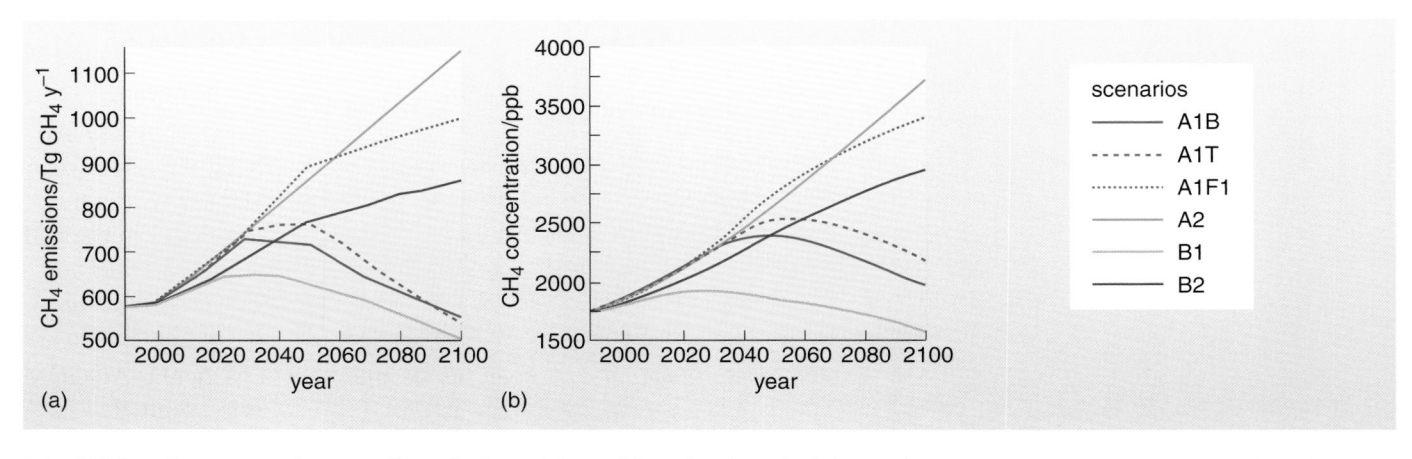

(a)   With reference to the storylines in Box 5.3, and bearing in mind the major anthropogenic sources of CH_4 (Box 2.6, Section 2.5), what factor is probably mainly responsible for the difference between the A1F1 and A1T emissions pathways in Figure 6.9a?

(b)   Use Figure 6.9b to estimate the range of projected CH_4 concentrations in 2100. How do these values compare with the pre-industrial level (i.e. 700 ppb)?

(c)   Now concentrate on the B1 scenario. How does the relationship between future emissions and the resulting atmospheric concentrations for CH_4 in Figure 6.9 compare with that for CO_2 in Figure 5.16 – the point we commented on at the end of Section 5.6.2? Explain the difference.

Figure 6.9   (a) Projected emissions of CH_4, and (b) the resulting atmospheric concentrations, according to the range of BaU futures in Box 5.3. (Note that the projections in (a) include emissions from both natural and anthropogenic sources.)

Question 6.3

In its second major report (1996), the IPCC projected a global warming of 1.0 to 3.5 °C by the end of the 21st century. Aware that the higher projected temperatures and wider range in the TAR could be used to challenge the credibility of climate model calculations, the Panel took pains to explain that this was not the cause. Rather it was mainly due to lower projected SO_2 emissions at the beginning of the analysis, reflecting growing action to tackle the acid rain problem (recall Figure 1.6c). Why would cleaning up this source of pollution be expected to lead to higher global temperatures in future?

Question 6.4

The projections in Figure 6.8d all show a smooth year-on-year rise in GMST. Why is this unlikely to be the case in the real world?

Chapter 7

Responding to the challenge: uncertainty, risk and dangerous climate change

7.1 Introduction

One thing is clear: the task of responding to human-induced climate change requires decision-making in the context of science that is both extremely complex and fraught with uncertainties. Much of this topic has been taken up with the potential consequences of simply carrying on with 'business as usual'. Though the science is still far from settled, arguments of the kind rehearsed in Activity 6.1 have convinced governments that this 'do little or nothing' option (effectively, a 'wait and see' response) is an inherently risky strategy. Instead, the international community has embarked on a 'precautionary' approach: the global climate policy regime enshrined in the UN Framework Convention on Climate Change (UNFCCC) and Kyoto Protocol (Boxes 1.1 and 1.3).

Yet if ardent 'greens' and diehard sceptics can agree on anything, it is that the commitments agreed at Kyoto will do little to stem the upward trend in greenhouse gas concentrations. Industrialised countries are required to make only relatively modest cuts in emissions of 5%, the US (the world's largest single emitter of CO_2) is not signed up to the protocol, developing nations are not involved, and the existing terms expire in 2012. Even more importantly, the Kyoto Protocol does not provide a blueprint for how the world should achieve the ultimate objective of the UNFCCC. Spelt out in a bit more detail than the quote in Box 1.1, the declared goal is:

> to achieve [...] stabilization of greenhouse gas concentrations in the atmosphere at a level that would prevent dangerous anthropogenic interference with the climate system. Such a level should be achieved within a time-frame sufficient to allow ecosystems to adapt naturally to climate change, to ensure that food production is not threatened and to enable economic development to proceed in a sustainable manner.

The problem is that this is *not* a clear goal. Indeed, the wording raises a host of difficult questions of the kind flagged up at the end of Section 1.6. What stabilisation level? And how are we going to get there? How deep do the cuts in emissions need to be, and who should make them? What kind of time-frame are we talking about: 20, 50, 100 or even 1000 years? Note too the reference to 'sustainable' economic development – another term giving rise to considerable ambiguity and heated debate (Section 1.4).

In this final chapter, we aim to give you a feel for the sorts of issues raised by questions like these, and thereby to reconnect the science of climate change with the broader social, economic and political context of the greenhouse warming problem, as outlined in Chapter 1. We hope you will then feel better prepared to take an active part in ongoing debates about what can, or should, be done to tackle this long-term, intergenerational problem.

We start by revisiting the question of what constitutes dangerous climate change.

7.2 Defining 'dangerous' climate change

In Chapter 1, we introduced the framework for interpreting 'dangerous interference with the climate system' established by the IPCC TAR: effectively, the criteria collected in Table 1.1 and the colour code used in Figure 1.15 (Section 1.5). Our tentative conclusion was that global warming somewhere within the range projected for the 21st century would take the world into the danger zone. But where within that range? Would it be 'safe' to let the GMST rise by a further 3 or 4 °C, for example? Or should we aim to keep the increase at or below 2 °C, say? In this Section, we look at the implications of defining 'dangerous' according to two of the criteria of 'concern' identified by the IPCC: the risks of increased extreme events (category II in Table 1.1); and the risks of 'large-scale discontinuities' in the climate system (category V).

7.2.1 Extreme weather in a warmer world

Consider a few recent examples of extreme weather events. In August 2002, unusual weather patterns dumped record amounts of rain over the Alps, adding to the rush of water in mountain rivers already swollen by meltwater from Alpine glaciers. Fed into some of the continent's largest rivers, the result was severe flooding across a swathe of central Europe (Figure 7.1), with damage costing some US$18.5 billion (bn). The following summer, Europe was in the grip of a prolonged and extreme heat wave (referred to in Section 1.5), the hottest since the global instrumental record began in 1860. In central England, where records go back to the 1660s, temperatures topped 100 °F (37.8 °C) for the first time ever. Across Europe, there were at least 20 000 excess deaths, along with widespread forest fires and agricultural losses of an estimated US$12 bn. In the south of France, the summer heat wave (classified as a 'one in 100-year event') gave way to a 'one in 100-year' flood in November, when the River Rhône burst its banks after heavy rainstorms. Meanwhile, other extreme events in 2003 took a huge toll elsewhere around the world. In China, for example, floods along the Huai and Yangtze rivers swept through 650 000 homes and caused more than US$7 bn of losses. Heat waves in India, Bangladesh and Pakistan took temperatures up to 50 °C. Forest fires scorched large areas of Australia, Canada and the US. In September, Hurricane Isabel wrecked 360 000 homes on the US east coast.

But are 'freak' summers in Europe the result of global warming? And what about major floods in many parts of the world, or the succession of violent hurricanes (the term for tropical cyclones in the Atlantic) battering the Americas and Caribbean in recent years (Figure 7.2), or the 3.5 *million* people at risk of famine in Niger in 2005, following a devastating two-year drought? In short, is the world becoming more prone to weather-related disasters of one sort or another?

Figure 7.1   Almost 50 000 residents of Prague were evacuated in August 2002 in the worst flood in more than a century, after the River Vltava burst its banks.

Figure 7.2   A satellite image captures Hurricane Wilma passing through the northwest Caribbean on 21 October 2005 – a fitting finale to an Atlantic hurricane season (officially August to November) that tied with 1969 as the worst since records began in 1851. Earlier in the season, people worldwide were shocked by images of the misery, destruction and calamitous floods brought to New Orleans and Mississippi's Gulf coast by Hurricane Katrina. For a while, the world's most powerful nation struggled to cope with the unfolding disaster.

Large reinsurance companies (such as Munich Re and Swiss Re) are the 'payers of last resort' for major natural disasters, and have good reason to monitor the human and economic costs arising from extreme weather events. They are already alarmed by the rising tide of large claims for damage from floods, storms, droughts and heat waves – a pattern evident in Figure 7.3.

Figure 7.3   The economic impact of major weather and flood disasters over the period 1950–1999.

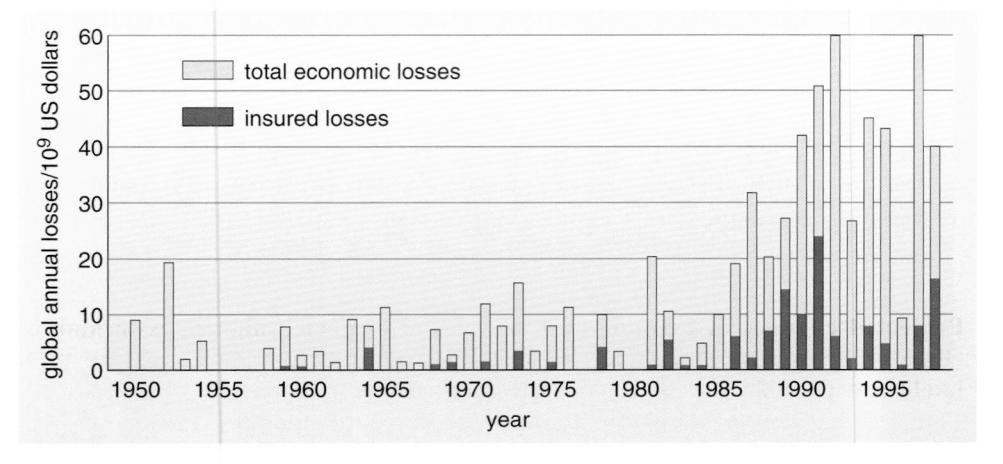

- Statistics like those collected in Figure 7.3 have sometimes been used to argue that recent decades have seen an increase in climate variability or in the frequency and intensity of extreme weather events. Why should you be wary of such claims?

- The impacts of floods, storms, etc. (economic and insured losses in this case) can depend on many factors in addition to the severity of the weather conditions that caused them.

Take the risk of flooding, for example. More people than ever before now live or work on river floodplains (including around 10% of all Europeans), or in coastal zones exposed to storm surges. Increased property values add to the economic impacts. Development patterns and other factors have tended to reduce the land's ability to soak up the rain, leading to rapid runoff and increasing the risk of massive and comparatively sudden surges of water down rivers. Examples include: the impervious concrete and asphalt of modern towns and cities; the draining of wetlands and 'hard' engineering of rivers, confining them between high reinforced banks; loss of forest from mountain valleys and other changes to the upland catchment areas of many rivers; various agricultural practices (e.g. the ploughing up of pasture and removal of hedges, etc.); and so on. Factors like these could well be leading societies in many parts of the world to become more vulnerable to the effects of unusually heavy rainfall.

- Look back at the entries under 'weather indicators' in Table 3.1 (Section 3.4.1). Is there any evidence there that analyses of available data point to significant changes in extreme weather and climate phenomena during the 20th century?

- To a limited extent. For example, the IPCC was confident (66–90% probability, at least) of having detected an increase in hot days, in heavy precipitation events (at mid- and high latitudes) and in the incidence of drought (in a few areas) – and a widespread decrease in cold/frost days (recall Question 3.2).

These rather tentative conclusions again reflect the difficulty of discerning any underlying trends amid the 'background noise' of natural variability – a problem we flagged up earlier (Section 4.4) in connection with detecting changes in tropical cyclone activity. Media stories about a record-breaking heat wave, flood or storm are now commonly qualified with the accurate comment that 'scientists don't know whether this was caused by global warming'. What we can say, however, is that an increase in some kinds of extreme events is a consistent theme of *all* model projections of 21st century climate change. The IPCC's judgements on this front in the TAR are collected in Table 7.1, along with some examples of what the projected changes could mean for people, wildlife and ecosystems. Clearly, this catalogue of (largely) damaging effects needs to be weighed in any analysis of what constitutes 'dangerous' climate change.

Table 7.1 Projected effects of global warming during the 21st century (IPCC, 2001d).

Projected changes in extreme climate phenomena and their likelihood (Box 3.2)	Examples of projected impacts with high confidence of occurrence (67–95% probability) in at least some areas
Higher maximum temperatures, more hot days and heat waves over nearly all land areas (*very likely*).	Increased incidence of death and serious illness in older age groups and urban poor. Increased heat stress in livestock and wildlife. Shift in tourist destinations. Increased risk of damage to a number of crops. Increased electric cooling demand and reduced energy supply reliability.
Higher (increasing) minimum temperatures, fewer cold days, frost days and cold waves over nearly all land areas (*very likely*).	Decreased cold-related human morbidity and mortality. Decreased risk of damage to a number of crops, and increased risk to others. Extended range and activity of some insect pest and disease vectors. Reduced heating energy demand.
More intense precipitation events (*very likely*, over many areas).	Increased flood, landslide, avalanche, and mudslide damage. Increased soil erosion. Increased flood runoff could increase recharge of some floodplain aquifers. Increased pressure on government and private flood insurance systems and disaster relief.
Increased summer drying over most mid-latitude continental interiors and associated risk of drought (*likely*).	Decreased crop yields. Increased damage to building foundations caused by ground shrinkage. Decreased water resource quantity and quality. Increased risk of forest fire.
Increase in tropical cyclone peak wind intensities, mean and peak precipitation intensities (*likely*, over some areas).*	Increased risks to human life, risk of infectious disease epidemics and many other risks. Increased coastal erosion and damage to coastal buildings and infrastructure. Increased damage to coastal ecosystems such as coral reefs and mangroves.
Intensified droughts and floods associated with El Niño events in many different regions (*likely*) (see also under droughts and intense precipitation events).	Decreased agricultural and rangeland productivity in drought- and flood-prone regions. Decreased hydro-power potential in drought-prone regions.
Increased Asian summer monsoon precipitation variability (*likely*).	Increase in flood and drought magnitude and damage in temperate and tropical Asia.
Increased intensity of mid-latitude storms (little agreement between current models).	Increased risks to human life and health. Increased property and infrastructure losses. Increased damage to coastal ecosystems.

* Changes in regional distribution of tropical cyclones are possible but have not been established.

Though the details of exactly which regions will experience more storms, greater floods or worse droughts remain uncertain (for all the reasons highlighted in Chapter 6), there is little doubt that the *human* costs of weather-related disasters in future are likely to fall disproportionately on the world's poorest people, just as they do today. Still it is sobering to note the potential effects on people in an affluent country like the UK, which has a relatively benign climate. In this context, a common starting point is a set of climate change projections for the UK generated by modelling studies at the Hadley Centre. These were published in 2002 in a report from the UK Climate Impacts Programme (UKCIP), established by the government in 1997 to provide a 'framework for an integrated national assessment of climate change impacts'. Some of the key results from this report are summarised in Box 7.1.

The potential implications of these climate change scenarios for flood risk in the UK were spelt out in a 2004 report, *Future Flooding*, from the Office of Science and Technology (Foresight, 2004). The report's findings (heralded in one of the headlines included in Figure 1.1) make disturbing reading.

Box 7.1 How will UK climate be affected by continued greenhouse warming? (UKCIP02, 2002)

To develop climate projections for the UK, the Hadley Centre focused on four of the IPCC's emission scenarios (A1F1, A2, B2 and B1; Box 5.3 and Figure 6.8), chosen to cover the range of possibilities. First, the Centre's global model (an AOGCM with a mid-range climate sensitivity of 3.3 °C) was used to simulate the resulting changes in climate for three future periods: the 2020s (2011–2040 average), the 2050s (2041–2070 average) and the 2080s (2071–2100 average). Results from the global model were then used to 'drive' a regional version of the model, which has a much higher spatial resolution (50 km × 50 km) over Europe (e.g. see Figure 7.4). This is one (albeit imperfect) way of incorporating the influence of relatively small-scale features, e.g. the mountains and uplands of the British landscape. Key features of the projected changes include the following.

- Depending on emissions, annual average UK temperatures may rise by 2 to 3.5 °C by the 2080s, with warmer, drier summers and milder, wetter winters. For the high emissions (A1F1) scenario, parts of the southeast may be up to 5 °C warmer in summer (Figure 7.4a), with 50% less rain (Figure 7.4b). Summer soil moisture could be reduced by 40% or more over large parts of England.

- Winters across the UK are expected to become wetter, with less snow and more rain falling in heavy downpours. By the 2080s, winter daily precipitation intensities that are experienced once every two years on average may become 5% to 20% heavier. In most parts of Scotland, snowfall could decrease by 40–50% by the 2050s, and by as much as 60–90% by the 2080s.

- Sea levels will continue to rise relative to most of the UK's shoreline, particularly in southeast England. For some east coast locations, extreme high water levels that occur, on average, once every 50 years today might occur as often as once every three years by the 2080s.

Britain's exposure to extreme seasonal anomalies in future may also be less than welcome. For the A2 (medium–high emissions) scenario, for example:

- Extreme summer heat and drought, e.g. an August as hot as that experienced in 1995 when central England temperatures averaged 3.4 °C above normal (currently expected only once or twice in a century), may occur one year in five by the 2050s, and as often as three years in five by the 2080s.

- Extremely wet winters like that of 1994/95 (66% wetter than average, again a 'one in 100-year' anomaly) could become seven times more frequent by the 2080s.

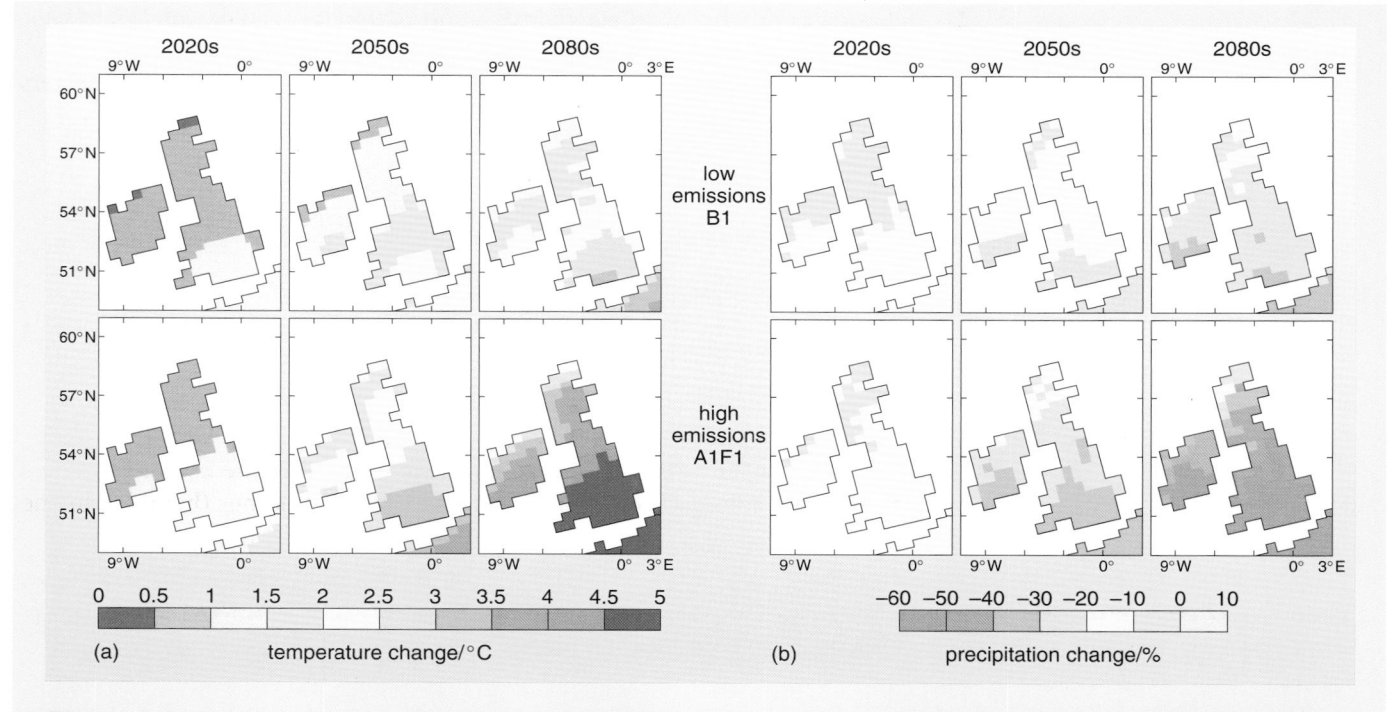

Figure 7.4 Projected changes in (a) average summer temperatures and (b) average summer rainfall across the UK during the 21st century for the IPCC's low (B1) and high (A1F1) emission scenarios. Note the much finer grid shown in these results compared with that evident in Figure 6.1.

For example, the current bill from flood damage across the country is around £1.4 bn a year, on average. At best, this figure could double by the 2080s; at worst, it could rise to over £20 bn a year, if no extra preventive action was taken. Meanwhile, the number of people at high risk from river and coastal flooding could increase from 1.6 million today to between 2.3 and 3.6 million. An additional hazard for our towns and cities is the localised flash-flooding that occurs when sewerage and drainage systems are overwhelmed by sudden downpours. By the 2080s, the report predicts a fourfold increase in the number of properties likely to be flooded in this way at least once every 10 years. An extra 600 000 people could have their lives blighted – not only by the stress of extensive damage, but also by the threat of repeat flooding, coupled with possible withdrawal of insurance cover, rendering their homes virtually unsaleable.

As well as considering a range of possible adaptive measures, this comprehensive report draws attention to the important influence of non-climatic factors in its estimates of future flood risks – notably the implications of continuing to build homes, factories and other infrastructure in flood-prone areas. But it also clearly identifies future climate change as a major driver behind the increased human and economic costs. The projected sea-level rise could increase the risk of coastal flooding by a factor of 4–10, for example. Heavier and/or more intense rainfall increases risks across the UK by 2–4 times, though specific locations could experience changes well outside this range. More telling, the report concludes: 'Reductions in flood risk resulting from climate-change mitigation would mostly accrue in the second half of the century – action to reduce emissions [of greenhouse gases] would have limited effect before then'.

■ What is likely to be the scientific reasoning behind this conclusion?

■ Recall your thoughts on Activity 6.1. The many time-lags in the climate system mean that much of the climate change (and sea-level rise) likely to occur over the next few decades is already 'built in' due to past greenhouse gas emissions; there is nothing we can do to stop it.

By the same token, these time-lags reinforce the need to take action *now* to reduce emissions, if we want to affect risks in the 2050s and beyond. From the limited perspective of urban flooding in the UK, that could make the difference between the existing system of drains and sewers coping, or reaching the limit of their capacity. But the message holds with equal force for the many other risks from an increase in extreme weather events. If the world chooses to follow a high-carbon pathway, for example, recent modelling studies suggest that a 2003-type summer in Europe could be unusually cool by the middle of the century.

Question 7.1

To get a feel for what life in the UK might be like towards the end of the century, it helps to interpret the climate projections in Box 7.1 in the following way. In terms of average seasonal temperatures and rainfall, changes at the top end of the projected range are roughly equivalent to moving southern England *south* into the Mediterranean region of France (though other aspects of climate, e.g. sunshine, winds and storms, etc. would be different). With this in mind, note down your immediate thoughts on the implications for (a) housing (apart from the increased flood risk in some areas); and (b) the appearance of the typical English landscape.

7.2.2 Climate 'surprises' in a warmer world

Modelling studies of the kind we looked at in Chapter 6 (Figure 6.8) project a gradual change in global climate over the course of the century ahead, however uncertain the precise trajectory might be. Yet the message from the palaeoclimate record is that the Earth is prone to sudden and drastic flips in climate; recall the rapid climate swings during glacial times noted earlier (Section 4.3.3), for example. The possibility that continued greenhouse warming could trigger abrupt changes of this kind, with severe consequences at regional or global scales, represents a different type of hazard – one that could again be considered dangerous.

In this context, climate scientists have identified several aspects of the climate system that may have a 'tipping point' – a threshold that, once exceeded, will make major (and possibly irreversible) changes inevitable, no matter how much we reduce greenhouse gas emissions thereafter. Here, we look briefly at current thinking on three kinds of 'imaginable surprises', and their potential implications.

Changes to the Gulf Stream

The background to concern about the mode of operation of the ocean conveyor (i.e. the thermohaline circulation, THC) in a warmer world was spelt out in Section 4.3.3, together with the implications for heat transport by the Gulf Stream.

■ What is the key point at the heart of this concern?

▨ The possibility that an influx of freshwater from rain, rivers and melting ice could, by lowering the salinity of surface waters, disrupt deep-water formation in the two 'pump' sites in the North Atlantic, and hence slow down or even switch off the Gulf Stream.

A recent 'what if' experiment with the Hadley Centre AOGCM predicts that switching off the heat supply brought by the Gulf Stream would lead to a rapid cooling of the Northern Hemisphere. In particular (Hadley Centre, 2005):

> the UK annual temperature would cool by up to 5 °C in a matter of a decade or two. But the effect on extreme temperatures would be worse […] winter daily minimum temperatures in central England could regularly fall well below −10 °C or so. If this were to happen, the disruption to society would be enormous; certainly not as extreme as depicted in the film *The Day After Tomorrow* [Figure 1.16] but enough to disrupt agriculture, transport and other infrastructure.

But is this likely to happen? Simulations of the response to various IPCC emission scenarios with different coupled AOGCMs all agree on one thing: none of them shows a complete switch-off of the Gulf Stream over the next 100 years, even with high (A1F1) emissions. Equally though, they all project a weakening of this vital ocean current, with reductions varying from a few percent to nearly 50%. Indeed, in experiments with the Hadley Centre model, high emissions lead to a shutdown of one of the deep-water pumps (in the Labrador Sea; recall Figure 4.9) by around 2020. Such a change might, by itself, be deemed a 'dangerous interference' with the climate system. In practice, however, the cooling effect on Europe of the decreased Gulf Stream flow was more than offset by the greenhouse warming effect, and regional temperatures continued to rise. (The net effect on Britain's climate is included in the projections referred to in Box 7.1.)

It would seem, then, that there is no immediate prospect of Britain and northwest Europe being plunged into a 'big freeze' even as the world heats up, despite the scary headlines to this effect that sometimes appear (Figure 1.1). On the other hand, the wide range of predictions noted above means that there is no single robust conclusion about the potential vulnerability of the Gulf Stream to ongoing greenhouse forcing, reflecting the many remaining gaps in our understanding of ocean currents and their apparent stability. In the words of the IPCC TAR (IPCC, 2001a): 'While none of the current projections with coupled models exhibit a complete shut-down of the THC during the next 100 years, one cannot exclude the possibility that such thresholds lie in the range of the projected climate changes'.

The caution implicit in this statement is reinforced by some recent measurements from research ships in the Nordic Seas. These seem to indicate that changes in ocean circulation, specifically a reduction in deep-water formation, are already taking place.

Collapse of the West Antarctic Ice Sheet

As noted earlier (Section 6.5), current thinking has it that the Antarctic ice sheet is likely to gain mass during the 21st century, partially offsetting sea-level rise due to thermal expansion and loss of ice elsewhere. However, signs of rapid change in this part of the world (Section 3.4.1) draw attention to one of the more dramatic scenarios in a global-warming future (again featured among the headlines in Figure 1.1): catastrophic collapse of the entire **West Antarctic Ice Sheet (WAIS)** (see Figure 7.5). This would release water roughly equivalent to a 6 m sea-level rise, inundating many coastlines and most of the world's great cities in developed and developing countries alike.

Figure 7.5   Satellite image of Antarctica. The Transantarctic Mountains run across the continent, dividing it into two contrasting components: the vast East Antarctic Ice Sheet, based on bedrock mainly above sea level; and the smaller West Antarctic Ice Sheet, largely grounded on bedrock that is *below* sea level, making it the world's only existing marine ice sheet.

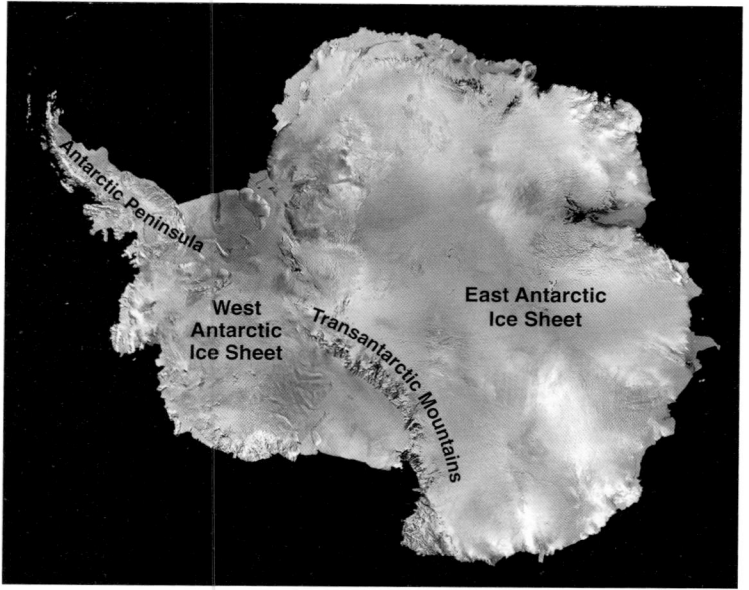

Unlike the huge mass of ice stored on the eastern part of the continent, most of the WAIS is grounded below sea level. It has long been argued that this situation could make the WAIS inherently unstable – that is, relatively small perturbations due to climate warming could trigger a rapid and unstoppable disintegration of the ice sheet, with massive outpourings of icebergs into the ocean. Time-scales as short as 200–400 years have been suggested.

It is now known that the activity of the WAIS is dominated by fast-flowing ice streams that feed into floating ice shelves, and appear to be able to respond rapidly to changes in the ice sheet–shelf system. However, the effect these dynamic ice streams might have on the stability of the WAIS is still debated. Over the years, plausible arguments both for and against WAIS instability have been put forward, and recent observational evidence is also somewhat equivocal on this front. Overall, the current consensus is that projected global warming is 'very unlikely' (1–10% probability; Box 3.2) to set in motion an irreversible collapse of the ice sheet during the present century. The prognosis on longer time-scales remains an unresolved issue.

'Runaway' carbon dynamics

The scope for a two-way interaction between climate change and carbon cycling by terrestrial ecosystems was an important theme in Chapter 5 – along with the potential implications for the uptake of anthropogenic CO_2 in future, and hence for the evolution of atmospheric CO_2 levels in response to a particular emissions pathway (a point revisited in Chapter 6). Recent modelling studies feed concerns that feedbacks triggered by ongoing climate change may not just weaken the land-based sink for fossil fuel CO_2; they could turn the world's ecosystems into a net source of the gas, further enhancing already increasing concentrations.

The results shown in Figure 7.6 illustrate the point. Here, the curve labelled 'with climate change feedbacks' was produced by a version of the Hadley Centre climate model that includes *both* a 'dynamic global vegetation model' (allowing vegetation type and amount to change as climate changes) *and* a fully interactive representation of the carbon cycle (including plant, soil and ocean processes). Note how the CO_2 concentration increases faster and to a higher level than in the simulation that does not incorporate climate-induced changes in vegetation and carbon cycling. In this case, the comprehensive model predicts that terrestrial ecosystems as a whole switch from being a weak sink for CO_2 to a strong source around the middle of the century, mainly due to the rapid loss of soil carbon beyond 2050.

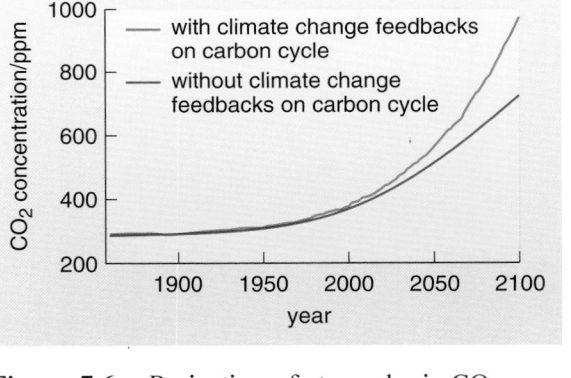

Figure 7.6   Projection of atmospheric CO_2 concentrations in response to a mid-range emissions scenario simulated by the Hadley Centre climate model coupled to a dynamic vegetation and carbon cycle model (red curve). For comparison, the results obtained when climate change is not allowed to feed back onto the carbon cycle or vegetation type are also shown (blue curve).

■ Why might a warmer climate be expected to lead to a loss of soil carbon?

▨ The activity of soil bacteria is very sensitive to temperature, and decomposition rates are expected to accelerate in a warmer world (Section 5.4). If organic matter breaks down faster than it is added to the soil, the result will be a net loss of carbon and a net release of CO_2 to the atmosphere.

Question 7.2

In the study referred to above, the model also predicts that vegetation carbon storage in South America will begin to decline in the second half of this century, due to the die-back of the Amazon rainforest. Look back at the climate change projections produced by the Hadley Centre model in Figure 6.1. What is likely to be the reason for the forest die-back in this simulation, and why might that be expected to accelerate the build up of atmospheric CO_2?

Climate scientists have been warning for some time that global warming could also trigger a more alarming positive feedback – by starting to release the methane currently trapped in Arctic permafrost (an eventuality foreshadowed earlier; Question 5.5); recall that methane is a more effective greenhouse gas than CO_2. There are now disturbing signs that this process may already be underway. In 2005, researchers reported that a vast area of frozen peat bog in western Siberia (present throughout the Holocene) has started to thaw (Figure 7.7). Estimates suggest that this region could hold some 70 billion tonnes of methane (i.e. 70 Gt CH_4; Box 5.1) – about a quarter of that thought to be stored in permafrost around the world. What impact might a slow but persistent thaw of the Siberian permafrost have on future levels of CH_4 in the atmosphere? We can get a rough idea by making a few simple assumptions.

Figure 7.7   The headlines from an article on the front page of *The Guardian*, 11 August 2005.

60p
Thursday
August 11 2005
Published in London
and Manchester
guardian.co.uk
* *

*The*Guardian

Siberia feels the heat It's a frozen peat bog the size of France and Germany combined, contains billions of tonnes of greenhouse gas and, for the first time since the ice age, it is melting

The permafrost in western Siberia is melting, leaving peatbogs exposed for the first time in 11,000 years and enabling the escape of billions of tonnes of methane which could accelerate global warming significantly Photograph: Francis Latreille/Corbis

Warming hits 'tipping point'

Question 7.3

(a)   As a fairly conservative estimate, suppose that the 70 Gt of CH_4 seeps out at a steady rate over the next 100 years. Calculate the annual rate of release averaged over this period, giving your answer in teragrams of CH_4 per year; i.e. $\text{Tg } CH_4 \text{ y}^{-1}$. (Refer back to Box 5.1, Section 5.2, for guidance on units.)

(b)   Now compare your answer to (a) with the projections of future emissions of CH_4 in Figure 6.9a (Question 6.2, page 175). On this basis, does the prospect of a persistent thaw of Siberian permafrost appear to be a legitimate cause for concern? Explain your answer.

(c)   The relative molecular mass of CH_4 is 16.0. Using the reasoning outlined in Box 5.1, estimate the mass of carbon in *all* of the CH_4 stored in permafrost around the world, giving your answer in GtC.

Concerns about warming-induced release of 'stored' methane do not end with melting permafrost. It is estimated that some *10 000* GtC of the gas is locked up in structures commonly known as **methane hydrates** (Figure 7.8a) in sediments on the ocean floor – double the amount of carbon in all the known reserves of coal, oil and natural gas (Figure 5.2). These hydrates are stable only at the low-temperature and high-pressure conditions found at depths of at least 500 m; they decompose rapidly above that depth (Figure 7.8b). Typically, hydrate deposits are found along the lower margins of continental slopes, where the sea floor drops sharply towards the abyss. If ocean warming penetrated sufficiently deeply to destabilise even a small portion of these deposits, huge quantities of CH_4 could be set free to exacerbate greenhouse warming.

At present, this is one of the more speculative scenarios in a global warming future, though something similar may have happened in the distant past. About 55 million years ago, the Earth experienced rapid climate warming. There is evidence to suggest that this could have been triggered by an explosive release of methane from marine hydrates, perhaps destabilised by gradual ocean warming.

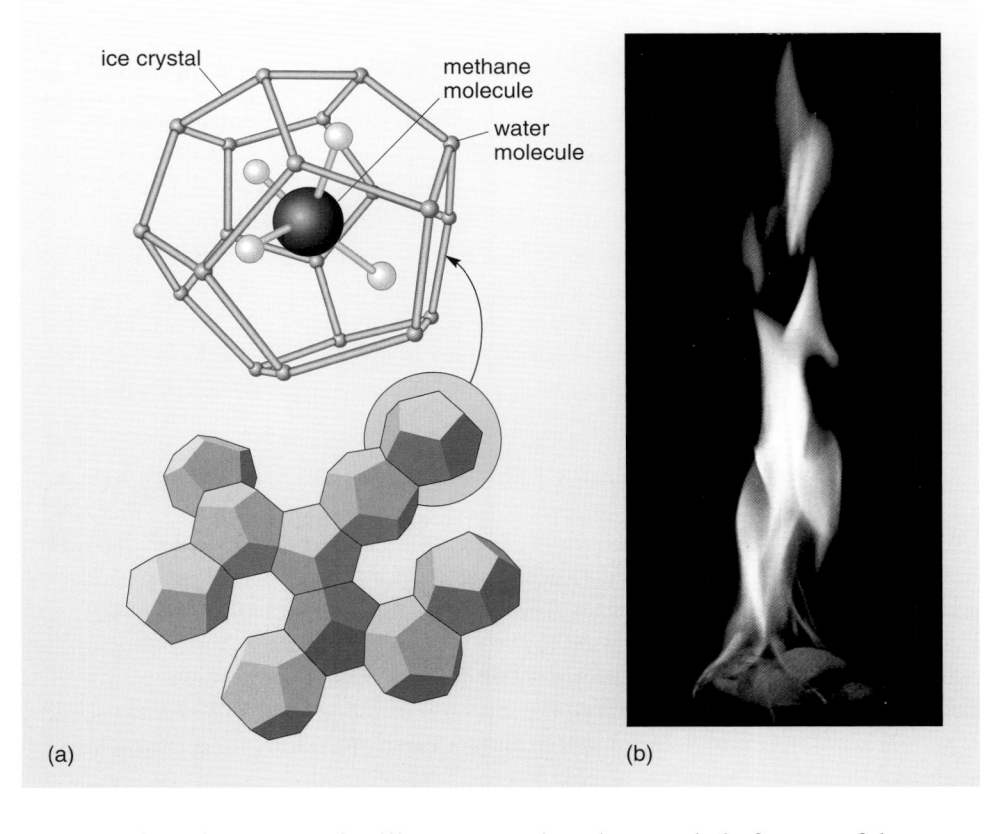

(a)

(b)

Figure 7.8 'Flammable ice'. (a) Methane hydrates (or more accurately, methane 'clathrates') consist of CH_4 molecules locked into a water–ice lattice. Deposits form when rising bubbles of methane (generated by microbial activity in sea floor sediments) become trapped under denser layers of mud. The gas reacts with near-freezing water to form what amounts to ice laced with methane. (b) Brought to the surface, the methane escaping from a lump of hydrate burns when ignited.

In conclusion: these examples illustrate another characteristic feature of the climate system. Once perturbed by sustained greenhouse warming, interactions and feedbacks within this complex, dynamic system can work to push some key factor over a critical threshold, and hence set in motion an uncontrollable (and often unstoppable) change that would have far-reaching implications. Perhaps human actions have already driven one component of the system (Siberian permafrost) across a potentially dangerous threshold. The likelihoods of the other outcomes noted above are not known, but there are good reasons to suppose that they will increase with the magnitude and rate of future global warming. And so could the risk of abrupt changes in many ecosystems. According to the IPCC TAR (IPCC, 2001d):

> Changes in disturbance regimes and shifts in the location of suitable climatically defined habitats may lead to abrupt breakdown of terrestrial and marine ecosystems with significant changes in composition and function and increased risk of extinctions.

Bear in mind too the perspective evident in the US Pentagon report referred to in Chapter 1 (Figure 1.1 and Section 1.5). By intensifying social, environmental and economic stress, the multiple impacts of climate change could well increase political instability, and the frequency and intensity of conflicts within and between nations. Mass migrations of environmental refugees, disputes over increasingly scarce resources (e.g. freshwater), clashes between ethnic groups or civil strife could all have potentially serious repercussions for the security interests of both developed and developing countries.

7.3 Defining a 'safe' level for stabilising greenhouse gas concentrations

The focus on severe impacts from climate extremes, and on possible 'tipping points' in physical systems, ecosystems and human societies alike, certainly brings home the message implicit in Figure 1.15: efforts to constrain the magnitude and rate of future climate change will reduce the risks of widespread damaging effects in all categories of 'reasons for concern'. But that does not, by itself, help us to pin down a specific target for climate stabilisation – in terms of an 'acceptable' increase in GMST over the next 100 or 150 years, say. Nor does it address the issue at the centre of the global political response in the UNFCCC: how low do we need to keep greenhouse gas concentrations to prevent this temperature target being reached?

A common framework for scientific assessment in this area is the construction of a range of 'stabilisation scenarios'; some typical examples are shown by the coloured plots in Figure 7.9 (ignore the black plots for now). Here, the analysis starts by defining a set of concentration profiles for atmospheric CO_2 that lead to eventual stabilisation at various levels (450 ppm, 550 ppm, etc; Figure 7.9b). Carbon cycle models are then used to 'work back' to the emissions pathway that would generate each concentration profile (Figure 7.9a). For all the reasons revisited above, assumptions about the strength of the terrestrial sink for CO_2 in future are an important determinant of the required emissions for a given stabilisation target. The grey area in Figure 7.9a spans the range of estimates produced by making various plausible assumptions about the strength of this sink: 'best guess' (the coloured lines); 'weak uptake' (requiring lower emissions for a given target); or 'strong uptake' (allowing higher emissions).

Figure 7.9   The time paths of global CO_2 emissions (a) that would lead to eventual stabilisation of atmospheric CO_2 concentrations at various specified levels (b), as estimated by carbon cycle models. The grey area in (a) illustrates the range of uncertainty in these model-based estimates; see text for further details. For comparison, three of the IPCC's alternative BaU futures are also included (black plots); see also Section 7.4.

■ What is the important general message to take from the stabilisation scenarios in Figure 7.9a?

■ The lower the chosen level for stabilising atmospheric CO_2, the sooner the decline in global emissions needs to begin, and the deeper the required cuts.

For example, these results indicate that stabilisation at 450, 650 or 1000 ppm would require global CO_2 emissions to drop below the year 1990 level (about 6 GtC from fossil fuels) within a few decades, about a century or about two centuries, respectively, and continue to decrease steadily thereafter. Indeed,

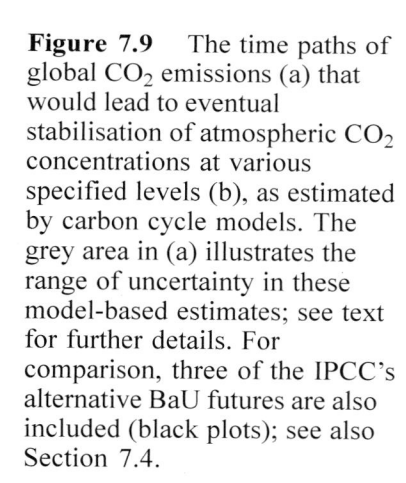

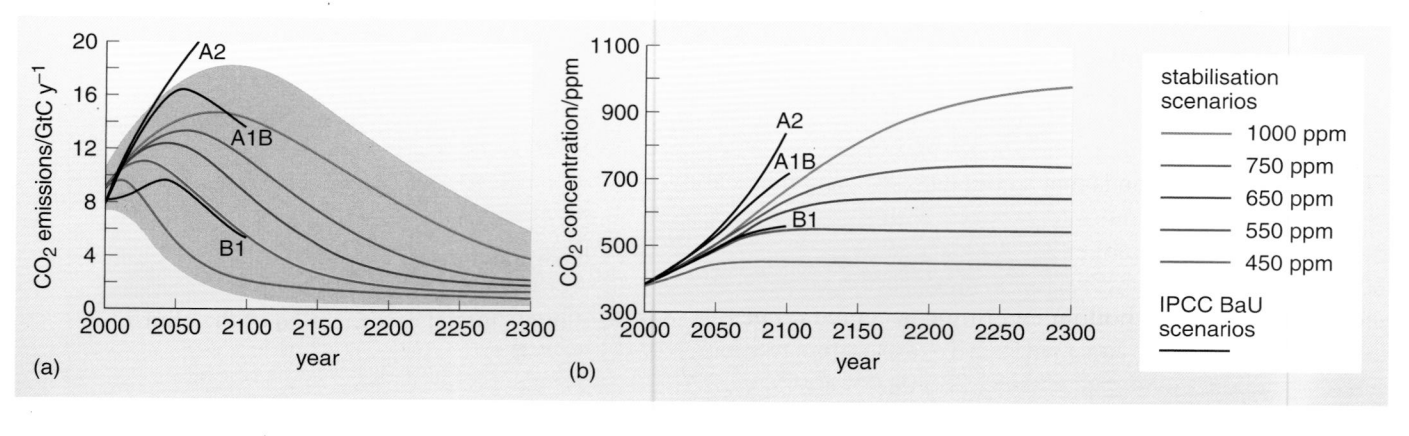

stabilisation at *any* level means that global emissions would need to decline eventually to a very small fraction of current levels, especially if the terrestrial carbon sink turns out to be weak. In the latter case, estimates suggest that CO_2-stabilisation at 450 ppm would require cuts of 60% or more by 2050.

Simple climate models (of the kind referred to in Section 6.4.2) have been used to explore the implications for global climate (i.e. GMST) of stabilisation scenarios like those in Figure 7.9. Again, uncertainty bedevils efforts to come up with a definitive answer to the question posed above. Or in the words of the IPCC (IPCC 2001d): 'for a specific temperature stabilization target there is a very wide range of uncertainty associated with the required stabilization level of greenhouse gas concentrations.'

■   What fundamental source of uncertainty about the global climate's response to greenhouse forcing is likely to lie behind this difficulty?

▨   The value of the climate sensitivity (i.e. the eventual equilibrium response to a CO_2-doubling; Section 6.4.1); recall that the 'official' range of values is 1.5 to 4.5 °C.

The results of a recent comprehensive modelling study summarised in Figure 7.10 illustrate the point. Here, the 'boundary' lines between the coloured bands (labelled 1.0 °C, 1.5 °C, etc.) record the projected rise in GMST by 2150 calculated by a simple climate model, as a function of two factors: the climate sensitivity value (on the horizontal axis) and the eventual CO_2-stabilisation level (vertical axis). In other words, each point on one of the labelled boundary lines is defined by a particular pair of values for climate sensitivity and CO_2-stabilisation.

There are several ways to interpret the information in Figure 7.10, but the one that illuminates the problem identified by the IPCC goes as follows. Suppose the international community agreed that the GMST rise by 2150 should be kept to 2 °C at most, for example.

■   On this basis, what would a climate sensitivity of 3 °C (the mid-point of the official range) mean for the CO_2-stabilisation level?

▨   It would need to be about 400 ppm – only 20 ppm or so above the current level. (You need to move vertically up from the point labelled '3.0' on the horizontal axis until you hit the boundary line labelled '2 °C', and then read across to the vertical axis.)

The further implication is that a climate sensitivity much above 3 °C would require stabilisation at CO_2 concentrations well below those of today – a virtually impossible task, given the scenarios in Figure 7.9. On the other hand, if the climate sensitivity was at the bottom end of the accepted range (i.e. 1.5 °C), stabilisation could be as high as 700 ppm and still allow the global temperature rise by 2150 to be limited to 2 °C.

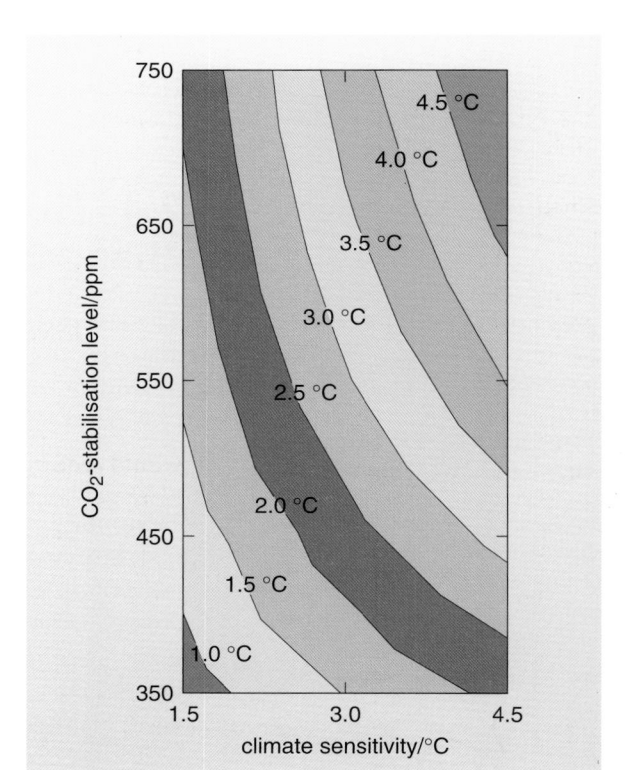

Figure 7.10   Projected rise in GMST by 2150 (above the 1990 value) calculated by a simple climate model as a function of the climate sensitivity and stabilisation scenario; see text for further details. (Hadley Centre, 2005.)

Clearly, the very large uncertainty about climate sensitivity is going to be unhelpful (to say the least!) in the political wrangling over what constitutes a 'safe' ceiling for atmospheric CO_2. Nor do the difficulties end there (Hadley Centre, 2005):

> In future, changes in other greenhouse gases are likely to contribute the equivalent of an additional 50–150 ppm of CO_2 to the warming effect. Thus, if we estimate that we need to stabilise climate at CO_2 concentrations of 550 ppm, this might mean – in practice – stabilising CO_2 itself at concentrations of, say, 450 ppm, allowing for an equivalent of a further 100 ppm from other greenhouse gases.

Finally, we need to bear in mind the all-important implications of inertia in the climate system (another key point in Activity 6.1). The analysis in Figure 7.10 relates to the *realised* warming by 2150. For most stabilisation scenarios, the world would be committed to a further rise in global temperature for centuries thereafter. Recent model-based estimates of the *eventual* (equilibrium) temperature rise (above the 1990 level) range from 1.5 to 3.9 °C for stabilising CO_2 (or its equivalent) at 450 ppm, for example; the range lies between 3.5 °C and a (frightening) 8.7 °C for stabilisation at 1000 ppm. Equally, modelling studies assessed in the IPCC TAR project an eventual sea-level rise of several metres over the centuries to millennia ahead – even for stabilisation levels of 550 ppm CO_2-equivalent.

How many other issues require policy makers to think through the implications of their decisions on a millennial time-scale!

7.4 Thinking through the challenge of climate change: an integrated approach

The emergence of a clear 'greenhouse warming' signal has changed perceptions about the urgency of tackling climate change. Around the world, there is now mounting pressure for governments to take further steps towards stabilising greenhouse gas concentrations, though the target level remains unclear. For their part, world leaders are concerned not only about the multiple impacts of unmitigated climate change, but also about the impacts of climate policies on economic growth, energy security, business cycles, unemployment, political instability and so on. How are they to weigh up the social, economic and political risks of different courses of action? Or in terms of the UNFCCC process, how are negotiators to establish effective, long-term climate policies in the face of many divergent interests – not just the differing priorities of developed and developing countries, for example, but also the long list of other 'actors' with a stake in influencing policy at the national or international level (e.g. large multinational fossil fuel companies, business, industry and commerce, consumers, environmental NGOs, the media, religious groups, etc.). Recall your thoughts on Activity 1.2, and the link with complex development and equity issues raised elsewhere in Chapter 1.

Leaving aside the 'do little or nothing' option, there are two basic ways of responding to the risks of climate change:

- **Mitigation**: Action to reduce emissions of greenhouse gases (e.g. the Kyoto 2012 targets for industrialised nations), or to enhance their sinks (e.g. planting forest 'sinks' to offset CO_2 emissions; Activity 5.1, Section 5.4).

- **Adaptation**: This takes in any adjustment to existing practices or infrastructure that would help to lessen or insure against the impacts of actual or anticipated climate change.

So far, the UNFCCC process has been focused almost entirely on mitigation, the aim being to address the driving force behind global warming. But bear in mind the point flagged up in connection with flood risk in the UK (Section 7.2.1): with or without further action on mitigation, regions around the world may well be facing significant risks from *unavoidable* climate change over the next 50 years or so, due to past greenhouse gas emissions. Societies will be obliged to cope with the changes that do occur.

Just as there is a spectrum of mitigation options (revisited later in Activity 7.1), so there is a wide range of possible adaptation measures that can be taken across different sectors (e.g. coastal zones, agriculture, water resources, human settlements, etc.; Figure 1.13, Section 1.5). For example, policies for adapting to sea-level rise could include improved flood defences of various kinds (Figure 7.11a), or the progressive abandonment of high-risk coastal areas. Adapting to the prospect of more frequent torrential downpours would usefully include action to address the many non-climatic factors that already exacerbate the risks of river and urban flooding, and add to their human and economic costs (Figure 7.11b). Equally, investment in reservoirs and in improved or more flexible water-distribution systems would make for more secure water supplies in the face of changing (or more unpredictable) rainfall patterns – as would policies to encourage reduced water use or recycling schemes. Similarly, there is a range of potential strategies to adapt agricultural production to changing climatic conditions (an area touched on in Section 1.5). Examples include: different crops or livestock; changed farming practices (e.g. planting/harvest times); improved irrigation systems; new heat/drought-tolerant crop varieties (developed through conventional breeding techniques or genetic manipulation; Topic 6). And so on.

By their nature, adaptation strategies are directed at addressing the local or regional impacts of climate change – just the aspect of climate model projections

Figure 7.11 Strategies for managing the risk of flooding in Europe. (a) Large engineering works have long gestation times and long lifetimes. In the UK, studies are starting for replacing or upgrading the Thames Flood Barrier around 2030; the new defences will be expected to work for many decades thereafter. (b) An innovative adaptation strategy in the Netherlands, Europe's lowest-lying country. These homes beside the River Meuse are designed to rise up and float on flood water the next time the river bursts its banks.

(a)

(b)

that is most uncertain. What we can say, however, is that the *slower* the rate of climate change, the lower the costs of adaptation are likely to be. Societies are in any case continually involved in upgrading facilities, or engaged in new investments. The effects of gradual trends in regional climates and sea level could be taken into account in planning decisions, allowing the social and economic costs of possible adaptation to be spread over a longer period. Even so, vulnerable developing countries are unlikely to have the resources needed to invest in effective adaptation measures – not without outside assistance, at least – leaving them more exposed to the damage wrought by future climate change (an ethical perspective emphasised in Chapter 1).

In the language of economists, the message to take from this brief discussion is simple: there are trade-offs between the costs of mitigation and adaptation on the one hand – and on the other, the damage costs arising from climate change that would occur in the absence of such precautionary action. For large greenhouse-gas emitters (e.g. the US, Europe and, increasingly, China and India), all three entries in the 'balance sheet' come into the assessment of options that would minimise the overall human welfare loss. Less climate change in future means that mitigation also benefits industrialised nations (Annex I countries; Box 1.3) in another way: a further ethical aspect of the UNFCCC is that they have obligations to assist poorer less-developed countries to adapt to climate change, or to compensate them for any damages. By contrast, small emitters (e.g. small island nations and, in fact, the majority of the 191 UN member states) are mainly interested in limiting the amount of residual climate damage they will suffer. Many of these countries account for only a fraction of 1% of total global emissions; whatever they do individually will make little difference to the future climate.

At the global level, the net balance of mitigation, adaptation and damage costs (and the distribution of winners and losers therein) lies at the heart of political debates about the best (such as least costly, or more equitable) course of action to take over the years and decades ahead. The challenge of dealing with climate change is to find solutions to this conundrum that have wide acceptance; it is anything but simple.

The ever more detailed (and expensive) calculations carried out by state-of-the-art climate models cannot, by themselves, provide solutions to this conundrum. Policy makers need guidance on the *full* implications of different climate policies (e.g. a particular time-evolving regime for reducing CO_2 emissions) – assessments that take into account both the direct costs of mitigation (i.e. the impact on society and the economy), and the indirect costs of adaptation and residual climate damage (through the impacts of climate change). The goal is to identify the mitigation strategies that would help to minimise the *total* costs of climate change (i.e. the sum of mitigation, adaptation and damage costs).

To that end, climate scientists are now collaborating with economists, sociologists, political scientists and others in an effort to understand, and then model, the highly complex two-way interactions between the climate system and the global 'socioeconomic system' (i.e. human societies around the world). This interdisciplinary approach has led to the development of a new generation of 'decision-support tools', known as integrated assessment models (IAMs). In principle, such models should incorporate detailed sub-models of both the climate system and the socioeconomic system, and allow these two systems to interact in a dynamic way in response to different 'what if' choices about global climate policy (Figure 7.12).

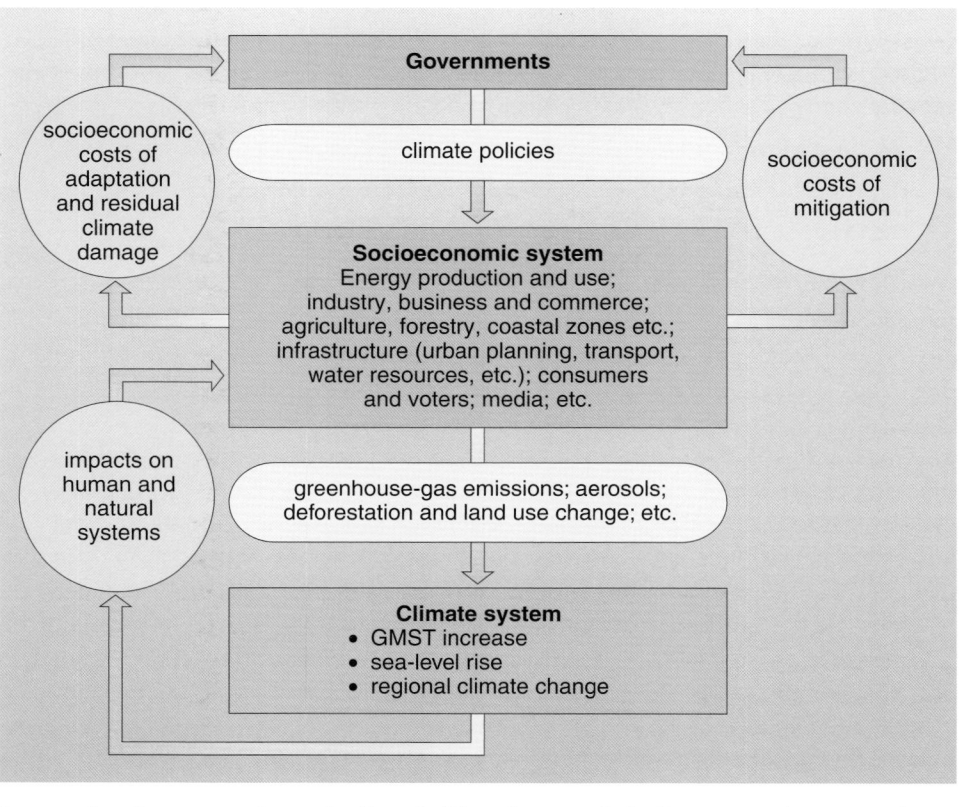

Figure 7.12 Integrated assessment models can help climate researchers understand the highly complex climate–socioeconomic system, providing input for decision-making on climate change. In these models, the climate system and the socioeconomic system are treated as separate subsystems that interact via the human activities that affect climate (emissions of greenhouse gases and aerosols, deforestation and land-use change, etc.); and conversely, through the impacts of climate change on human societies – both directly (via sea-level rise, food production, etc.) and indirectly (via the effects of less tangible but important factors such as the loss of biodiversity, increased migration pressures, etc.).

In practice, however, the task of modelling the coupled climate–socioeconomic system presents a formidable challenge. For a start, it takes the resources of the world's largest supercomputers to fully simulate the workings of the climate system alone (Chapter 6). The global socioeconomic system is undoubtedly as complex as the climate system; worse still, there is not even a consensus about how a 'realistic' model should be put together. Different experts bring very different perspectives to the question of how the 'real world' socioeconomic system actually functions, and how it is likely to be affected by the actions and divergent interests and values of the many 'stakeholders' in the climate change issue referred to earlier. Recall too that any assessment of the 'costs' of climate change raises another set of difficult and controversial questions (Chapter 1): how do you assign monetary values to the loss of species and habitats, to the interests of future generations, and even to such intangible factors as the aesthetic value of a cherished landscape?

Difficulties and controversies of this kind are unlikely to be resolved on the time-scale needed to support decision-making on climate change. Instead, current IAMs sacrifice detail in favour of speed. Typically, they include a highly simplified model of the climate system, capable of running through a climate change simulation in a matter of minutes on a modern PC or laptop. This allows researchers to carry out a large number of coupled simulations with different candidate socioeconomic models – and for a wide range of possible mitigation strategies. Unsurprisingly, the 'solutions' generated by such integrated assessments are strongly dependent on the assumptions embedded in the socioeconomic component. If the outputs from IAM studies are to be used to inform decision-making on climate change, it is important to interrogate these assumptions, and make clear the origins of different views on what might constitute the 'best' course of action to take. With this in mind, we close this section with a brief look at some of the key factors that affect perceptions of the climate change challenge, and the costs of dealing with it; specifically:

- the target level for stabilising greenhouse gas concentrations
- the speed of mitigation
- the range of countries sharing the burden of mitigation
- the costs and acceptability of various mitigation options.

In general, the lower the stabilisation level sought, the more challenging and costly it is likely to be, since this is working against the prevailing upward trend in emissions (evident in Figure 5.12, Section 5.6). However, there is also a more subtle point in this context, brought out by including three of the IPCC's alternative 'business-as-usual' (BaU) emission scenarios in Figure 7.9a (the black plots labelled A2, A1B and B1). *Perceptions* of the challenge posed by stabilising atmospheric CO_2 at a particular level also depend critically on what assumptions are made about how global emissions would evolve *in the absence* of direct 'climate policy' intervention. Thus, for example, if you believe that the world is likely to follow a low-carbon (B1) pathway anyway, we could already be on course to stabilise CO_2 at roughly double the pre-industrial level (i.e. around 550 ppm) by the end of the century; it would take relatively little extra effort (i.e. cost) to keep the eventual level even lower (at 450 ppm, say). By contrast, if you believe that a BaU future would entail ever-rising emissions (as in the A2 scenario, say), then the perceived costs of stabilisation at (or below) 550 ppm are going to be very high. In other words, the gap between climate goals (stabilisation targets) and the 'baseline' (whatever BaU future you think is more likely) is a measure of the size of the challenge that lies ahead.

Turning to the second bullet point, the timing of cutbacks in CO_2 emissions also critically affects costs. However, there are arguments both for and against early mitigation. As summarised in a recent article (O'Neil and Oppenheimer, 2002):

> Some studies find justification for preferring reductions sooner rather than later in order to account for the inertia in energy systems, to stimulate technological development, or to hedge against uncertain future concentration limits. Others conclude that although early investment in research and development may be justified, undertaking emissions reductions later can lower costs, even when accounting for uncertain concentration limits, by avoiding premature retirement of capital [e.g. coal-fired power stations, industrial plant, etc.] [...] and allowing for technical progress. However, at a certain point, postponing mitigation requires unrealistically rapid emissions reductions, especially for low stabilization targets.

The third bullet point in our list very much reflects the *realpolitik* of the climate change issue: it is a global problem, which requires a global response – an imperative brought into sharper focus by the following question.

Question 7.4

The information in Figure 5.12 can be used to make a rough estimate of how rapidly CO_2 emissions from developed (Annex I) and developing (Non-Annex I) countries have risen over recent decades. On this basis: in 1960, annual emissions were about 2 GtC y^{-1} (Annex I) and 0.6 GtC y^{-1} (Non-Annex I); by 2000, these figures had risen to about 3.6 GtC y^{-1} and 3.0 GtC y^{-1}, respectively. Calculate the percentage increase in annual emissions from developed and developing countries over the period 1960 to 2000.

In short, CO_2 emissions from developing countries are currently growing five times faster than in the industrialised world. Indeed, the rapidly 'emerging' economies of China and India already account for some 14% and 4%, respectively, of global CO_2 emissions. Bear in mind, though, that there are still major disparities in the average *per capita* emissions between developed and developing countries; currently, these stand at about 3.5 tC y^{-1} and 0.6 tC y^{-1}, respectively. Nevertheless, several studies with IAMs have concluded that achieving the ultimate goal of the UNFCCC depends crucially on increasing the participation of developing countries in the climate regime; the industrialised world cannot continue to 'go it alone'. Yet there are real tensions and conflicts inherent in this scenario – notably over the issue of equity. Any target for CO_2-stabilisation implicitly puts an absolute limit on cumulative emissions over the century ahead. But how should that global total be allocated among nations?

One avowedly fair approach, known as 'contraction and convergence', is based on the principle that every person on the planet should have an equal right to emit CO_2 to the atmosphere; in effect, each of us should be allocated the same 'carbon budget' to spend. This approach goes back to the 1990s, and there are now several variations on the theme of 'equitable allocation'. Some of these are based on geographical area, for example, some on historical responsibility for emissions, on the level of economic activity, or a combination of all of these.

Whatever the details, approaches of this kind envisage a global market in emissions entitlements. Those nations with per capita emissions below their entitlement (currently likely to be less-developed countries) would be able to sell these surpluses to countries (almost certainly industrialised) with a deficit of permits. As well as encouraging emissions reductions or avoidance among all parties, this approach would also set in motion a huge flow of resources (for which read money) from rich to poor countries. Here we can make connections with an issue that is likely to be a major source of conflict in climate negotiations: in addition to reducing their own emissions, how much should industrialised countries contribute to the reduction of future emissions by developing nations?

The final bullet point in our list takes us back to the difficult questions raised in Chapter 1 and laid out in more detail in Chapter 5. Although ongoing deforestation in the tropics is a significant source of anthropogenic CO_2 (and a major conservation issue), addressing the CO_2-induced component of climate change is essentially an energy problem. Worldwide, primary power consumption today is around 12 TW (12×10^{12} W), of which 85% is fossil-fuelled. Can we break the link between economic growth, energy demand and the burning of fossil fuels? Or as one author has put it: 'Can we "decarbonize" the global economy without stifling it?'.

It would take a whole book to explore the full implications of these questions. What we can say, however, is that stabilising atmospheric CO_2 at (or below) double the pre-industrial level presupposes a radical break with the historical carbon-intensive path to economic development (recall the B1 storyline in Box 5.3). It will involve major changes over the coming decades – not only in energy technologies, but also in social and economic patterns. Take a few minutes to think about this.

Activity 7.1

Allow about 15 minutes

(a)   Drawing on the material in Chapter 5, list the major options for curbing global CO_2 emissions.

(b)   Now think about your *personal* (i.e. non-work-related) lifestyle for a moment. Jot down any ways in which you could 'do your bit' to reduce CO_2 emissions. What stops you? (It may help to organise your lifestyle under various headings, e.g. 'home', 'travel', etc.)

Major debates today revolve around the social and economic costs, technical performance and acceptability of the various energy supply-side and demand-side options touched on in Activity 7.1, and their potential contribution to the task of mitigating climate change. Though experts agree that efforts to rein in end-use energy demand could have a significant impact on global emissions, many studies have concluded that this will not be nearly enough to allow CO_2-stabilisation (at 550 ppm, say) alongside ongoing economic development. According to one recent assessment (Hoffert *et al.*, 2002), to achieve that goal: 'Mid-century primary power requirements that are free of carbon dioxide emissions could be several times what we now derive from fossil fuels, even with improvements in energy efficiency.'

This assessment may be overly pessimistic, but it does bring the spotlight to bear on the portfolio of possible carbon-free or carbon-neutral energy options (Activity 7.1), and their potential for large-scale commercialisation, especially in the all-important area of electricity generation. Here, some countries already rely heavily on nuclear and hydroelectric power. Collectively, other 'renewable' energy sources (biomass, solar, wind, wave, tidal, etc.) currently account for less than 1% of global power supplies. Lack of investment in the past has left some of these technologies far from fully developed and/or the electricity generated is uncompetitive at present prices.

As with the take-up of energy-saving measures, however, economic and technical factors are not the only obstacles to a major scale-up in the contributions from non-fossil-fuel energy systems; not all the possible options are welcomed by everybody. For example, the possibility that the 'clean development mechanism' (included in the terms of the Kyoto Protocol; Box 1.3) will encourage developing countries to adopt nuclear or certain renewable energy options (e.g. 'big hydro' projects or large-scale biomass plantations) has generated considerable concern among environmental NGOs and other stakeholders. Closer to home, the prospect of renewed investment in nuclear power in the UK is hotly contested, and there is growing opposition to the siting of wind farms as well (Figure 7.13).

(a) (b)

Figure 7.13 To exploit the renewable energy resource offered by Britain's windy climate, wind farms have usually been sited in open, exposed locations – either (a) offshore or (b) in upland rural areas. Objections to the proliferation of wind farms tend to revolve around three main issues: the noise of the turbines; the potential dangers to bird life (if sited close to a migration route, say); and the visual impact of the turbine towers. To some, they represent an elegant source of 'green' electricity; to others, they threaten to blight areas of outstanding natural beauty with ugly eyesores.

Other mitigation options can be equally controversial. Chief among these is the notion of '**carbon capture and storage**' (i.e. carbon sequestration).

■ Where have you met this idea before?

▨ In the context of proposals to remove CO_2 from the atmosphere and lock up the carbon in long-term storage, either on land (by planting forest sinks) or in the deep ocean (by manipulating the biological pump).

The risks and uncertainties associated with these 'biological' sequestration schemes were well rehearsed in Activities 5.1 and 5.2. An alternative 'technical' option is to capture the CO_2 generated by burning fossil fuels *before* it is released to the atmosphere – by removing it from power station flue gases, for example, much as SO_2 is now 'scrubbed out' in response to the acid rain problem. Though technically feasible (Box 7.2), CO_2 capture can be expensive, and itself consumes significant amounts of energy.

Box 7.2 'Scrubbing out' CO_2

CO_2 emissions produced by fossil-fuelled power plants can be captured using commercially available 'chemical absorption' technology. The underlying chemistry involves the reaction between CO_2 and an aqueous solution of an organic amine (represented here as $R-NH_2$): the CO_2 goes into solution as the bicarbonate ion ($R-NH_2 + H_2O + CO_2 \longrightarrow R-NH_3^+ + HCO_3^-$), and is recovered by heating. When oil prices were high in the late 1970s and early 1980s, CO_2 was routinely captured from US power plants for use in 'enhanced oil recovery' operations; pumped down into depleted oilfields, it helps to squeeze out the remaining reserves of oil. When oil prices fell in the mid-1980s, such operations became uneconomic and most CO_2-recovery plants were shut down. However, opportunities for significant cost reductions exist, since very little R&D has been devoted to CO_2 separation and capture technologies. Several innovative schemes are currently being explored – another area where science connects with the climate change issue. The US government is investing billions of dollars in the process – a 'magic bullet' that will allow continued use of its abundant coal stocks for electricity generation?

More telling is the concomitant problem of disposing of the vast amounts of captured CO_2. Scenarios that are the focus of current research include piping the gas to sites where it can be pumped down into various geological reservoirs; examples include exhausted oil and gas fields or deep waterlogged rock formations (aquifers) either on land or under the sea bed (e.g. beneath the North Sea). Alternatively, researchers envisage direct injection into the deep ocean: liquefied CO_2 would be released 1000 m or more deep, either from stations on shore or from tankers trailing long pipes at sea. Yet another proposal draws inspiration from the weathering reactions of silicate rocks, which remove CO_2 from the atmosphere on geological time-scales. The idea is to vastly accelerate this natural process, and thereby sequester carbon as solid 'bricks' of magnesium carbonate ($MgCO_3$). In highly simplified chemical terms, the overall process can be represented as:

$$MgSiO_3 \text{ (e.g. the mineral serpentine)} + CO_2 \longrightarrow MgCO_3 + SiO_2 \text{ (silica)}$$

Whatever the details, carbon capture and storage looks set to become a key battleground in the debate about tackling climate change. Supporters contend that sequestration technologies will be a necessary part of the transition to a non-carbon energy economy. Critics argue that the whole approach, which amounts to continuing to dump 'waste' CO_2, is wrong-headed. For many environmentalists, the idea is an expensive and unproven smokescreen for continued reliance on fossil fuels, and likely to divert funds from what should be the top priority: targeted investment in R&D into the efficient, zero-carbon energy systems of the future. There are also unanswered questions about the safety and long-term security of proposed CO_2-disposal sites. Could the gas stored underground or beneath the sea floor leak out over time and make its way back into the atmosphere, or have other environmental effects? Certainly, the largely unknown implications of leakage into the marine environment is a valid concern – an issue likely to be a major obstacle to any plans for direct ocean disposal of CO_2 (which could also contravene various treaties aimed at restricting dumping wastes at sea).

Finally, no discussion of global warming mitigation would be complete without a brief mention of 'geoengineering'. Typically, 'technical fixes' of this kind envisage ways of *deliberately* manipulating the Earth's radiation balance, in an effort to counteract the *inadvertent* modification brought about by increased greenhouse gas concentrations. Most such proposals are variations on the sunlight-blocking theme (i.e. they would aim to increase the planetary albedo). Examples include injecting billions of tiny metallic particles into the stratosphere, increasing cloud cover by artificial seeding, and shadowing the Earth by objects deployed in space. We leave you to ponder on the risks inherent in such high-tech 'solutions' to the greenhouse warming problem.

7.5 Final thoughts

When the definitive history of how humanity woke up to the full implications of its 'experiment' with the climate system is written, certain dates and events will stand as enduring milestones (notably those referred to in Chapter 1). It is possible that 2005 will also feature somewhere in that canon. At the beginning of that year, the legally binding Kyoto targets finally came into force, following ratification of the protocol by the Russian Duma (parliament). In the early hours of 10 December 2005, weary negotiators at climate change talks in Montreal (a meeting of parties to the UNFCCC) achieved a series of breakthroughs. First, the 157 nations signed up to Kyoto agreed to extend the protocol when its first phase expires in 2012; harsher cutbacks in emissions from industrialised countries are firmly on the agenda for the next phase, though the details and timing remain unclear. Secondly, China and India agreed to take an active part in a parallel process, aimed at increasing the participation of other big emitters. And so, eventually, did the US government delegation (Figure 7.14) – provided any such process does not amount to negotiating mandatory cuts in emissions!

Figure 7.14 Citizen pressure for action on climate change. In December 2005, cities around the world saw demonstrations timed to coincide with the start of climate talks in Montreal – the first in a series of annual meetings of parties to the UNFCCC (known as a 'Conference of the Parties' or COP meeting) to be held in North America. As a result, US journalists flooded in, along with environmental campaigners and delegations from many parts of American society: state governments, cities, business, trade unions, religious and youth groups, etc. Stung by press criticism of its obstructive stance at the talks, and faced with the rest of the world's resolve to press ahead regardless, the Bush Administration made a last-minute U-turn and signed up to a statement calling for international cooperation on the climate change issue. It remains to be seen what this will mean in practice. The US is still outside the global climate policy regime (i.e. the Kyoto agreement), and seems to be wedded to an approach based on voluntary actions and 'partnerships'.

It would be naïve to interpret this agreement as a seismic shift in the long-standing intransigence of the Bush Administration. Still, there are signs that the pressure for action on climate change is growing within the US: several groups of states have already launched their own carbon-trading schemes; 192 cities and dozens of leading US companies are making efforts to cut their emissions. On the other hand, the gap between rhetoric and reality appears to be growing elsewhere in the developed world. Within the EU, for example, the general

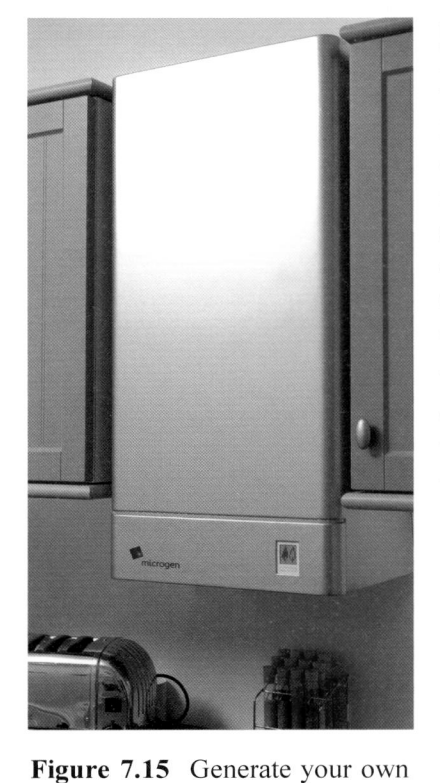

Figure 7.15 Generate your own electricity and, at the same time, heat your home. The image shows an example of the clean-burning, highly efficient 'micro-CHP' (combined heat and power) systems that are now becoming available for individual households. Usually fuelled by natural gas, these systems are capable of converting over 85% of the energy content of fuel into useful heat and electrical power. By contrast, in a conventional fossil-fuelled power station, only some 30–40% of the heat released by burning the fuel is actually converted to electricity; the rest is dissipated as 'waste' heat into the environment. In a micro-CHP unit, the latter is used to operate a domestic heating system, allowing a significant reduction in fuel consumption, and hence CO_2 emissions, for a given level of end-use energy (i.e. combined heat and power) demand. Any surplus power generated can be fed back into the national grid, further reducing household electricity bills.

picture is of rising emissions; few countries are currently on track to meet their Kyoto 2012 targets. Britain is one of these, but is still likely to fall well short of the government's own (more ambitious) target of a 20% cut on 1990 emission levels by 2010. Commentators point to a complicated mix of factors: the near-exhaustion of UK North Sea gas fields, leaving the country exposed to global markets that currently favour the economics of coal; electricity trading arrangements that favour big, centralised generation over more dispersed options (e.g. Figure 7.15); cutbacks in support for renewable technologies; no clear long-term energy policy, combined with a lack of 'joined-up' thinking among relevant government departments; and so on.

These comments rehearse in microcosm the highly complex realities of tackling climate change – the message we have sought to stress throughout this topic. In the words of Irving M. Mintzer, written as the world took its first tentative step towards a global climate policy regime, but still relevant today (Mintzer, 1992):

> If you come away from this volume with one understanding, it should be of the importance of linkages: the interconnections between the risks of rapid climate change and so many other problems of central concern to national governments, corporate leaders, non-governmental organisations, and individual citizens. Climate change is inexorably linked to ozone depletion, acid deposition and urban pollution, deforestation and loss of biological diversity, and desertification. It is intimately tied to the most vital economic undertakings of our time – energy production and use, transportation, agriculture, forestry, building construction, industry and manufacturing, and so on. It affects (and is affected by) the fundamental concerns of human society: population growth, urban density and planning, management (and mismanagement) of institutions, and the quality of life for individuals and families. It is no accident that environmental matters, and particularly global warming, have captured the attention of schoolchildren around the planet. What we decide now is shaping their world.

> Finally, consideration of climate change is necessarily involved in the great policy negotiations of our time – not only through new environmental treaties, but also through trade negotiations, water rights disputes, and international security debates. The implementation of a framework convention on climate change [i.e. the UNFCCC] could affect all these issues.

> Certainly, dealing with the risks of rapid climate change would be easier if the risks themselves were well characterised and carefully quantified. Today, neither is completely possible […]. The best efforts of the international scientific community – embodied in billions of dollars of research – will leave major uncertainties unresolved for decades to come.

> […] scientific uncertainties have allowed governments to assume that climate change dangers were unimportant, exaggerated or premature. Such nonchalance can no longer be maintained without sobering political and environmental consequences […]. How then are governments, corporations, and individuals to respond? Science offers us no quick fix or magic solution. We face instead a problem of risk management.

Nearly a decade later, the IPCC TAR referred to this task as 'sequential decision making under uncertainty'. To decide about actions on climate change is to anticipate and weigh-up consequences. As you have seen, that means bringing together insights from all kinds of intellectual endeavour – not just virtually every branch of science, but also cutting-edge technology, the politics and economics of development, the sociology of consumption, and so on. Given the uncertainties in our knowledge and understanding, and the sheer ambition of the interdisciplinary exercise, there are bound to be many fuzzy edges.

The IAMs referred to earlier are beginning to provide insights into the pros and cons of different policy choices, but these are very early days for such integrated assessments. In the meantime, 'hedging' strategies and 'sequential decision making' seem to be appropriate responses to the combination of uncertainty and inertia that characterises the climate change issue. In IPCC language: 'The challenge now is not to find the best policy today for the next hundred years, but to select a prudent strategy and to adjust it over time in the light of new information.' We are right at the start of this process. In the years and decades ahead, we are likely to witness intense and controversial debates over how all nations can move forward together in the effort to map out an equitable approach to climate stabilisation – the ultimate objective of the UNFCCC. It will be all too easy to lose heart. So let's end, with Mintzer, on a more upbeat note:

> In conclusion, we want to emphasise that the international process of managing the risks of rapid climate change is not just an exercise in damage control. It offers an important – and in some ways unique – opportunity: to use the threat of global environmental change as a vehicle for expanding international cooperation […] and as an incentive for the development of the advanced, more efficient, and less polluting technologies that can propel humankind forward into the 21st century. If the human race embraces the challenges which this opportunity presents – enthusiastically, energetically and with good courage – then we may truly be on the path to a sustainable world.

Or, to put the matter more simply (Oreskes, 2004): 'our grandchildren will surely blame us if they find that we understood the reality of anthropogenic climate change and failed to do anything about it'.

Learning Outcomes for Topic 5

In order to grasp a topic as complex as climate change, it is necessary to know about and understand a considerable amount of interdisciplinary science (Kn1) and also appreciate the importance of uncertainty in the underlying data (Kn2). In addition to understanding climate in the 'real world', it is also necessary to understand the power and limitations of climate models. Equally important are knowledge and understanding of how information about climate change is communicated between scientists, decision makers and members of the public (Kn3); the possible adverse consequences of climate change (Kn4); ethical issues related to inter-regional and intergenerational responsibilities (Kn5); and the process of decision making in the context of the entire planet for hundreds or thousands of years into the future (Kn6).

The complexity of the 'science' underpinning climate change and the interaction of its consequences with the lives of ordinary people everywhere, provide considerable scope for developing cognitive skills. These include interpreting, evaluating and synthesising scientific information bearing in mind any limitations in the data (C1), recognising influences on the debate that emanate from outside science (C2), making judgements in the face of contradictory scientific and other evidence (C3) and assessing the relative importance of scientific information and other factors in decision making about climate change (C4). Unexpected developments within climate change or related to it will almost certainly occur during the lifetime of S250 and may need to be considered (C5).

There is, of course, a huge amount of information related to climate change from which appropriate selections have to be made (Ky1). Although much of the data related to climate change are quantitative, it is sometimes necessary to work with qualitative information (Ky2, Ky3). Given its complexity and 'real world' relevance, this topic provides plenty of opportunity for you to hone your skills of communication (Ky4) and working with others (Ky5). Again, the very complexity of this topic might provide the motivation necessary to develop your skills of effective learning (Ky6).

Answers to questions

Question 2.1

White light contains *all* visible wavelengths (Box 2.1), whereas red light is at the long wavelength end of the visible band (Figure 2.1). 'White-hot' objects therefore emit light of shorter average wavelength than cooler 'red-hot' ones. Generalising, as the temperature of an object rises, so the average wavelength of the radiation it emits will decrease.

Question 2.2

The basic problem is the notion of a 'barrier across the terrestrial rays'. This could suggest that the atmosphere somehow 'reflects' back outgoing radiation (an error that sometimes appears in newspaper accounts to this day) and/or that *none* of it ever goes out to space – in which case the planet would simply heat up without limit! In reality, some of the longwave radiation from the surface escapes directly to space (at wavelengths in the 'atmospheric window'). The rest is *absorbed and re-emitted* (up and down) by greenhouse gases in the atmosphere. Back radiation from the atmosphere keeps the surface warmer than it otherwise would be (the natural greenhouse effect). But some of the re-emitted radiation ultimately goes out to space, maintaining an overall radiation balance at the top of the atmosphere.

Question 2.3

(a) The planetary albedo is the proportion of incoming solar radiation reflected (or scattered) directly back to space – 31 units according to Figure 2.11. Surface reflection contributes 9 units or $(9/31) \times 100\% = 29\%$. Snow- or ice-covered surfaces (predominantly at high latitudes) are likely to be mainly responsible, given their high albedo.

(b) (i) The total rate of energy gain by the Earth's surface is the sum of the appropriate downward-pointing arrows in Figure 2.11; i.e. $(49 + 95)$ units $= 144$ units. The total loss rate is the sum of the upward-pointing arrows that originate at the Earth's surface: $(30 + 114)$ units $= 144$ units. The difference is zero, so the surface is in a steady state; the GMST is not changing.

(ii) Proceeding as in (i), the total rate of energy gain by the atmosphere is: $(20 + 30 + 102)$ units $= 152$ units. The total rate of loss is: $(95 + 57)$ units $= 152$ units. The difference is again zero.

(iii) For the whole Earth–atmosphere system, the total rate of energy gain (solar radiation intercepted) is 100 units, and the total rate of loss is $(31 + 57 + 12)$ units $= 100$ units, confirming that the whole system is also in a steady state.

(c) The proportion is $(102/114) \times 100\% = 89\%$ (to 2 significant figures).

(d) 100 units is equivalent to 342 W m^{-2}, so 114 units is equivalent to $(342 \text{ W m}^{-2}/100) \times 114 = 390$ W m^{-2}. This is significantly higher than the rate of emission (236 W m^{-2}; Section 2.1.1) from a body with an effective radiating temperature of $-19\ ^\circ$C. Since the rate of emission increases with increasing temperature, this implies that the Earth's GMST is higher than $-19\ ^\circ$C.

Question 2.4

The radiative forcing is the difference between the rate at which the Earth–atmosphere system absorbs solar radiation and the rate at which it emits longwave radiation to space. From parts (b) and (c) of Figure 2.12, the *magnitude* of the radiative forcing is (69.69 − 69) units or (69 − 68.31) units = 0.69 units, which is equivalent to (342 W m^{-2}/100) × 0.69 = 2.4 W m^{-2} (to 2 significant figures). The forcing is positive for a 1% increase in the solar constant (Figure 2.12b) and negative for a 1% decrease (Figure 2.12c).

Question 2.5

(a) Both snow- or ice-cover on land and sea ice have a very high albedo (up to 90%), and so will reduce the amount of solar radiation absorbed.

(b) Replacing large areas of dark forest cover with vegetation that reflects a higher proportion of incident solar radiation effectively increases the planetary albedo; this constitutes a negative radiative forcing. (See Figure 3.14, Section 3.5.1 for an estimate of the effect this has had.)

Question 2.6

The main point here is that methane is a more powerful greenhouse gas than CO_2 (at least on a mass-for-mass basis; Table 2.2, Section 2.5).

Question 2.7

Something along the lines shown in Figure 2.20 would be appropriate. Note how a simple annotated diagram like this can communicate a lot of information, much of which would not need to be repeated in detail in the accompanying text (useful if you are working to a tight word limit). Note too that diagrams should always have a caption.

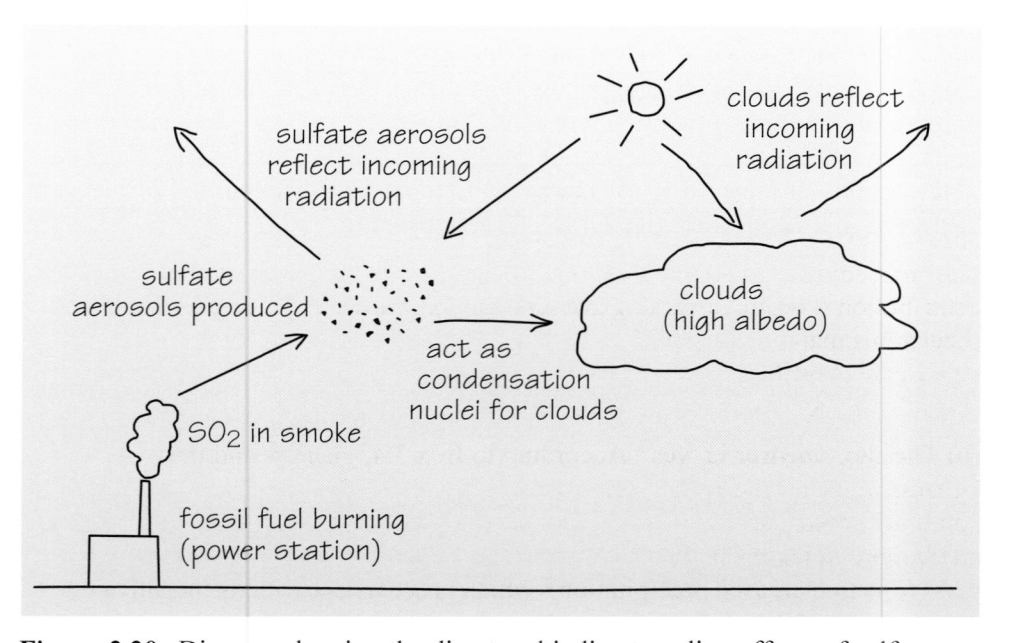

Figure 2.20   Diagram showing the direct and indirect cooling effects of sulfate aerosols in the lower atmosphere.

Question 3.1

The more recent estimate (0.6 °C) is 0.15 °C larger than that estimated in the IPCC's second report for the period up to 1994 (0.45 °C), mainly due to the exceptional warmth of the additional years (1995 to 2000; see Figure 3.3a). [According to the IPCC TAR, the recent estimate also involved improved methods of processing the data.]

Question 3.2

(a) Figure 3.16 shows how an increase in mean temperature shifts the whole bell-shaped curve to the right. This reduces the frequency of unusually cold days (effectively to zero, in the somewhat exaggerated situation depicted to the left in Figure 3.16), and increases the frequency of unusually hot days (i.e. the area under the curve above a given temperature, to the right in Figure 3.16, is now much larger). This pattern is consistent with the first two entries in Table 3.1.

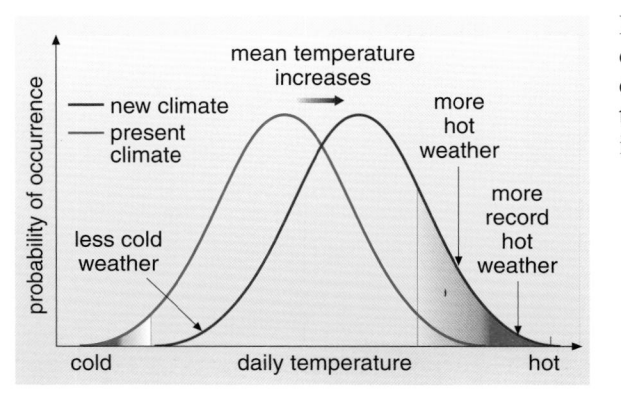

Figure 3.16 Schematic diagram showing the effect on extreme temperatures when the mean temperature increases.

(b) Shifts of the kind identified in (a) could have both beneficial effects (reducing the number of cold-related deaths in winter in some regions) and adverse effects (increasing the number of deaths due to heat stress). (See also Chapter 7.)

Question 3.3

(a) From the central estimates in Table 3.2, the major contribution to the observed rate of sea-level rise has come from the thermal expansion of seawater; this accounts for $(0.5/1.5) \times 100\% = 33\%$. The next-largest contribution was due to melting glaciers (20%), followed by 'long-term ice-sheet adjustment' (17%; this is something that will continue to make a significant contribution in future), and then loss of ice from the Greenland ice sheet due to 20th century warming (just 3%).

(b) The short answer is 'yes'. According to Box 3.4, glaciers and the Greenland ice sheet are expected to lose mass in a warmer climate (greater ablation exceeds any gains from increased precipitation), but glaciers respond much more quickly. By contrast, the Antarctic ice sheet is expected to gain mass (due to increased precipitation), which is consistent with the negative entry in Table 3.2 (i.e. this has partly offset the loss of ice elsewhere).

Question 3.4

(a) As noted in Section 3.1.2, the smoothed curve in the instrumental record (Figure 3.3a) traces a very irregular pattern of warming during the course of the 20th century. There is little direct correlation with the observed build up of greenhouse gases, which translates into a relatively *smooth and accelerating* increase in radiative forcing since pre-industrial times (Figure 3.13). In this context, the most striking inconsistency is the pause in the upward trend in GMST (or even a slight cooling; Activity 3.2) from the mid-1940s to the mid-1970s – whereas the greenhouse forcing shows the steepest increase from around 1950.

(b) Natural sources of radiative forcing include possible variations in the solar constant during the 20th century (could be either positive or negative forcing), together with the short-term negative forcing associated with volcanic activity. Other anthropogenic factors include: the cooling effects (both direct and indirect) of sulfates and most carbonaceous aerosols; the warming effects of 'black carbon' (Section 2.5); and the effect on surface albedo of widespread deforestation (likely to be negative forcing; Question 2.5b).

[The important general point is that variations in the Earth's GMST reflect the influence of the *total* radiative forcing of climate, and how this has evolved over time during the past century: deviations from the 'expected' steady warming trend due to greenhouse forcing alone are only to be expected. Keep this in mind as you work through the rest of Section 3.5.]

Question 3.5

'Switching on a kettle' is linked to sea-level rise by the following chain of 'cause-and-effect' relationships:

* burning fossil fuels (e.g. in a power station) causes the release of CO_2 to the atmosphere
* and has resulted in a build up of the gas since pre-industrial times.
* The effect is a temporary reduction in the longwave emission to space, disturbing the radiation balance at the top of the atmosphere and producing a positive radiative forcing of climate
* which has a warming effect, causing an increase in GMST.
* Higher temperatures, in turn, cause the thermal expansion of seawater and the melting of land ice
* increasing the volume of water in the ocean, and leading to sea-level rise.

Now compare the above with your notes on Activity 1.3a. Did you include all the steps at that stage? By now, of course, you will also be aware that many of the links in this chain are not that simple. For example, burning fossil fuels releases particulate matter as well, and that acts to partially offset greenhouse warming. Equally, there are 'time lags' between climate warming and the melting of land ice. And so on. These and other complexities in the climate change puzzle will occupy us for the rest of the topic.

Question 4.1

According to Figure 4.3, high precipitation is associated with rising air; e.g. the rising branch of the convective (Hadley) circulation at low latitudes. Rising air often has a high moisture content (due to evaporation at the surface); as it is carried upwards, it cools and may become saturated, leading to the condensation of water vapour onto condensation nuclei (Section 2.2.4). Clouds form, and may result in precipitation.

Question 4.2

(a) According to the global estimates in Figure 4.7, the total amounts of water entering and leaving the atmosphere each year (in units of 10^{15} kg y^{-1}) are as follows:

Entering: 434 (from the ocean) + 71 (from the land) = 505.

Leaving: 398 (to the ocean) + 107 (to the land) = 505.

The totals do indeed balance. Were this not the case, the water-vapour content of the atmosphere would gradually increase or decrease (a point we revisit in Question 4.5).

(b) No. Again in units of 10^{15} kg y^{-1}, over the ocean there is a *net* input of water to the atmosphere of (434–398) = 36, and a *net* loss over the land of (107–71) = 36. The overall cycle is balanced by the transport of airborne moisture from the ocean to the land by winds (36×10^{15} kg y^{-1}), and back again via a combination of 'surface runoff' (19×10^{15} kg y^{-1}) and 'underground flow' (17×10^{15} kg y^{-1}).

Question 4.3

The two roles identified so far are:

- The ocean is the main source of water vapour (the most important natural greenhouse gas), and hence latent heat, to the atmosphere (Figure 4.7).
- The influence of the ocean's thermal inertia (i.e. the differential heating of land and sea) on climate (Section 4.2) – both at the local level (e.g. its role in moderating seasonal temperature variations in maritime areas), and at the global scale (e.g. its role in the monsoon climates experienced by many low-latitude regions).

Question 4.4

(a) According to Figure 4.4a, the general pattern across the tropical South Pacific is warmer sea-surface temperatures to the west and cooler to the east.

(b) The two main factors can by deduced from the information in Figure 4.9:

- the influence of cooler subsurface water upwelling along the west coast of South America, and
- the influence of the surface ocean currents that make up the gyre in the South Pacific: the western limb brings warm waters from equatorial regions, whereas the eastern limb brings cold waters from higher latitudes.

Question 4.5

Higher temperatures give rise to increased evaporation and a warmer atmosphere can 'hold' more water vapour (a greenhouse gas) before becoming saturated. This further enhances the greenhouse effect which, in turn, leads to more warming of the surface and atmosphere. These stages form the components of the positive feedback loop illustrated in Figure 4.19.

Figure 4.19 Schematic diagram of the positive feedback loop whereby the warming induced by the build up of CO_2 (and other greenhouse gases) is amplified by the effect that has, in turn, on the total amount of water vapour in the atmosphere.

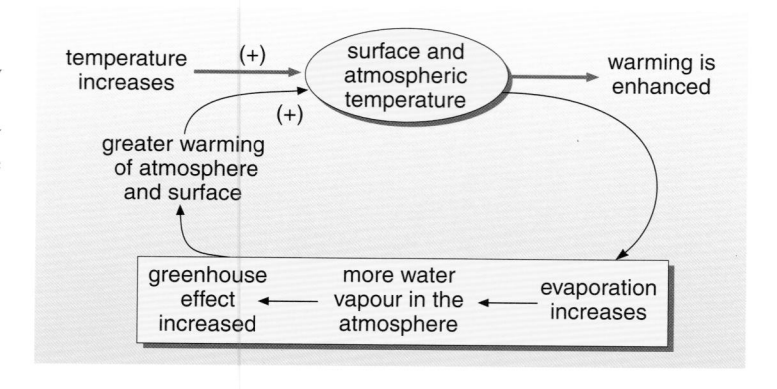

Question 4.6

(a) Hot, moist areas of tropical rainforest release large amount of water vapour (and hence latent heat) into the atmosphere through vigorous evapotranspiration (behaving rather like the tropical oceans in this respect). You might (correctly) expect latent heat transfer to be relatively low from arid desert regions and semi-arid grassland.

(b) Rainforest also traps and recycles water on a regional scale, so replacing large areas with grassland might be expected to lead to an overall 'drying' of the local climate.

Question 4.7

The relevant entries in Table 3.1 are the final three points under 'weather indicators' – changes to precipitation and to the frequency/severity of drought in different parts of the world. Shifts of the kind identified there are broadly consistent with an increase in the rate of the hydrological cycle; i.e. an increase in the overall rates of both evaporation and precipitation (due to the higher moisture content of a warmer atmosphere). Since any increase in rainfall is very unlikely to be distributed uniformly around the globe (or through the year), we might well expect to see both higher (and/or heavier) rainfall in some regions and an increased risk of seasonal drought elsewhere (e.g. due to the combined effects of reduced rainfall and enhanced evaporation).

Question 5.1

(a) From Figure 5.2, the carbon stored in plant biomass amounts to 500 GtC, and the total rate of input (or output) is 120 GtC y^{-1}. So the average residence time of carbon in this reservoir is (500 GtC/120 GtC y^{-1}) or about four years.

(b) Proceeding as in (a), the average residence time of carbon in the soil is (1500 GtC/60 GtC y^{-1}) or about 25 years.

Question 5.2

The comparisons show different geographical patterns: (a) total carbon stocks in the world's forests are in the order tropical > boreal > temperate; (b) the ratios of carbon in plants to that in the soil are in the order tropical > temperate > boreal.

Question 5.3

One consequence of converting large areas of forest to agricultural land is that less carbon is stored in plant biomass (0.5 kgC m^{-2} as against 13 kgC m^{-2} and 19 kgC m^{-2} for temperate and tropical forest, respectively). Burning the wood or allowing it to decay – either on site (stumps, branches, roots, etc.) or in wood products (timber, paper and so on) – sooner or later releases its carbon content to the atmosphere as CO_2. Secondly, ploughing aerates the soil, and this speeds up the decomposition of organic matter, thus depleting this store of carbon as well.

Question 5.4

Proceeding as in Question 5.1, the average residence times are as follows:

(i) atmosphere: $\{760 \text{ GtC}/(120 + 90) \text{ GtC y}^{-1}\} = (760 \text{ GtC}/210 \text{ GtC y}^{-1})$ or about four years.

(ii) surface ocean: $\{1000 \text{ GtC}/(90 + 42) \text{ GtC y}^{-1}\} = (1000 \text{ GtC}/132 \text{ GtC y}^{-1})$ or about eight years.

(iii) deep ocean: $(38\,000 \text{ GtC}/42 \text{ GtC y}^{-1})$ or 905 years.

The answer to part (iii) has the same order of magnitude as the figure quoted in Section 4.3.3 for the residence time of *water* in the deep ocean (about 1000 years) – as it should, since DIC is carried around by the ocean circulation.

Question 5.5

(a) The most obvious justification is that CO_2 is far more abundant than CH_4 (or indeed, any other carbon-containing molecules in the atmosphere, e.g. the CFCs); its current atmospheric concentration is over 200 times that of CH_4, for example. [The traditional emphasis on CO_2 is also justified through its importance to the biosphere, and the very large amounts cycled naturally through the atmosphere each year.]

(b) The enhanced warming at high latitudes is already thawing and degrading permafrost in some polar and sub-polar regions (Table 3.1 and Box 3.3). If this trend continues, large amounts of methane (a more potent greenhouse gas than CO_2; Question 2.6) could be released to the atmosphere, accelerating greenhouse warming. [See also Chapter 7.]

Question 5.6

To decide which is the better deal, you need to express both offers in the same terms, using the information in Box 5.1. So, for example, what is $40 per tonne of carbon expressed as $ per tonne of CO_2?

1 tC is equivalent to 3.67 tCO_2. In other words, you would need to sequester 3.67 tCO_2 to earn $40. So, sequestering 1 tCO_2 would earn you $40/3.67 or

$10.9. $40/tC is therefore the same as $10.9/tCO_2 – slightly less than the alternative offer. What would you rather earn: $40/tC or $11/tCO_2? The first sounds much more attractive, but the two offers are very nearly the same thing.

Question 5.7

Burning ethanol derived from biomass still releases CO_2, but it does not unlock further amounts of *fossil* carbon. Rather, it effectively recycles the carbon 'fixed' in the plant material during its lifetime – the proportion actually returned to the atmosphere being dependent on the details of the fermentation process and subsequent combustion of the alcohol in a vehicle engine.

[Detailed assessments of the scope for (and impacts of) this type of fuel switching would need to address a host of questions. Does the type of plant material matter? How much land would be needed? Would 'biomass plantations' need heavy applications of fertiliser to be cost effective (possibly enhancing emissions of NO (an ozone precursor) and N_2O, for example)? What about its economic viability, as compared with conventional fuels or other options for the transport sector (e.g. hydrogen; Figure 5.15)? And so on.]

Question 6.1

(a) The magnitude, and hence the average rate, of the projected warming is a little over twice to nearly ten times that experienced over the past century.

(b) The projected sea-level rise over a period of 110 years (1990 to 2100) is 0.09 to 0.88 m, i.e. 90 to 880 mm. This translates into an average annual rate of increase of 0.8 to 8 mm y^{-1}. The observed rate of increase during the 20th century is estimated as 1 to 2 mm y^{-1}. So the century ahead could see a significant acceleration in the rate of sea-level rise.

Question 6.2

(a) From Box 2.6, there are three major anthropogenic sources of methane: food production (rice cultivation and livestock); waste management; and emissions linked to the extraction of *all* fossil fuels (i.e. not just natural gas). The A1F1 and A1T storylines share the same assumptions about population trends, patterns of economic development and income levels, etc., but differ as regards the energy supply side (Box 5.3): in A1F1 this remains fossil-fuel-intensive, whereas A1T envisages a transition to non-fossil fuels. So this is likely to be the main factor behind the very different emissions pathways.

(b) From Figure 6.9b, projected CH_4 concentrations for the year 2100 range from about 1600 to 3750 ppb – from roughly twice to over five times the pre-industrial level.

(c) The relationship between emissions and atmospheric concentrations is quite different for the two gases. For CH_4, the projected concentrations in Figure 6.9b track closely the corresponding emissions pathways in Figure 6.9a; in the B1 case, both are lower in 2100 than they were in 1990. By contrast, the B1 scenario for CO_2 again projects falling emission rates within a few decades (Figure 5.16a), yet the atmospheric concentration continues to rise, and only begins to level off at the end of the 21st century (Figure 5.16b). The difference is due to the very different atmospheric lifetimes of CH_4 and CO_2 (about 12 years and 100 years, respectively; Table 2.2, Section 2.5). The concentration of the shorter-lived CH_4 responds much more quickly to changes in emissions than the long-lived CO_2.

Question 6.3

Reduced SO_2 emissions leads to reduced concentrations of sulfate aerosols in the lower atmosphere, which *removes* a cooling effect – and its impact is immediate. Recall that these aerosols have only limited tropospheric lifetimes – a few weeks at most (Section 2.5).

Question 6.4

The projections in Figure 6.8d were generated by a simple climate model in response to various scenarios for the total *human-related* radiative forcing of climate during the 21st century. They do not include the influence of natural factors, namely:

- Any underlying trend in the average value of the solar constant, which could either add to or partially offset greenhouse warming in future (as it has in the past; Section 3.5.2).
- The short-term cooling effect of major volcanic eruptions in future.
- Internally generated natural variability; i.e. the spontaneous fluctuations in global temperature (on annual and decadal time-scales) generated largely by ocean–atmosphere interactions.

In short, a downturn in global temperatures for a few years should not be interpreted to mean that the greenhouse warming problem has 'gone away'!

Question 7.1

(a) Most UK housing stock is built for a cool, temperate climate and not to cope with summer heat. A considerable proportion might have to be adapted (e.g. by fitting air-conditioning, which would increase electric cooling demand; Table 7.1) or redesigned to reduce the risk of heat stress for the population. Buildings would also need to be protected from drought-induced subsidence (Table 7.1) – as well as the risk of flooding, of course.

(b) The effect on the typically English landscape would be dramatic. Agriculture would need to adapt to something more appropriate to a Mediterranean type of climate. As regards the 'natural' landscape, many of the trees, shrubs and other plants characteristic of the present moist temperate zone (Figure 4.6, Section 4.2) would be unable to survive the shift to the more arid conditions that currently support the vegetation zone of Mediterranean scrub. The 'green and pleasant land' celebrated by poets and artists would disappear.

Question 7.2

The forest die-back probably results from the particularly strong warming (Figure 6.1a) and large reduction in rainfall (Figure 6.1b) projected by the Hadley Centre model for the Amazon region. If the region becomes unable to support tropical rainforest (but only plants adapted to a drier climate, e.g. shrubs or grasses), much less carbon will be stored above ground in plant biomass. Sooner or later, the carbon in dead trees will be released to the atmosphere as CO_2 – either slowly (via decomposition) or more rapidly (via more frequent wildfires in a hotter, drier climate).

[Indeed, the modelling study referred to here predicts that over 75% of the total carbon stored in Amazonia (above and below ground) is gone by the end of the century. Bear in mind, however, the caution noted in Section 6.5: coupled AOGCMs developed by other modelling groups sometimes indicate increased rainfall in Amazonia, or little change.]

Question 7.3

(a) In this calculation, you need to convert from multiples of tonnes to multiples of grams, so it is a good plan to do this at the outset. Using the information in Box 5.1: $1 \text{ t} = 10^3 \text{ kg} = 10^6 \text{ g}$; and $1 \text{ Tg} = 10^{12} \text{ g}$. So:

$$70 \text{ Gt} = 70 \times 10^9 \text{ t}$$
$$= 70 \times 10^9 \times 10^6 \text{ g}$$
$$= 70 \times 10^{15} \text{ g}$$
$$= 70 \times 10^3 \times 10^{12} \text{ g}$$
$$= 70 \times 10^3 \text{ Tg}$$

Thus, averaged over the next 100 years, the annual release of CH_4 is an estimated $(70 \times 10^3 \text{ Tg CH}_4)/100 \text{ y} = 700 \text{ Tg CH}_4 \text{ y}^{-1}$.

(b) Comparing your answer to (a) with the projections in Figure 6.9a indicates that a slow, but persistent, thaw of Siberian permafrost would roughly double the amount of methane added to the atmosphere each year. This would effectively double projected atmospheric levels of the gas over the century ahead, meaning that current estimates of future global warming may need to be revised upwards.

(c) From the estimates given in the text, the total amount of CH_4 stored in permafrost worldwide is about $4 \times 70 \text{ Gt} = 280 \text{ Gt}$. Using the reasoning in Box 5.1, 16.0 g CH_4 contains 12.0 gC, so 280 Gt CH_4 contains $280 \text{ Gt} \times (12.0/16.0) = 210 \text{ GtC}$.

Question 7.4

Over the period 1960 to 2000:

- Developed (Annex I) countries saw an increase of $(3.6 - 2.0) \text{ GtC y}^{-1} = 1.6 \text{ GtC y}^{-1}$. So the percentage increase was $(1.6/2.0) \times 100\% = 80\%$.

- Developing (Non-Annex I) countries saw an increase of $(3.0 - 0.6) \text{ GtC y}^{-1} = 2.4 \text{ GtC y}^{-1}$. So the percentage increase was $(2.4/0.6) \times 100\% = 400\%$.

Comments on activities

Activity 1.1

Keep your notes for use when you come to Activity 1.2.

Activity 1.2

(a) (i)   The more 'formal' means of communication touched on so far include: expert-panel studies by prestigious scientific bodies (e.g. the US National Academy of Sciences, the Royal Society, etc.); consensus statements issued by such bodies or by large international gatherings of climate scientists (e.g. the conferences noted in Box 1.1); and latterly, of course, the reviews, negotiating sessions and reports of the IPCC. [Individual scientists can also play an important role – as official government advisers (e.g. Sir David King in the UK), as 'witnesses' before government committee hearings, or by seeking to influence officials/politicians in other ways (a theme we revisit in Chapter 3).]

(ii)   The main vehicle is undoubtedly media coverage (often informed by press releases) of the kinds of reports, events, etc. noted above, together with newspaper or broadcast stories of new scientific developments (e.g. the articles in Figure 1.1). Over the years, some leading climate scientists have also adopted a high public profile – by talking to journalists (e.g. Revelle) or taking part in broadcast interviews or debates, or writing popular scientific articles or books, etc. (e.g. see Figure 1.18). [In turn, of course, the media and public opinion influence government attitudes.]

(b)   As in other scientific areas, government funding for research in the many fields that have fed into the development of climate science is a key factor, whatever the underlying motivation (e.g. insights gained from US government support for space, atmospheric and ocean science during the 'Cold War' years). At the intergovernmental level, UN agencies have played a major role in building a worldwide network of climate scientists (by sponsoring conferences, coordinating multinational research programmes, etc.) and in drawing together the science of climate change, and connecting it to the world's agendas, via the work of the IPCC. [As you will see in Chapter 3, in policy-sensitive areas like climate change, governments can also seek to 'block' communication of scientific findings that run counter to their existing arguments or beliefs.]

(c)   As 'citizens of the world', we all have a stake in influencing the wider debate about climate change. The other 'stakeholders' mentioned so far include: environmental NGOs and campaigners; large multinational fossil fuel companies and other corporations; industry, business and commerce at all levels; religious leaders; and so on. Given the link with complex development and equity issues, you may also have thought of other groups: the many organisations (e.g. charities like *Oxfam*) with a focus on the problems of the world's poorest people; the antiglobalisation movement; economic analysts; and a whole range of commentators and pundits with an interest in promoting their own worldview.

(d) This would be an interesting area for an exchange of views with other students – or indeed, with friends, family or colleagues. The point of the exercise was just to get you thinking about your existing attitude to the climate change 'problem'. That will depend on your own personal circumstances, of course, but it's likely to involve a fairly complex mix of, possibly conflicting, preconceptions, values and feelings. Perhaps you are already convinced that climate change is a credible threat, for example, but are equally concerned about the implications of tackling the problem. What might it mean for your lifestyle or the economic well-being of your family, say: higher fuel and energy prices, less air travel, a smaller car (or even no car)? How does your own attitude to risk come into the equation? Perhaps you are a climate sceptic. You've heard 'doom-and-gloom' stories before: climate change may turn out to be just another false alarm. On the other hand, you may live in a flood-prone area where insurance premiums are already going through the roof. Are you influenced by the ethical dimension to climate change? Do you feel a moral responsibility to reduce the harm we might be doing to people elsewhere on the planet or to the world we 'hand on' to our children? And so on.

Keep your notes: they will help you to reflect on whether your views change as you work through the topic and gradually build up a deeper understanding of the underlying science.

Activity 1.3

(a) Keep your notes for comparison with your work on Question 3.5 at the end of Chapter 3.

(b) Like George Carey (Section 1.4), George Monbiot is invoking the argument that, to date, climate change is mainly the responsibility of the energy-intensive lifestyles of those who live in the affluent West, whereas people in the developing world are likely to bear the brunt of its negative impacts.

Activity 3.1

1   Basically, Baliunas and Soon sought to re-establish the 'conventional' view that the Northern Hemisphere experienced a 'Medieval Warm Period' (put at AD 800 to AD 1300 in their study), followed by a 'Little Ice Age' (1400 to 1900). They did this by asking a series of questions of the proxy data records for *particular* regions:

- Was there a period (of 50 years or more) with one type of climate anomaly (e.g. unusual warmth) between 800 and 1300?
- Was there a similar period with the opposite type of climate anomaly (e.g. unusual cold) between 1400 and 1900?
- How did anomalies in the past compare with 20th century climatic conditions (e.g. was it warmer during Medieval times than it is today, etc.)?

On the basis of their analysis, the Harvard team claimed to have cast doubt on Mann's 'hockey stick' reconstruction, and hence to have undermined the IPCC's all-important conclusions about the significance of 20th century warming – the implication being that what's happening now is merely natural variability (and less than the warming in the Middle Ages).

[Note too the authors' long-standing interest in another agent of climate change (solar variability), their link with the Marshall Institute and the fact that the research was funded in part by the American Petroleum Institute.]

2   The main point in Mann's rebuttal was the one we emphasised in Section 3.1.2. To challenge his (and the IPCC's) conclusions, any re-analysis of the proxy data record would have to show that disparate regions during the *same* 50-year period experienced *simultaneous* warming similar to that observed during the second half of the 20th century (when warming *has* been happening almost everywhere). Baliunas and Soon did not do this; they simply found evidence for a patchwork of different 50-year warm periods in different parts of the globe. In short, their conclusions did not follow from the evidence they presented. One of the editors of *Climate Research* (Professor Hans von Storch) made it clear that this 'flaw' was picked up during the journal's peer-review process (see Section 3.3); in his opinion, the paper should not have been published because this issue was not addressed.

3   There are several strands to the political impact of the Harvard study:

• It was published in a reputable peer-reviewed journal.

• It apparently provided scientific grounds for scepticism about the evidence for a human influence on climate, and hence support for the Administration's hostility to mandatory cuts in CO_2 emissions.

• It was quickly brought to the attention of powerful political figures: President Bush himself and Republican Senator James Inhofe, chair of the Environment Committee of the US Senate (quoted as characterising the hockey stick reconstruction as 'the greatest hoax ever perpetrated on the American people').

4   William O'Keefe characterised the Marshall Institute as the guardian of the 'integrity of science' in policy-sensitive areas like climate change. In the latter context, the Institute's main agenda seems to be selective promotion of the doubts raised by scientific sceptics like Baliunas and Soon; i.e. to make sure that work challenging the 'mainstream' view is conveyed to policy makers and (through the media) to the public. [In practice, it does this in a very effective way by running regular workshops and seminars, issuing press releases, etc. O'Keefe's long association with the oil industry gives pause for thought about the true 'objectivity' of the Institute's perspective on climate change.]

5   As noted in the caption to Figure 3.6, there were allegations of 'political bullying' by White House officials – demands for changes in the draft EPA report that would, in the opinion of the agency's scientists, have misrepresented the 'current state of knowledge' on climate change, and its implications for human health and the environment. For example, the White House wanted the (flawed) Harvard study to be included, and the removal of language (approved by the US National Academy of Sciences) that 'climate change is a real and established threat'. In the event, the EPA bowed to political pressure: its final report ran to 450 pages covering every conceivable threat to the environment in detail, except climate change.

6   The criticisms focused on the credibility of the climate models used in this assessment of the likely regional impacts of climate change across the US (an issue we revisit in Chapter 6). The disturbing feature was the attempt to get an official government report withdrawn by filing a lawsuit against it under the 'Data Quality Act' – new US legislation that could end up putting scientific disputes in policy-sensitive areas (notably, environmental protection) 'on trial' in a federal courtroom.

7   In many ways, Ebell is the archetypal anti-Kyoto, anti-regulation American conservative. His stance on the global warming issue is evident in his colourful sound bites and apocalyptic rhetoric. For example, he initiated the CEI's lawsuit on the grounds that the *National Assessment* was based on 'junk science' (i.e. 'non-objective, biased and laughably inadequate' science), and he sees the Kyoto Protocol as a vast conspiracy by the 'forces of darkness' (including, apparently, European governments!) to 'stop' industrial civilisation and 'start turning out the lights'.

Activity 3.2

(a) If you cover up the last bit of the record in Figure 3.3a, it's fairly easy to see how the slight cooling in the post-war years (from the early 1940s to the mid-1970s, say) could be interpreted as evidence that a long-term downward trend in global temperature might be underway.

[In fact, cooling during this period was stronger in the Northern Hemisphere, and particularly marked in the well-monitored regions around the North Atlantic. This northern cooling was offset to some extent by a slight warming in the Southern Hemisphere, but this only became apparent with the generation of the first reliable records of *global* temperature (i.e. GMST) in the mid-1980s.]

(b) The language used conjures images of wholesale 'doom and gloom', made more potent still by reference to the deepest fear of the 'Cold War' years – the threat of nuclear war. Indeed, the devices used in these quotes are strikingly similar to those sometimes used today to communicate the implications of global warming. Recall, for example, the image of 'a world riven by water wars, famine and anarchy' in the recent Pentagon report (Section 1.5), and references to the 'threat of terrorism' by Sir David King (Section 1.1) and the Prime Minister of Tuvalu (Section 1.5).

(c) The most likely basis for a cooling influence from expanding industrial activity is the large amount of particulate matter (sulfate and carbonaceous aerosols) pumped out by burning fossil fuels, especially coal. [See Section 3.5 for the part this has played in 20th century climate change.]

(d) This episode exemplifies points flagged up at the beginning of Chapter 3. Given evidence of an apparent, but relatively short-term, trend in global temperature, we need to be wary of jumping to conclusions – both about the significance of that trend (i.e. it needs to be set in a long-term context, the message of Sections 3.1 and 3.2), and about the underlying cause or causes (the issue taken up in Section 3.5).

[It is worth noting that this episode would continue to haunt the climate science community. In the years that followed, it was often used to cast doubt on the credibility of climate science and the emerging consensus that greenhouse warming would, sooner or later, prove to be a major factor in the Earth's climate future.]

Activity 5.1

(a) A newly planted forest is not in a balanced state. It acts as a (local) sink for atmospheric CO_2 because there is a *net* storage of fixed carbon in the living tissues of its rapidly growing trees and in its soils; i.e. the rate of carbon input (NPP) exceeds the rate of carbon loss by decomposition.

(b) (i) The forest would need to accumulate carbon at the *same* rate as the fossil carbon emissions, i.e. at 1.5 GtC per year or 1.5×10^9 tC per year (Box 5.1).

So the area required $= (1.5 \times 10^9 \text{ tC y}^{-1})/(5.0 \text{ tC ha}^{-1} \text{ y}^{-1}) = 3.0 \times 10^8$ ha.

(ii) This represents $(3.0 \times 10^8 \text{ ha})/(9.8 \times 10^8 \text{ ha}) = 0.31$ or 31% of the continental USA – a pretty unrealistic scenario, quite apart from the logistics of actually planting such a vast area!

(iii) The short answer is 'no'. Even with relatively stable climatic conditions, the net uptake of atmospheric CO_2 would decline as the forest reached maturity and decomposition gradually caught up with growth.

(c)   Relevant points include the following:

- Tree-planting schemes on a realistic scale could only ever mop up a small fraction of direct fossil-fuel related emissions (from b); i.e. they would at best help to slow the build up of atmospheric CO_2. However, the uncertainties and practical problems noted below suggest that relying on forest sinks as a substitute for reducing energy-related emissions could well be a 'high-risk' strategy for managing future CO_2 levels.

- Growth rates of trees depend on climate (temperature, rainfall, soil moisture, etc.), itself uncertain in a global warming future.

- A CO_2-enriched atmosphere boosts photosynthesis, stimulating plant growth (NPP) and increased CO_2 uptake. But this CO_2-fertilisation effect eventually saturates, and is affected by complicated interactions with other environmental factors (Extract 5.1).

- Decomposition rates are predicted to accelerate in a warmer world. This could negate the beneficial effects on plant growth of CO_2-fertilisation, longer growing seasons, increased rainfall and nitrogen availability, etc., slowing or even reversing the net uptake of CO_2 by 'forest sinks'.

- Other knock-on effects of continued global warming could also reduce the effectiveness of these sinks (e.g. increased damage from insect pests, storms or wildfires; tree death due to drought in some regions; etc.).

- Planting forests requires clearing land, which itself releases CO_2.

- What to do with the wood once the forest matures; it could not be burnt or allowed to decay since this would again release CO_2 to the atmosphere.

Activity 5.2

(a)   The final sentence could be taken to imply that planktonic debris simply settles on the ocean floor and remains there for hundreds of years. In reality, very little of the organic matter in 'marine snow' (i.e. the fixed carbon in export production; Section 5.2.2) reaches the sea bed and is permanently buried. Most of it is consumed or decomposed by bacteria, and ultimately converted to DIC in the deep ocean via heterotrophic respiration.

(b)   As part of the natural carbon cycle, ocean regions that support high phytoplankton productivity (e.g. spring blooms in the North Atlantic) currently act as natural sinks for atmospheric CO_2. In effect, the gas is drawn into solution to compensate for the fixed carbon exported to the deep ocean via the biological pump.

Several studies have confirmed that lack of iron limits phytoplankton growth in some ocean areas (e.g. parts of the South Atlantic and Southern Ocean); fertilising these ocean waters with iron does indeed trigger enhanced productivity. However, it is not yet clear what proportion of the carbon fixed by these artificial blooms is actually exported to the deep ocean – an issue that is central to their effectiveness as a long-term sink for anthropogenic CO_2. One estimate (quoted in the article) suggests that deliberately manipulating the biological pump could remove 10–20% of annual fossil-fuel emissions, but only if iron-fertilisation were carried out on a large-scale, continuous basis.

(c)   The main driving force is the mechanism for trading 'carbon credits' enshrined in the Kyoto Protocol. Though there is a more 'eco-friendly' slant to the non-profit-making Planktos Foundation, both organisations aim to sell carbon credits that can be used to offset direct CO_2 emissions by companies or individual households.

(d)   Three main areas of concern are identified in the article:

- Limited understanding of marine ecosystems makes it impossible to assess the potential impacts of the 'cascade of unwanted side effects' that could be triggered by large-scale iron-fertilisation of selected ocean areas.

- Some of the possible side effects could themselves affect climate. Examples given in the article include increased absorption of solar radiation (effectively, a change in ocean albedo), and increased release of dimethylsulfide. [Like other sulfur-containing gases of biogenic origin, this is converted into sulfate aerosols, whence the reference to cloud formation.]

- Currently, there is no legal framework or other internationally agreed mechanism (e.g. under UNEP auspices) whereby those engaged in commercial iron-fertilisation projects could be compelled to do a full environmental-impact assessment.

(e)   This might be another area for an exchange of views with other students. My own thoughts ran along the following lines.

'Human actions have already set in motion a planetary-scale experiment on Earth's climate system, however inadvertently. It would seem imprudent (foolhardy?) to attempt to 'manage' that experiment by deliberately interfering with one of the natural controls over atmospheric CO_2 (the biological pump) – especially given the uncertainties about how effective this is likely to be as a long-term sink for fossil-fuel CO_2, and the largely unknown ecological and climatic effects it could have.'

Activity 5.3

There are lots of possible answers to this question. Hopefully, you may have come up with some of the factors collected below.

- Total UK population. The UK birth rate has been relatively stable and is, if anything, predicted to decline. But people are living longer. How will an ageing population affect patterns of car ownership and use? What about the effects of immigration/emigration in the years ahead?

- Will the trend towards more people choosing to live alone continue? And how will this affect car ownership patterns? The number of households owning more than one car has been steadily growing. Will that trend continue? What about other social changes? How might more people working from home affect car ownership and use?

- How fast will the UK economy grow over the next 20 years? How much disposable income will people have to spend on additional cars?

- How will government policies affect traffic levels in the years ahead? Will government choose to increase taxes on car purchases, car ownership or fuel? What about the influence of congestion charging or road tolls? How much will government choose to invest in road building or public transport? And so on.

- What about technological developments over the next 20 years? How will this affect fuel efficiency and CO_2 emissions per passenger-mile? What about alternative fuels or electric vehicles?

Activity 6.1

(a)   The implicit assumption is that the many sources of uncertainty about the Earth's climate future will all act in 'one direction', i.e. such that global warming over the century ahead is *necessarily* kept to a minimum. In turn, this implies a belief that global society will definitely evolve along the lines of the IPCC's most 'optimistic' (i.e. low emissions) B1 scenario (even in the absence of explicit climate-protection policies), the climate sensitivity will turn out to be at the bottom end of the model-projected range (i.e. 1.5 °C, or below), and so on. If there is currently no basis for assigning relative likelihoods to various emission scenarios, climate sensitivity values, etc., there is certainly none for asserting that one particular outcome has a 100% probability of occurring!

(b)   You will have your own thoughts on this, but the following points should be enough to convince most people that climate change is a credible threat, and that a 'wait-and-see' response is an inherently risky strategy.

- There is no doubt that greenhouse gas concentrations in the atmosphere have risen dramatically in the last 250 years. Before the industrial age, the CO_2 level had been steady at around 280 ppm since the world emerged from the last glacial period about 10 000 years ago. The concentration hit 378 ppm in 2004, and is now higher than at any time in the past 400 000 years. Without concerted action to curb CO_2 emissions from fossil fuel burning, we could see concentrations double or rise to over three times the pre-industrial level by the end of the 21st century. (Chapters 2 and 5)

- The Earth really is warming up; global-mean surface temperature increased by 0.6 °C during the 20th century, and the 1990s were the warmest decade on record. For the Northern Hemisphere, at least, the warmth of recent decades is likely to have been unprecedented in the past millennium. The relatively modest 20th century warming has already had widespread effects: precipitation patterns are changing; glaciers and snow cover are shrinking across the globe; Arctic sea ice is thinning; sea levels are rising; and plants and animals are changing their behaviour in ways that are consistent with rising temperatures. (Chapter 3)

- Natural causes of climate variability have undoubtedly influenced the Earth's recent temperature history, but there is now a strong scientific consensus that the evidence for human modification of climate is compelling. In 2001, the

IPCC concluded that 'most of the warming observed over the last 50 years is attributable to human activities'; i.e. to greenhouse warming due to the build up of CO_2 (and other greenhouse gases) in the atmosphere. (Chapter 3)

- There is still plenty of uncertainty about the amount and details of future climate change. Nevertheless, it is inevitable that, if CO_2 concentrations continue to rise, so too will the Earth's temperature. Warming in the 21st century at the low end of the model-projected range (over 0.1 °C per decade) would still exceed that experienced over the last 100 years. The high end of the projected range (a rise of 5.8 °C by 2100) approaches the size of the temperature increases seen only during the transition from glacial to interglacial conditions. (Chapters 3 and 6)

- The impacts of future climate change on human societies and the natural environment are uncertain, but they are likely to be profound – especially for vulnerable communities in developing countries, and for species and ecosystems that are already threatened by other pressures. The risks of widespread damaging effects grow with the amount of global warming: increases in extreme events (floods, storms and droughts) become more likely, and there is an increased chance that the climate system could be 'nudged' into a sudden and dramatic change in its mode of operation (as it has been in the past). (Chapters 1, 3 and 4) [See also Chapter 7.]

- There are many 'time lags' in the climate system, including the long atmospheric lifetime of CO_2, the thermal inertia of the ocean and delays in the melting of land ice. Postponing cuts in CO_2 emissions means an inevitable commitment to higher levels in the atmosphere. Temperatures will go on rising for centuries after atmospheric CO_2 stabilises; sea-level rise will continue for millennia. (Chapters 4, 5 and 6)

Activity 7.1

(a) In general, the main options are:

- Improved energy efficiency and other measures aimed at reducing per capita energy use.
- Switching the mix of fossil fuels from coal→oil→natural gas, and thereby reducing CO_2 emissions per unit of energy generated (Figure 5.14; bear in mind, though, that this runs counter to the relative abundance of fossil fuel reserves).
- Recycling carbon through biomass utilisation, for power plants as well as vehicle fuels (Question 5.7).
- Using carbon-free sources such as nuclear (or hydroelectric) power, renewables (such as solar, wind, wave, etc.), or hydrogen as a fuel (provided it is generated without the use of fossil fuels; e.g. Figure 5.15).

(b)   Once you start thinking about this, it's hard to stop (recall Figure 5.13).

Here are the ideas I came up with:

Home: The obvious areas of energy use have to do with heating (space and water), lighting and the many electrical/electronic appliances and gadgets you may have (cooker, washing machine, fridge/freezer, TV, DVD/video player, computer, etc.). So the sorts of questions to ask yourself are: How well insulated/ draught-proofed is your home (roof space, walls, doors, windows)? How energy-efficient is the heating system? What about turning the thermostat down a notch or two? Or investing in a new boiler, or solar heating panels? Do you switch off unnecessary lights, or use low-energy bulbs? How energy-efficient are the other electrical/electronic goods, and how do you use them? Do you switch off the TV/DVD/computer, or regularly leave these on standby? And so on.

Bear in mind too that *all* the manufactured goods in your home also have an energy cost; at present, this is often very different from the financial cost. That goes for the food you eat as well, especially if it is flown in 'out-of-season' from the other side of the world.

Travel: What proportion of the travelling you do is by public transport, private car, bicycle, on foot – and why? If you have a car, how fuel-efficient is it – and did you buy it, and do you drive it, with this in mind? Are you part of a car pool for regular journeys (to work, taking children to school, etc.)? Have cheap air fares encouraged you to take more short breaks (or buy a holiday home) abroad? And so on.

Many of the questions above (just a sample of those you may have thought about) contain implicit hints to ways of saving energy, but they also touch on some of the barriers to doing so in practice. For example, financial constraints may be paramount. Even if not, the 'pay back' period over which investment in energy-saving measures (new equipment, home insulation, etc.) becomes cost effective probably is – and that, in turn, depends on capital costs as against energy (i.e. fuel and electricity) costs. Awareness of (which means ready access to information about) alternative options and products comes into the equation, as do your own attitudes and priorities, of course. Do you know where your electricity comes from (i.e. how it is generated), for example? Have you thought about switching to an alternative 'green' provider (advertised as guaranteeing lower CO_2 emissions), or investing in options for generating your own power (e.g. solar photovoltaic panels or a small wind turbine on the roof, say)? Or are you wary of unfamiliar changes or equipment, perhaps for fear of being manipulated or swindled? How resistant are you to making changes in the way you use energy, especially ones that trespass on your sense of personal freedom (use of the car, cheap flights, even the food you eat)? And what would it take to erode that resistance?

Finally, this might be a good point to reflect on whether your answers to questions like these have been swayed by a deeper understanding of the science of climate change.

References

Allen, M., Raper, S. and Mitchell, J. (2001) Uncertainty in the IPCC's Third Assessment Report, *Science*, **293**, pp. 430–433.

Clark, N. (2003) Shrinking worlds: islands and environmental change, in Brandon, M. and Clark, N. (eds) *Environmental Changes: Global Challenges*. Milton Keynes: The Open University (Book 1 of U316 *The Environmental Web*).

Edwards, P. N. and Schneider, S. H. (2001) Self-governance and peer review in science-for-policy: the case of the IPCC Second Assessment Report, in Miller, C. and Edwards, P. N. (eds) *Changing the Atmosphere: Expert Knowledge and Environmental Governance*. Cambridge, MA: MIT Press. Available from: http://stephenschneider.stanford.edu/Mediarology/Mediarology.html (accessed 23 February 2004).

Falkowski, P. *et al.* (2000) The global carbon cycle: A test of our knowledge of Earth as a system, *Science*, **290**, pp. 291–296.

Foresight (2004) Foresight Flood and Coastal Defence Project, *Future Flooding: Executive Summary*, Office of Science and Technology, UK. Available from: http://www.foresight.gov.uk (accessed 26 April 2004).

Hadley Centre (2005) *Stabilising climate to avoid dangerous climate change – a summary of relevant research at the Hadley Centre* (January 2005), Meteorological Office, UK. Available from: http://www.metoffice.com/research/hadleycentre/pubs/brochure/ (accessed 3 February 2005).

Hasselmann, K., Schellnhuber, H. J. and Edenhofer, O. (2004) Climate change: complexity in action, *Physics World*, **17**(6), pp. 31–35 (June 2004).

IPCC (2000) *Land Use, Land Use Change and Forestry*, IPCC Special Report. Cambridge: Cambridge University Press.

IPCC (2001a) *Climate Change 2001: The Scientific Basis. Contribution of Working Group I to the Third Assessment Report of the Intergovernmental Panel on Climate Change*. Cambridge: Cambridge University Press.

IPCC (2001b) *Climate Change 2001: Impacts, Adaptation and Vulnerability. Contribution of Working Group II to the Third Assessment Report of the Intergovernmental Panel on Climate Change*. Cambridge: Cambridge University Press.

IPCC (2001c) *Climate Change 2001: Mitigation. Contribution of Working Group III to the Third Assessment Report of the Intergovernmental Panel on Climate Change*. Cambridge: Cambridge University Press.

IPCC (2001d) *Climate Change 2001: Synthesis Report. Contribution of Working Groups I, II and III to the Third Assessment Report of the Intergovernmental Panel on Climate Change*. Cambridge: Cambridge University Press.

IPCC (2004) (online) About the IPCC. Available at: http://www.ipcc.ch/about/about.htm (accessed 10 January 2004).

Mathews, B. (2004) (online) Available at: http://www.chooseclimate.org. (accessed 26 September 2004).

Mintzer, I. M. (1992) Living in a Warming World, in Mintzer, I. M. (ed.) *Confronting Climate Change: Risks, Implications and Responses*. Cambridge: Cambridge University Press.

O'Neill, B. C. and Oppenheimer, M. (2002) Dangerous climate impacts and the Kyoto Protocol, *Science*, **296**, pp. 1971–1972.

Oreskes, N. (2004) The scientific consensus on climate change, *Science*, **306**, p. 1686.

Peake, S. (2003) The climate strikes back, in Peake, S. and Smith, J. (eds) *Climate Change: From Science to Sustainability*. Milton Keynes: The Open University (Book 3 of U316 *The Environmental Web*).

Smith, J. (2003) Listening out: climate, politics, and philosophy, in Peake, S. and Smith, J. (eds) *Climate Change: From Science to Sustainability*. Milton Keynes: The Open University (Book 3 of U316 *The Environmental Web*).

Stainforth, D. A. *et al.* (2005) Uncertainty in predictions of the climate response to rising levels of greenhouse gases, *Nature*, **433**, pp. 403–406.

Stokstad, E (2001) Myriad ways to reconstruct past climates, *Science*, **292**, pp. 658–659

UCS (2004) (online) http://www.climatehotmap.org (accessed 19 February 2004).

UKCIP02 (2002) *Climate Change Scenarios for the United Kingdom: The UKCIP02 Briefing Report*. Norwich: Tyndall Centre, University of East Anglia. Available from: http://www.ukcip.org.uk (accessed 5 June 2002).

Weart, S. (2004) (online) *The Discovery of Global Warming*. Available from: http://www.aip.org/history/climate (accessed 3 June 2004).

Acknowledgements

The contributions of several authors to a number of other Open University courses were of considerable value in the preparation of this topic, in particular: Roger Blackmore, *Changing Environments* (Book 2 of U216 *Environment: Change, Contest and Response*); Angela Colling, *The Dynamic Earth* (Book 2 of S269 *Earth and Life*); Nigel Clark, *Environmental Changes: Global Challenges* (Book 1 of U316 *The Environmental Web*); and Stephen Peake and Joe Smith, *Climate Change: From Science to Sustainability* (Book 3 of U316).

Grateful acknowledgment is also made to the following sources for permission to reproduce their material:

Figure 1.2 copyright © Honduras.com; *Figures 1.3, 1.11* Lutgens, F. K. and Tarbuck, E. J. (2001) *The Atmosphere: An Introduction to Meteorology*, Pearson Education; *Figure 1.4* copyright © ICSU; *Figure 1.5* copyright © Fred Espenak/Science Photo Library; *Figure 1.6a* copyright © Camera Press; *Figure 1.6b* copyright © Connor Caffrey/Science Photo Library; *Figure 1.6c* copyright © Chris Martin/Still Pictures; *Figures 1.6d, 3.10, 4.5, 4.14* copyright © NASA; *Figure 1.9* copyright © Stephen Peake; *Figure 1.10* United Kingdom Climate Change Impacts Review for the Department of the Environment, *The Potential Effects of Climate Change in the United Kingdom*, January 1991, Crown copyright material reproduced under Class Licence No. C01W0000065 by permission of Controller of HMSO and Queen's Printer for Scotland; *Figure 1.12* courtesy of Bob Girdo; *Figures 1.15, 3.13, 3.15, 6.6, 6.8, 6.9* copyright © GRID-Arendal; *Figure 1.16* courtesy of Ronald Grant Archive; *Figure 1.17* copyright © Phil Noble/PA/Empics; *Figure 1.18* reprinted from Giles, J. (2002) 'Scientific uncertainty: When doubt is a sure thing', in *Nature*, **418**(6897), Aug., copyright © 2002 by permission of Macmillan Publishers Ltd; *Figure 2.5* Science Photo Library; *Figure 2.7* copyright © PPM GmbH; *Figure 2.9* Stevens, W. K. (1990) 'Clouds are yielding clues to climate change', *New York Times Science Times*, 24 April, copyright © 1990 The New York Times, reprinted by permission; *Figures 2.13, 7.5* copyright © US Geological Survey; *Figure 2.14* copyright © Ken Abbot/National Ice Core Laboratory; *Figures 2.15a, 3.3, 3.14, 4.16, 5.1* adapted from *Climate Change 2001-1*, Intergovernmental Panel on Climate Change; *Figures 2.15b,c, 3.16, 5.16* Houghton, J. T. *et al.* (2001) *Climate Change 2001, The Scientific Basis*, Intergovernmental Panel on Climate Change; *Figure 2.17 Special Report of Emissions Scenarios*, Intergovernmental Panel on Climate Change; *Figure 2.19* Kaufman, Y. J. *et al.* (2002) 'A satellite view of aerosols in the climate system', *Nature*, **419**, 12 Sept., copyright © Nature Publishing Group; *Figure 3.1* copyright © Stephen J. Krasemann/DRK PHOTO; *Figure 3.2 Introduction to Climate Change*, UNEP/GRID, Arendal, Norway; *Figure 3.5* Kunsthistorisches Museum, Vienna/ Bridgeman Art Library; *Figure 3.6* Harris, P. and Rodrigues, J. (2003) 'Bush covers up climate research', *The Observer*, 21 Sept., copyright © 2003 Guardian Newspapers Ltd; *Figure 3.7* copyright © Ashley Cooper/Alamy Images; *Figure 3.9* copyright © Michelle Gray/British Antarctic Survey; *Figure 3.11* MODIS images courtesy of NASA's *Terra* satellite, supplied by Ted Scambos, National Snow and Ice Data Center, University of Colorado, Boulder, USA; *Figure 4.1* copyright © Tom Van Sant, Geosphere Project/Planetary Visions/Science Photo Library; *Figure 4.12* Rahmstorf, S. (2002) 'Ocean circulation and climate during the past 120,000 years', *Nature*, **419**(6903), 12 Sept., copyright © Nature Publishing Group; *Figure 4.13* copyright © Paul Harcourt Davies/Science Photo Library; *Figure 4.15a* copyright © Pierre Laboute/IRD Phototheque Indigo; *Figure 4.15b* copyright © Georgette Douwma/Science Photo Library; *Figure 5.4* copyright © 1988 Tom Bean/DRK PHOTO; *Figure 5.5* copyright © Ecoscene; *Figure 5.6* copyright © Tantyo Bangun/Still Pictures; *Figure 5.8* copyright © Southampton Oceanography Centre; *Figure 5.12* copyright © Ben Mathews; *Figures 6.1, 7.6* Hadley Centre (2003) *Climate Change: Observations and Predictions – Recent Research on Climate Change Science*, Crown copyright © 2003, published by The Meteorological Office; *Figure 6.3* Houghton, J. T. (1997) *Global Warming: The Complete Briefing*, Cambridge University Press; *Figure 6.5* copyright © climateprediction.net; *Figure 7.1* copyright © Reuters/Joe Klama; *Figure 7.2* copyright © US National Oceanic and Atmospheric Administration; *Figure 7.3 Climate Change 2001: Impacts, Adaptation and Vulnerability*, Intergovernmental Panel on Climate Change; *Figure 7.4* 'Climate Change Scenarios for the United Kingdom', *The UKCIP02 Scientific Report*, April 2002, copyright © UK Climate Impacts Programme; *Figure 7.7 The Guardian*, 11 Aug. 2005, copyright © Guardian Newspapers Ltd; *Figure 7.8a* copyright © Francis Latreille/Corbis; *Figure 7.8b* courtesy of Pacific Northwest National Laboratory, USA; *Figure 7.9* Watson, R. T. *et al. Climate Change 2001: Synthesis Report*, Intergovernmental Panel on Climate Change; *Figure 7.10* Stabilising climate to avoid dangerous climate change – a summary of relevant research at the Hadley Centre, January 2005, Crown copyright © 2005, published by The Meteorological Office; *Figure 7.11a* copyright © Tim Ayers/Alamy; *Figure 7.11b* copyright © Vera Schimetzek/Alamy; *Figure 7.13a* copyright © BYB/Rex Features; *Figure 7.13b* copyright © PA/Empics; *Figure 7.14* copyright © AP PHOTO/CP, Jacques Boissinot; *Figure 7.15* courtesy of JDS Consulting Associates Ltd.

Every effort has been made to contact copyright holders. If any have been inadvertently overlooked, the publishers will be pleased to make the necessary arrangements at the first opportunity.

Appendix: Abbreviations

AGCM	atmosphere general circulation model
AOGCM	(coupled) atmosphere–ocean general circulation model
BaU	business as usual
CFC	chlorofluorocarbon
DIC	dissolved inorganic carbon
EAIS	East Antarctic Ice Sheet
ENSO	El Niño–Southern Oscillation
GMST	global mean surface temperature
GPP	gross primary production
GWP	global warming potential
IAM	integrated assessment model
IPCC	Intergovernmental Panel on Climate Change
ITCZ	Intertropical Convergence Zone
NADW	North Atlantic Deep Water
NAO	North Atlantic Oscillation
NPP	net primary production
OGCM	ocean general circulation model
SPM	Summary for Policymakers (in IPCC reports)
TAR	Third Assessment Report (from the IPCC)
THC	thermohaline circulation
UKCIP	United Kingdom Climate Impacts Programme
UNEP	United Nations Environment Programme
UNFCCC	United Nations Framework Convention on Climate Change
WAIS	West Antarctic Ice Sheet
WMO	World Meteorological Organisation

Index

Entries in **bold** are key terms defined, along with other important terms, in the Glossary. Page numbers referring only to figures and tables are printed in *italics*.